THE CARE OF THE GOLF COURSE

Edited by

P. HAYES, Ph.D., N.D.A., C.Biol., M.I.Biol., F.I.Hort.
Director: S.T.R.I.

R.D.C. EVANS, B.Sc.
Advisory Agronomist

S.P. ISAAC, B.Sc.
Advisory Agronomist

Published by:-

THE SPORTS TURF RESEARCH INSTITUTE
BINGLEY, WEST YORKSHIRE, ENGLAND, BD16 1AU

First Published 1992 by:-

THE SPORTS TURF RESEARCH INSTITUTE, BINGLEY, WEST YORKSHIRE, BD16 1AU, ENGLAND

ISBN: 1-873431-02-3

NOTE 1:   The fact that particular items of equipment or machinery are mentioned in this text should not be taken to imply that the STRI endorses one firm's products over another. When purchasing equipment for a golf club it is always wise to obtain details of all rival products and to make a choice based on full on-course demonstrations and on the exact requirements of the particular club, bearing in mind the supply of spare parts, local servicing facilities, etc.

NOTE 2:   The application rates given in the following text for pesticides should be regarded as being for guidance only, although every effort has been made to ensure that quoted rates are appropriate. It should be understood that pesticide users are under an obligation to comply with legal requirements governing the usage of such materials and that the instructions included with each product are mandatory, including instructions regarding application rates. Users should be familiar with the Food and Environment Protection Act of 1985 and the Control of Pesticides Regulations 1986.

❖ ❖ ❖

ACKNOWLEDGEMENTS

The original articles which form the basis for the present text were written by the following members (and ex-members) of the STRI staff:–

S.W. Baker, BSc, PhD
N.A. Baldwin, BSc, PhD
D.F. Boocock, NDA
P.M. Canaway, BSc, CBiol, MIBiol
T.W. Colclough, BSc
A.R. Cole, BSc
P. Hayes, PhD, NDA, CBiol, MIBiol, FIHort
S.P. Isaac, BSc
D.M. Lawson, BSc, PhD
T.A. Lodge, BSc
G.C. Macadam, SDH
A.J. Newell, BSc, PhD

S.J. Ormondroyd, BSc
J. Perris, BSc
S.T. Pool, NDH, MIHort
J.P. Shildrick, BA, CBiol, MIBiol
D.M. Stansfield, BSc
R.S. Taylor, BSc
S.L. Thornton, BSc
J.W. Tucker, BSc
J.R. Westwood, BSc
D.D. Wishart, BSc
A.R. Woolhouse, BSc

The Editors most gratefully acknowledge their contribution to the present volume.

Thanks are also due to the United States Golf Association for permission to reproduce Figure 7. Mr. John W. Holroyd of Shipley is thanked for the cover design.

The task of producing the text on desk top publishing equipment fell to the STRI's Head Typist, Ann Bentley, who deserves warmest thanks for long hours of accurate and conscientious work.

DEDICATION

To the Memory of the late R.B. Dawson, Esq., O.B.E., M.Sc., the Institute's first Director (1929–1963), author of *'Practical Lawn Craft'* and a notable Pioneer of British Turfgrass Research.

CONTENTS

SECTION 8: WEEDS

SECTION 9: PESTICIDES AND LEGISLATION

SECTION 10: ADMINISTRATION & FACILITIES

BIBLIOGRAPHY

———————————————————— ✣✣✣ ————————————————————

LIST OF ILLUSTRATIONS

INTRODUCTION

There has long been a need for a comprehensive manual on the maintenance of the British golf course. Golf is now after all one of the most popular participant games in the U.K., and ever-increasing numbers of players are demanding higher and higher standards of course presentation from their greenkeepers and Green Committees. In recent years scientific research, combined with practical experience, has provided a much clearer understanding of the underlying factors which contribute towards good golfing surfaces and a considerable body of knowledge has been accumulated.

Much has appeared in print, but scattered through various books, greenkeeping magazines, scientific journals and conference proceedings. The greenkeeper or Chairman of Green seeking a comprehensive source of background information on golf course management has therefore so far been deprived of an obvious single publication. This present volume seeks to correct that deficiency and provide a ready reference which can hopefully be relied upon to provide answers to the innumerable questions which arise during the day to day care of the golf course.

The above paragraph should not be taken as implying that no useful book on modern greenkeeping currently exists. A number of invaluable works have indeed been published and to give a comprehensive picture of available literature, an extensive Bibliography covering all aspects of golf course design, construction and management has been included at the end of the present volume. As an outstanding work on the subject, one might cite as an example Professor James B. Beard's *"Turf Management for Golf Courses"*, published by the U.S. Golf Association in 1982. From a British point of view however, the value of this definitive textbook is limited by the climatic, environmental and managerial differences which exist between the U.S. and U.K. golf course scenarios, and a specifically British contribution to the literature is therefore an obvious requirement. Booklets such as the Royal & Ancient's *"Way Forward"* and Nicholas Park's *"The Management of British Golf Courses"* have recently played a part in focusing attention on the subject, but the Editors remain confident that there is still room for another volume on the book-shelf.

The body of accumulated international knowledge on golf greenkeeping, in both its practical aspects and in terms of background scientific research, is indeed now so vast that many volumes would be required to provide a fully comprehensive coverage of the subject. The Editors of the current work, however, feel that a general (and not too technical) book giving reasonably detailed information on the range of greenkeeping problems which arise in British golf course management will be of value to all individuals involved in this exacting and demanding task.

Over recent decades, one consistently popular and well-received periodical covering both turf maintenance and the construction of new sports facilities has been the quarterly Bulletin of the Sports Turf Research Institute. Appearing four times each year since 1951, and written largely by experienced members of the STRI staff (both research scientists and advisory agronomists), its accumulated articles are a rich source of information on all aspects of the subject. Many of the articles which have appeared over the years refer specifically to golf course management, and it is these which form the basis for the text of this book. To ensure their relevance to the modern up-to-date situation, the vast majority of articles selected are those which have appeared in the Bulletin issues of the past five years. Where appropriate to provide a comprehensive treatment of the subject, additional articles have also been gathered from other STRI publications.

As a compendium of articles by various authors, the present volume is perhaps not primarily intended to be read through from cover to cover – although it is hoped that at least some readers would find such an approach an interesting and rewarding exercise. In most circumstances however, it might be more appropriate for the reader to consult the Contents page, and then select a section or sections most appropriate as a source of information on any question which might be foremost in the mind at the time. Most sub-sections of the book can stand alone as sources of information on a particular subject, although they are inevitably inter-related to a certain degree, and the consultation of one section or article might logically lead to the need to consult another relevant topic.

Aimed primarily at Head Greenkeepers and their assistants, and at Chairmen or Members of Green Committees, it is hoped that the appeal of the book will extend to all those concerned in any way with the care of the British golf course. Indeed, it is hoped that the average club golfer himself will find something of interest within these pages, as an appreciation of some of the problems of course management can give the golfer a deeper insight into the characteristics of his course, and hopefully heighten his enjoyment of his game.

The Editors
STRI, Bingley, W.Yorks.
1992

SECTION 1

GENERAL

FESCUES, BENTS AND *POA ANNUA*

The origins of golf stretch back into antiquity and no-one can say with certainty just when or how the game started. We can be sure, however, that the Scots played a big part in popularising the game. King James VI of Scotland took up golf on the North Inch at Perth and in 1658 re-affirmed the golfing rights of the people of Earl's Ferry and Elie. It is fairly certain that in those days golf flourished initially on the upland downs and heaths and seaside links – areas that were of limited use agriculturally and devoted mainly to sheep grazing which 'maintained' a playable turf before the advent of mowers. Such ground would be inherently infertile, very often free draining and drought prone, only capable of supporting the dwarf growing, hardy bent and fescue grasses that are so well adapted to that harsh environment.

The first recorded experiments with grasses for turf were carried out by J.B. Olcott between 1885 and 1910 at Connecticut in the United States. He came to the conclusion that the best types of grasses for turf in that region were to be found in the genera *Agrostis* and *Festuca*. Subsequent work over the years both by the Sports Turf Research Institute at Bingley and elsewhere has confirmed this. Characteristics which enable these grasses to perform well as turf maintained for golf are summarised below.

Bents (*Agrostis* Species)
There are 5 species of bents which may be considered for turfgrass purposes but in the UK only 3 of them are normally used – browntop bent (*A. tenuis*), creeping bent (*A. stolonifera*) and velvet bent (*A. canina*).

For fine turf, the virtues of the best bents are high shoot density which, on close mown golf greens, can reach 120,000 shoots per m^2. Their leaves are small, relatively broad and flat, giving good ground cover and, with satisfactory growing conditions, they can maintain a reasonably green appearance the year round. All of them are capable of vegetative spread, 'Highland' browntop bent quite vigorously by rhizomes, whilst other cultivars of browntop spread more moderately by both stolons and rhizomes. Creeping bent widely used for putting greens in the United States and Mediterranean countries spreads vigorously by stolons, is tolerant of greater extremes of heat and cold than 'Highland' and probably other browntop bents as well. However, it has never been popular in the UK, despite having been used on a number of courses and included in trials here at Bingley. It is possible that our mild, wet climate allows 'weed' grasses such as annual meadow-grass and, indeed, other turf species a greater competitive advantage, especially in spring following winter wear and tear. American experience suggests that for optimum growth this grass requires summer temperature regimes of the order of 15–20°C at night and 18–24°C during the day – rarely achieved for more than a few days at a time in our typical summers. Thus grasses better adapted to our cooler summer weather do better. Clearly, American selections of creeping bent have a handicap from the start – we need perhaps to be looking at creeping bents of UK provenance. Nonetheless, this grass has a lot to offer and although its stoloniferous habit has disadvantages – a tendency to form nap and thatch rapidly unless regularly verticut – its vigorous growth and ability to recover from damage are such that further trials with it will undoubtedly be carried out.

Velvet bent is even finer-leaved than browntop bent and the cultivar 'Kingstown' is dense and attractive in appearance during the summer and outstanding in drought, though with much poorer winter appearance. For this reason, as well as a tendency for its stolons to form a nap, it is rarely used, and then only in mixtures.

Close mown bentgrass turf with high shoot density and only limited thatch formation is quite wear tolerant given good management, especially plenty of aeration and avoidance of over-feeding and watering.

Fescues (*Festuca* species)

There are also 5 species of fescue on the market but only 3 of these – Chewings fescue (*F. rubra* ssp. *commutata*), slender creeping red (*F. rubra* ssp. *litoralis*) and strong creeping red (*F. rubra* ssp. *rubra*) – are used to any extent for golf turf.

Useful characteristics of fescues include quite high shoot numbers – up to 90,000 per m^2 – a fine-bladed leaf that blends well with bentgrass and differences in surface texture and seasonal colour which complement those of bent. They are particularly well adapted to drier, infertile soils. Since germination and early growth is rapid, they help provide a quick ground cover whilst the slower-growing bents establish – the two are frequently sown together.

Chewings fescue has neither rhizomes nor stolons so is very slow to colonise bare places but it is fine-leaved, of low growth habit, very tolerant of close mowing, fairly resistant to two common diseases, red thread and dollar spot. Once this grass is established and has developed a little surface thatch, it supports abrasive and golf spike wear during the summer quite well.

Slender creeping red fescue spreads moderately by rhizomes, is fine-leaved, low growing and can survive close mowing well. It is, however, susceptible to red thread disease and the sea-marsh varieties of this grass are also susceptible to dollar spot, though these types are most tolerant of salt. When established, it is quite capable of withstanding abrasive and golf spike wear during the summer and recovers from such wear moderately well.

Strong creeping red fescue has more numerous, longer rhizomes but a rather coarser leaf and thus produces a much more open sward. It is non-persistent under close mowing, but satisfactory at fairway heights of cut. It is susceptible to red thread but quite resistant to dollar spot, although its tolerance of heavy wear is poor.

Annual Meadow-Grass (*Poa annua*)

Almost universally derided as a poor species for fine turf, and that includes all three main playing areas on a golf course, annual meadow-grass is still a very ecologically successful weedgrass. The single species name covers a wide range of plant types, those most commonly found in turf being biennials or short-lived perennials. In fine turf, annual meadow-grass often occurs as tufts or in isolated patches which look unsightly and, by their variable growth rate, affect the smoothness of the playing surface, especially in spring and autumn. The grass is capable of producing seed heads below the normal cutting height on greens and this is the main way by which it spreads – this characteristic too affects appearance and smoothness of the playing surface at times.

There is no doubt that this grass is extremely tolerant of heavy wear and even when completely worn away it has the capacity to regenerate quite rapidly from seed shed in previous years lying dormant in the soil – seed can remain viable in the soil for up to 10 years. Although criticised as shallow-rooting, it will in fact develop an extensive and deep-rooted turf in open, well aerated soil conditions; like any other grass, it becomes shallower-rooting in compact soils but in such conditions has a competitive edge over other grasses and tends to survive better. Thus annual meadow-grass is often seen as practically the only species present through central areas of golf greens that are most used for pin positions.

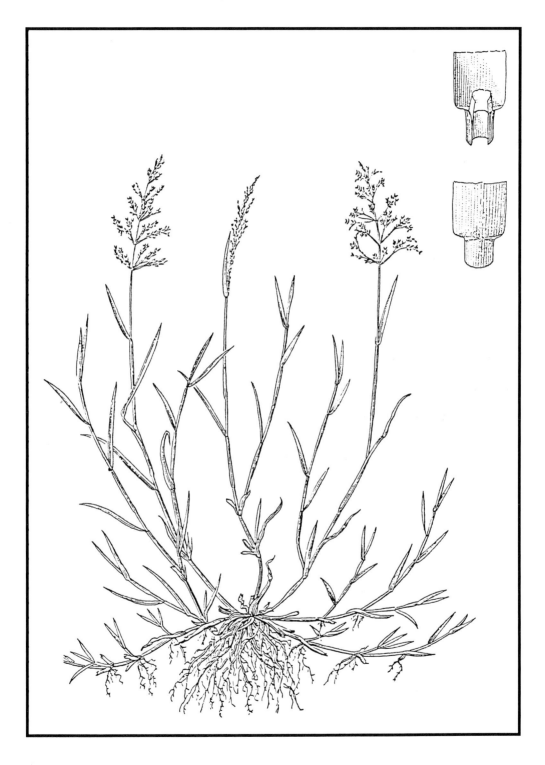

FIGURE 1: Bentgrass (*Agrostis* spp.)

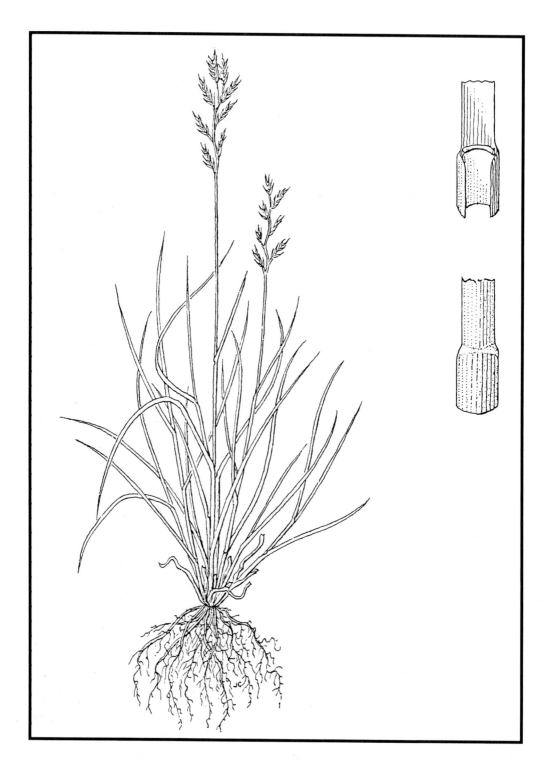

FIGURE 2: Fescue (*Festuca* spp.)

Other disadvantages include its susceptibility to fusarium patch disease, poor colour in drought and during the winter. It is less tolerant of extended periods of ice and snow cover than the finer grasses and, particularly relevant in the UK, is readily killed in low lying areas where standing water develops in extended freezing and thawing cycles over winter. When these effects, loosely termed 'winter kill', are added to the natural annual die-back of some plants in a population of biennials and short-lived perennials, there is small wonder that putting greens colonised extensively by annual meadow-grass can be weak, thin and open through the spring and early summer.

Management Factors

We have seen that annual meadow-grass has many disadvantages – far too many for it ever to provide the reasonable putting surfaces for 12 months of the year that today's golfer demands. One object of management therefore must be to reduce the proportion of annual meadow-grass throughout the golf course – not just on putting greens – to insignificant proportions.

This goal will not be achieved quickly or easily and all aspects of management must strive towards this end. It is not simply a question of using nil phosphate fertilisers and forgetting everything else. Annual meadow-grass becomes dominant in fine turf areas because it is better adapted to the prevailing conditions than anything else and it will not be possible to reduce it, never mind eliminate it, unless those conditions are changed.

The most important aspect in control is to ensure that growing conditions and all inputs will favour the browntop bent and fescue grasses. These finer grasses, particularly the fescues, are naturally adapted to drier, infertile soils which is one reason they do so well on seaside links, and they clearly have a wide tolerance of pH from acid heath to alkaline links and downland. Bents are equally at home on heavier, more moisture retentive soils of heath and moor, also characterised by low soil fertility. Neither of these grasses likes poorly drained, compact soil or excessive use of fertiliser and water. First, ensure that soils and drainage are good enough and make improvements where they are not. The main thrust of maintenance must be aimed at regular spiking appropriate to season to relieve compaction, keeping the soil open, well aerated and free draining. Compaction, and all the ills that follow, is the main enemy on intensively used areas of the golf course.

Fertiliser use must be correct, with the main emphasis on nitrogen – though without creating lush conditions from excessive applications. In particular, avoid excess phosphate since this element assists seedling establishment, rooting and seed production, all three essential stages to eventual dominance of annual meadow-grass. Many golf green soils are so over-supplied with phosphate that it will take years to deplete these reserves. Maintain inland fescue/bent turf at a low pH and ensure top dressing materials are not alkaline (including bunker sand) and also that they have the right physical characteristics to maintain or improve existing soils on greens.

Irrigate sensibly to keep the grass alive but avoid over-watering, especially on low lying and central areas which take most play. Never apply water simply to produce a soft, holding putting surface. Verticutting must be a light and regular operation throughout the summer to control thatch formation and remove flattened, straggly growths as well as seed heads. Avoid late season severe verticutting which will leave the turf surface open and thus more vulnerable to invasion by annual meadow-grass seed. Avoid cutting the greens at 4 mm or less as this will scalp the grasses and the better ones will die out and the ingress of annual meadow-grass will take place.

Only through adopting an integrated management plan with each component designed to favour the right types of grass will it be possible to look forward to a gradual reduction in annual meadow-grass.

BENTGRASSES FOR FINE TURF

There are three species of bentgrass currently available in the UK. These are: *Agrostis castellana* (Oregon browntop bent also called dryland bent), *A. tenuis* (Dutch browntop bent) and *A. stolonifera* (creeping bent). There are a number of different cultivars of Dutch browntop and creeping bents. These are listed in "Turfgrass Seed 1992", which also gives merit ratings for the different bentgrass types and cultivars. Only one cultivar of Oregon browntop bent is available and this is 'Highland'. Historically, 'Highland' was classified as *A. tenuis* but was found to be so distinct from the others in this group that it was re-classified as *A. castellana*. This cultivar has generally been more readily available and cheaper than other bentgrass cultivars. As a result, it has in the past made up the majority of the bentgrass proportion of seed mixtures containing bentgrasses.

The cultivars of Dutch browntop bent which are available and listed in "Turfgrass Seed 1992" are 'Egmont', 'Sefton', 'Lance', 'Bardot', 'Duchess', 'Saboval', 'Tracenta', 'Allure', 'Heriot' and 'Litenta'. The common name, used here, for these bents may be a little misleading as not all of them originated in Holland. Indeed, 'Egmont' and 'Sefton' were selected in New Zealand.

In the UK, 3 cultivars of creeping bentgrass are currently listed in "Turfgrass Seed 1992". These are 'Carmen', 'Prominent' and 'Emerald'. There has been much debate over the years regarding the use of creeping bents for fine turf in the British Isles. Much of this discussion has revolved around observations of creeping bent-grass performance in the USA. In America, the creeping bents ('Penncross', 'Penneagle', etc.) are regarded as the best grass for golf greens. However, what needs to be stated very strongly is that good performance in the USA does not necessarily mean good performance in the British Isles. There is a marked difference in climate between Britain and America, as a result we would expect grasses to perform differently in these two areas. In the regions of America where creeping bents are used, the summers are generally warmer and the winters colder. Creeping bentgrasses grow aggressively in warm temperatures, but become dormant under cool temperatures. A problem occurs if play is continued on dormant grass, as would happen in Britain. In America, this does not tend to occur as bentgrass greens are snow-bound for the winter months or in the Southern States of the USA the temperatures are high enough in the winter for active growth of Penn cultivars to take place. That creeping bents do not grow aggressively in the British summers and that they have a particularly short growing season, in comparison to browntop bents, was noted as long ago as the early 1960s in trial work at the STRI.

In contrast to the creeping bents, 'Highland' tends to maintain some growth during normal British winters, it also has a longer growing season than the Dutch browntop bents. 'Highland' is also more drought tolerant than the other available bentgrasses. However, in close mown turf trials at Bingley, many of the other characteristics of 'Highland' have been more comparable with the creeping bentgrasses than the other browntop bentgrasses. 'Highland' has therefore been consistently out-performed by other browntop bentgrasses. It is now STRI policy to encourage the greater use of Dutch browntop bents (*A. tenuis*) at the expense of 'Highland' in seed mixtures and purpose-grown turf for golf greens. 'Highland' is still strongly recommended for other fine turf uses, such as golf fairways, golf tees and golf roughs. In these situations the cheaper 'Highland' is probably the best bentgrass, especially when irrigation is not feasible.

CHOICE OF CULTIVARS FOR GOLF COURSES

There are two main grass species which should be used on golf courses in Britain. They are as follows: fescues and bents.

The following merit lists are taken from the STRI publication "Turfgrass Seed 1992".

Chewings, Slender Creeping and Strong Creeping Red Fescues (Tables 1, 2 and 3)

Cultivars of chewings fescue and slender creeping red fescue are shown in order of their suitability for use in close mown turf (mown at 5–10 mm). This order was determined from the mean of each cultivar's tolerance of close mowing and shoot density found in close mown trials. Strong creeping red fescues are shown in order of their suitability for use in low maintenance amenity turf. This ranking was derived from the mean ratings for cover, compactness and short growth in low maintenance trials. The new cultivar section of each table contains cultivars which have recently become available but have only been assessed in the latest STRI trials. Information for cultivars in this category should be treated with less certainty than that given for the more established cultivars in the main body of each table.

Cultivars of strong creeping red fescue are not generally suitable for use in close mown turf (cutting height less than 13 mm). Whereas, the better cultivars of Chewings and slender creeping red fescues are suitable for use in close mown turf and will tolerate mowing at 5 mm, for use in golf greens. Cultivars of slender creeping and Chewings fescues also tend to produce finer and denser turf at other heights of cut. In low maintenance situations where wild flowers are to be encouraged the less dense cultivars of fescue may be more appropriate than the high density (A or B for compactness) turf-type cultivars. However, the high density cultivars would be more desirable if ground cover and soil stabilisation was the primary objective of the low maintenance mixture.

Cultivars at the top of each list may not be the best cultivars for every use. Users should identify which characteristics are most important for their intended use and then select cultivars accordingly. Short growth will be important where the frequency of cutting is low, such as low maintenance areas. Resistance to disease will be important where the incidence of disease is likely to be high or if disease is unlikely to be controlled.

The merit ratings for each characteristic are comparable between tables. Therefore, seed specifications may be prepared which contain a mixture of the different types of fescue, using the range of desirable characteristics found in different cultivars and types of fescue. For instance, in close mown turf a mixture of chewings and slender creeping red fescues may be advantageous. This would combine the greater drought tolerance and ability to spread from rhizomes of the slender creeping red fescues with the greater disease resistance of the chewings fescues. It should be noted that there are often several cultivars of equal merit for any particular use. In such cases, the final selection of cultivars can be made according to price or other commercial factors.

TABLE 1
CHEWINGS FESCUE (*Festuca rubra* ssp. *commutata*)

Cultivar	Tolerance of close mowing	Compactness (shoot density)	Freedom from red thread[1]	Winter greenness	Summer greenness	Short growth
Baruba	A	B	B	DG	DG	C
Frida	A	B	B	MG	MG	B
Center	A	B	B	DG	MG	C
Olivia	A	B	C	MG	DG	B
Lobi	A	B	B	DG	MG	C
Enjoy	B	B	B	DG	MG	C
Waldorf	B	B	B	DG	MG	B
Bingo	A	B	B	DG	MG	D
Wilma	B	B	C	MG	LG	B
Mary	B	B	C	MG	DG	C
Atlanta	B	C	B	DG	MG	C
Alltop (LA)	B	B	B	DG	MG	B
Epsom	B	C	B	DG	DG	C
Beauty	B	C	B	MG	LG	B
Agram	B	C	B	DG	MG	B
Bellamy	B	C	B	DG	MG	C
Tamara	B	C	B	DG	MG	C
Menuet	B	C	B	DG	DG	D
Lustre	B	C	C	DG	MG	C
Weekend	B	C	C	DG	MG	B
Lifalla	B	C	B	DG	MG	D
Scarlet	B	C	B	DG	DG	C
Capitol	B	C	C	DG	MG	B
Koket	B	C	B	DG	LG	C
Tatjana	C	D	C	DG	LG	E
Barnica	C	D	B	DG	LG	D
Banner	C	C	B	MG	MG	D
Ivalo	C	D	B	DG	MG	D
New cultivars						
Nimrod (LA)	B	B	D	DG	MG	C
Bargreen (LA)	B	B	B	DG	DG	B
Rainbow (LA)	B	B	B	DG	DG	B

[1] Symptoms caused by *Laetisaria fuciformis*

TABLE 2
SLENDER CREEPING RED FESCUE (*Festuca rubra* ssp. *litoralis* etc.)

Cultivar	Tolerance of close mowing	Compactness (shoot density)	Freedom from red thread[1]	Freedom from dollar spot	Winter greenness	Summer greenness	Short growth
Barcrown	A	A	B	–	DG	MG	A
Jupiter	A	B	C	A	DG	DG	B
Logro	A	B	C	B	MG	MG	A
Recent	A	B	E	A	MG	MG	B
Estica	B	B	D	B	DG	MG	B
Oriflamme	A	B	C	B	DG	DG	B
Horizon	B	B	C	–	DG	MG	C
Dawson	B	B	C	B	DG	DG	C
Liprosa	B	B	B	C	DG	MG	C
Lovisa (LA)	B	C	C	–	MG	MG	C
Rufilla	B	C	C	–	MG	DG	C
Artist	B	C	C	A	DG	DG	C
Suzette	B	C	D	A	DG	DG	D
Hawk (LA)	B	C	D	–	DG	MG	A
Merlin	B	C	B	B	DG	LG	B
Virtus	C	D	C	–	MG	DG	C

TABLE 3
STRONG CREEPING RED FESCUE (*Festuca rubra* ssp. *rubra*)

Cultivar	Tolerance of close mowing	Compactness (shoot density)	Freedom from red thread[1]	Winter greenness	Summer greenness	Short growth
Cindy	C	D	B	DG	DG	C
Elanor	C	D	B	MG	MG	C
Pernille	C	D	C	DG	MG	D
Victor	C	D	D	DG	MG	D
Ensylva	C	D	C	DG	MG	D
Flyer	D	D	C	MG	LG	D
Ceres	C	D	C	NG	MG	D
Boreal	C	E	D	MG	MG	D
Claudia (LA)	D	D	B	MG	LG	D
Franklin (LA)	C	D	C	MG	MG	D
Commodore	C	E	B	DG	MG	E
Reptans	D	E	D	DG	MG	D
New cultivars						
Herald	C	D	D	DG	DG	D
Jasper	C	D	E	DG	MG	C
Lirosy	D	E	B	DG	MG	D
Cornet	D	E	C	MG	LG	D

[1] Symptoms caused by *Laetisaria fuciformis*

TABLE 4
BROWNTOP AND CREEPING BENTS (*Agrostis* ssp.)

Cultivar	Compactness (shoot density)	Fineness of leaf	Summer greenness	Winter greenness	Freedom from red thread[1]	Short growth
A. tenuis						
Egmont	A	B	B	B	B	B
Bardot	C	B	B	C	B	A
Duchess (LA)	C	B	B	C	B	A
Saboval	D	D	B	B	B	B
Tracenta	D	D	B	C	B	B
Allure	D	D	B	C	–	B
A. castellana						
Highland	E	D	D	A	D	E
New cultivars						
Sefton	A	A	–	–	C	A
Heriot (LA)	A	A	–	–	C	A
Lance	B	B	–	–	B	B
Litenta	–	–	–	–	–	–
A. stolonifera						
Carmen	D	C	C	C	A	C
Prominent	D	D	C	C	A	B
Emerald	E	C	C	C	A	A

[1] Symptoms caused by *Laetisaria fuciformis*

Browntop and Creeping Bents (Table 4)
Cultivars of browntop bent (*Agrostis tenuis*) and creeping bent (*A. stolonifera*), with the exception of new cultivars, are listed in order of their suitability for use in close mown turf. The new cultivar section for browntop bents includes cultivars which have recently become available but have only been tested in the latest STRI trials. Although the data for the new cultivar category should be treated with less certainty than that for cultivars in the main body of the table, the new cultivars listed have so far been found to be comparable with the very best of the established cultivars and should therefore be considered for use on golf greens. 'Highland' browntop bent is generally acceptable for most UK situations, especially golf fairways, in which bent is sown and seed of this species is usually more readily available than that of other cultivars of bent. However, for very fine turf such as golf greens the STRI now advises that finer and denser cultivars of *A. tenuis* are used in preference to 'Highland'. In other situations the compactness, summer appearance and disease resistance of bentgrass turf can be improved by replacing some of its 'Highland' content with a finer browntop bent, to the extent of 30–50% of the bentgrass fraction of a bent/fescue seeds mixture.

Golf Greens
For turf mown at 5 mm or less the traditional mixture is approximately 80% Chewings fescue and 20% browntop bent by weight. (NB The difference in seed size means that proportions of 80% fescue and 20% bent by weight are reversed when expressed by seed number, i.e. for every 2 fescue seedlings there are 8 of the smaller, weaker bent seedlings.)

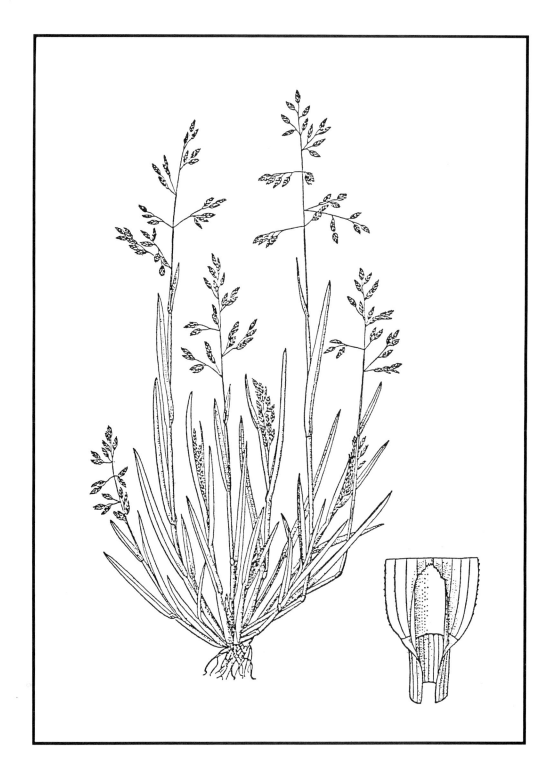

FIGURE 3: Annual Meadow-grass (*Poa annua*)

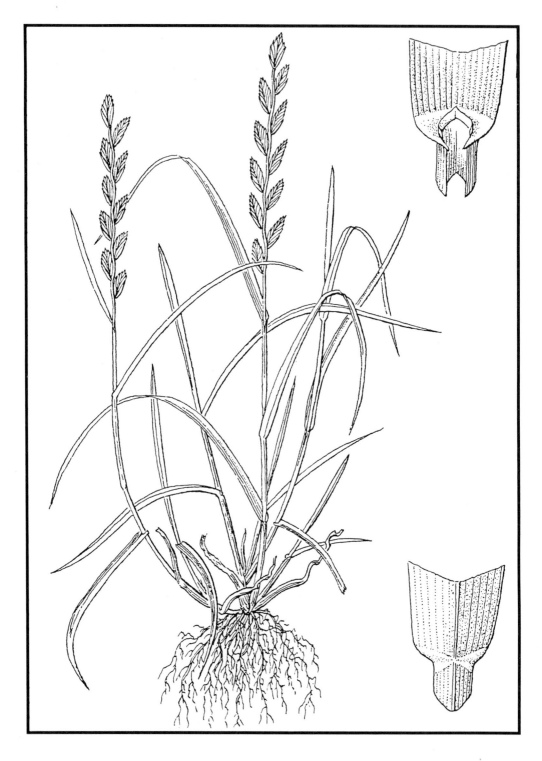

FIGURE 4: Perennial Ryegrass (*Lolium perenne*)

14

The two species will not remain evenly balanced. High fertility and adequate water will favour the bent, low fertility and dry conditions the fescue. Disease, management and weed competition will help to tip the balance. Two variations on the basic mixture can be considered – a combination of two or more cultivars or species of bent, and partial replacement of the Chewings fescue by other fescues. A monoculture of bent may also be considered.

Fairways

The most natural and appropriate grasses for UK fairways are the bents and fescues (70 or 80% fescue). There is, however, less need for the best and most compact cultivars, and therefore some possibility of financial saving. Strong creeping red fescue, which is quite unsuitable for greens, can nevertheless be used on fairways, which are mown more leniently, and the seed of acceptable cultivars will generally be cheaper than that of acceptable Chewings fescue or slender creeping red fescues.

Fairways should receive enough seed bed fertiliser to ensure vigorous establishment of the sown grasses, but thereafter they are unlikely to receive much fertiliser, if any, and they will tend to become increasingly like the mown or grazed areas of natural grassland in the locality. It may therefore be sensible to help this process by introducing other species into the fairway mixture if they are clearly well adapted to the soil and climate. Smooth-stalked meadow-grass and fine-leaved sheep's fescue are two species of which seed could be obtained, to add to the fairway mixture if appropriate.

POA ANNUA – FACTS AND FALLACIES

Poa annua (annual meadow-grass) is the commonest unsown grass species found on British golf courses. The majority of greenkeepers regard the species purely as a weed and yet close examination shows that there are some good as well as many undesirable features to this common grass. For example, many turf surfaces would be void of any cover if *Poa annua* was not present. No other species has generated so much folklore about its attributes and control as *Poa annua* from both greenkeepers and research workers. So what do we know about the species? There are many negative factors which are associated with this grass – it produces soft, slow playing surfaces, thatch problems, patchy appearance, shallow rooting in certain circumstances, disease problems, poor drought tolerance, poor winter colour and flower heads are troublesome. It also produces a large pool of dormant seed in the soil and when the conditions are right these seeds will germinate and fill any gaps in the turf.

Many Forms

Poa annua occurs as two major subspecies, each having its own characteristic growth form. One subspecies is a very upright growing plant that flowers and sets seed very rapidly, under good conditions in less than 60 days from germination. This form of *Poa annua* is strictly an annual and dies shortly after producing seed. It has been named subspecies *erecta* which describes its upright form or, alternately, subspecies *annua* after its annual life cycle. The second subspecies is a creeping plant that can, under the right conditions, form roots where its shoots trail on the ground. Known as subspecies *reptans* from its creeping habit, this form of *Poa annua* may be either an annual, a biennial or a short lived perennial. It is slower growing than subspecies *erecta* and is far less prolific in its production of flowering heads. A turf area therefore could contain populations of *Poa annua* that vary from upright annuals to lower growing creeping forms that may be biennials or perennials.

Identification of the Subspecies

This can be difficult, young plants of both subspecies are upright but as the creeping form matures it produces horizontal shoots unlike the erect annual. In general, the erect annuals are light green in colour whereas the creeping perennials are much darker green – but fertiliser treatments can change the colour. As a rule, the more intensive management and the closer the mowing, the more likely it is that the *Poa annua* will be a perennial form.

Effects of pH

Low pH does inhibit *Poa annua* – but to maintain turf at a level at which the weedgrass is excluded can lead to other problems. Acid turf may become patchy and suffer from moss colonisation. It may also begin to build up a thick thatch layer as decomposition slows down. It may be particularly susceptible to damage in droughts. On fine turf, containing the wiry grasses of fine-leaved fescues and bents, *Poa annua* can be controlled more easily by producing acid turf, as fine-leaved fescues and bents can grow at lower pH's.

Is Phosphate to Blame?

There is firm evidence that *Poa annua* is a lover of readily-available phosphate. In common with many fast growing plants, it has a high requirement for this nutrient. It does not, unfortunately, follow that withdrawing phosphate fertiliser from turf will immediately reduce the *Poa annua* content, but in the long term it will help. Apparently *Poa annua* is adapted to extracting its phosphorus requirement even from soils with low phosphate levels. It seems likely that in turf *Poa annua* will not suffer from a phosphate deficiency unless all the other species are similarly affected. Needless phosphate application should nevertheless be avoided. The application of phosphate to golf greens should only take place following a soil nutrient analysis which shows a definite deficiency of this element.

A Shallow Rooted Grass?

Poa annua is often wrongly assumed to be a shallow rooting grass. In fact, it is no more shallow rooting than most grasses, and on a loose friable soil it can develop roots to a considerable depth. It is, however, one of the few grasses that can survive with a shallow root system. It frequently invades areas where the soil is so compacted that other species are unable to survive. Under these conditions it forms an often extensive but very shallow root system. In these circumstances it is therefore susceptible to drought. A problem, yes, but do not criticise the grass when the underlying soil conditions are to blame. Hence the need for frequent deep slitting and other forms of aeration to relieve compaction.

Will it Stand Wear?

This partly depends upon the subspecies present. In trials at Bingley our native *Poa annua*, a small perennial form of subspecies *reptans*, has proved to be the most wear-tolerant of all species tested. Subspecies *erecta* is not so wear-tolerant but with its large seed output there is a constant renewal of the species in the sward. Coupled with the ability of *Poa annua* to re-root itself after disturbance, the overall wear tolerance of the species has to be rated highly.

Stress and Disease

Is *Poa annua* more susceptible to stress and disease than other turfgrass species? It certainly is intolerant of salinity in the soil and it does not thrive in shade, but generally it is fairly tolerant of other stresses. High temperature coupled with lack of moisture will kill *Poa annua* on a compacted soil or where excessive thatch build up has caused shallow rooting, but the average spells of hot weather or drought in the United Kingdom rarely last sufficiently long for this to happen. It will not tolerate snow or ice cover as long as other species but, again, it will survive in any but the most exceptional of UK winters. High levels of sulphur dioxide in industrial areas will injure *Poa annua* but no more so than perennial ryegrass. Disease susceptibility can be a problem in *Poa annua* however. The species is very susceptible to fusarium patch disease and this can kill large areas of grass under the right conditions. Disease susceptibility is probably the major disadvantage of *Poa annua* – fusarium is, after all, our commonest and most damaging disease.

Poorer Surface?

Does the invasion of *Poa annua* into turf cause a deterioration in playing conditions? There are so few turf areas without *Poa annua* that it is very difficult to say. In fine turf, with increasing demands for use from the public, *Poa annua* invariably forms a large component of the cover. However, when large proportions of *Poa annua* are present on golf greens, all agree that its presence does produce slow surfaces. Again, *Poa annua* on golf greens produces a great deal of thatch, which in turn holds large amounts of water, and the consequence of this is that greens become very soggy during winter play. This can be a major problem on the modern day golf course where golfers wish to play for 12 months of the year. Whether this is acceptable is a choice for the player and the greenkeeper. From the research side, we need more information on how *Poa annua* affects playability.

No *Poa annua*?

We cannot as yet eliminate *Poa annua* from turf. If all the *Poa annua* on our golf courses were to disappear overnight there would be a lot of frustrated golfers and embarrassed greenkeepers throughout the country. The long term aim on golf greens should be to change the management of the greens so that the ecological conditions favour the growth of bents and fine-leaved fescues and do not favour the growth of *Poa annua*. The weedgrass is thereby gradually, not suddenly, reduced. Management systems which would encourage the growth of bents and fescues would be frequent aeration to relieve compaction, avoiding needless application of phosphate fertilisers, keeping pH on the 'acid-side' and the careful use of automatic watering systems.

PLANT NUTRITION

The growth of a fully developed mature plant from a tiny, apparently lifeless seed has forever fascinated mankind. In this process the mysterious forces of life become manifest. Thus, when man began to cultivate plants for his own needs he felt it his duty to entreat the co-operation of Nature's forces in his work. However, scientific investigation has shed much light on the factors required by plants from their environment. Early European scientists put forward many interesting ideas as to which substances plants used to form their structures; indeed it was once proposed that plants were formed solely from water. It was only when chemistry became a more precise science that the composition of plants could be ascertained and hence the elements needed by plants from their surroundings could be determined.

In the early 19th century a great step forward in our understanding was made when Théodore de Saussure showed that the carbon in plants was obtained from carbon dioxide in the atmosphere. He also showed that the air supplied plants with oxygen and that water from the soil was used to construct plant tissue. De Saussure's pioneering discoveries were later bolstered by the work of the German chemist Justus von Liebig. He proposed also that nitrogen was taken in by the plant as ammonia and that other elements found in plant ash, such as potassium and phosphorus, were taken up from the soil. At Rothamsted, England, J.B. Lawes and J.H. Gilbert took up Leibig's work by setting up field experiments in the 1840's to show the elemental requirements of crop plants. Some of these experiments are in progress to this day.

Basic research into plant nutrition has become so sophisticated that now scientists investigate, in minute detail, the mechanisms used by plants to absorb chemical elements from the soil into their roots. However, the plant kingdom has not yet yielded all of its secrets.

In strict terms nutrition is the function by which plants use glucose to obtain energy. The plant itself manufactures the glucose using carbon dioxide from the air, water from the soil and sunlight by the process of photosynthesis. Although this is a highly complex and extremely important subject, it need not be gone into in any further detail here. The intention in this section is to describe the individual mineral elements which plants need to take up from the soil in order to grow healthily. It will show what these mineral nutrients are needed for, the forms in which they are absorbed and symptoms observed when a particular nutrient is deficient. The nutritional requirements of grasses are in general similar to those of all plants, but where interesting differences do exist these will be pointed out.

Nitrogen

Nitrogen (N) is the mineral element required in greatest abundance by plants. Leaves commonly contain between 2 and 5 per cent N in their tissue. It is present in proteins; in the DNA which carries genetic information, in chlorophyll (the green pigment which absorbs sunlight for photosynthesis) and within other chemicals which are needed for energy production in the plant. Thus, nitrogen has a vital role to play in the plant's well being. There are numerous other nitrogen-containing compounds, many of whose functions are not known.

The plant absorbs nitrogen from the soil solution mainly in the form of the nitrate molecule (NO_3) which, being the most soluble form found in the soil, is the most freely available to the plant root. The ammonium molecule (NH_4) can also be absorbed, along with other molecules of larger size such as urea and amino acids.

Some experiments with perennial ryegrass have shown that when the roots are grown in solutions containing both nitrate and ammonium forms of N, a greater proportion of its N is taken up as ammonium at lower temperatures. As the temperature at the root surface increases up to 25°C, a greater proportion of nitrogen is taken up as nitrate. (See Grassland Research Institute, Annual Report, 1981, pp. 19–20.)

Plants taking up their nitrogen in the ammonium form release acidity into the soil. This leads to a lowering of soil pH in the area immediately surrounding the root surface (the rhizosphere). On the other hand, if the plant is supplied with nitrate–N, the decrease in pH is not so pronounced and in some plant species an increase in rhizosphere pH has been observed. This latter phenomenon has been observed with certain grass species.

Once inside the plant, nitrate–N is converted to ammonium which in turn is used to produce glutamate, an amino acid. This can then be converted to other amino acids, for protein formation, and to other nitrogen-containing compounds. It is important for the plant that the concentration of ammonium does not become excessive as this could lead to toxicity.

The amounts of nitrate and ammonium available in the soil for the plant root vary enormously during the growing season and depend largely on the release of ammonium from soil organic matter by soil microorganisms. The ammonium is subsequently converted to nitrate by soil bacteria. In addition, the rate at which soluble forms of nitrogen are leached out of the soil has important consequences for the amounts of plant-available N. The cultivation of plants by man has led to supplementary nitrogen being added to soils through fertilizing. The materials used may be organic compounds such as dried blood or mineral fertilisers such as ammonium sulphate. Some plant species have developed additional systems for obtaining nitrogen. Here, gaseous nitrogen present in the earth's atmosphere is 'fixed' by bacteria which live in conjunction with the plant roots. (Clover and other leguminous plants can, for example, perform this feat.)

The air contains 78 per cent nitrogen but it is in such an inert form that only relatively small amounts can be converted to nitrates which the plant can use. The conversion occurs during lightning discharges in the earth's atmosphere. The fertiliser industry has to expend a vast amount of energy in order to convert the atmospheric nitrogen into natural fertiliser. However, leguminous plants have nodules on their roots containing nitrogen fixing bacteria which convert the gaseous nitrogen to organic nitrogen compounds. These are released into the plant root. The bacteria tend to be rather choosy about the conditions under which they will function and they generally require a soil of neutral pH with a sufficient supply of phosphate, a low nitrogen content and with adequate amounts of trace elements such as molybdenum. Through the techniques of genetic engineering, scientists are trying to introduce the faculty of atmospheric nitrogen fixation into crop plants such as wheat.

Because nitrogen-containing compounds are required for so many different biological processes within plants, its deficiency leads to an overall decrease in leaf growth. In grasses, the amount of tillering is suppressed. However, root growth may be enhanced by conditions of nitrogen starvation. The amount of chlorophyll (green colouration) in the plant decreases markedly, leading to a fading of the green colouration and yellowing of the leaves. Because nitrogen compounds move from the older into younger leaves during growth, it is the older leaves which first show nitrogen deficiency symptoms. In addition, as nitrogen becomes deficient leaves become more fibrous and contain less water. On the other hand, if the nitrogen supply is excessive then leaves become extremely succulent and cell walls thin. These 'softer' leaves are more susceptible to fungal and insect attack as well as being less wear tolerant and frost hardy. Excess nitrogen and soft grass growth lead to slow pace on golf greens.

Phosphorus

In nature, phosphorus is not found as a free element as it prefers to combine with other elements to form a large variety of compounds. One such combination is with oxygen to form phosphate which is the compound found in rocks, soils, animal bones and in teeth. Man has manufactured many phosphorus-containing chemicals such as the highly poisonous phosphine gas, which is phosphorus in combination with hydrogen.

Plants commonly contain from 0.3 to 0.8 per cent of their dry weight as phosphorus within various compounds. Although this is less than one eighth of the nitrogen concentration, the phosphorus-containing materials are just as vital to the plant as those of nitrogen. A group of the phosphorus compounds carry out the job of storing and transporting energy within the plant; the most important of this group being adenosine triphosphate (ATP). This stores energy in its three phosphate groups and releases it by losing one of them to form adenosine diphosphate. In order to produce adenosine triphosphate in the first place, energy is obtained from sunlight by the process of photosynthesis.

Another vital role for phosphorus in both plants and animals is for the formation of the nucleic acids DNA and RNA which hold the organism's genetic code. The growth and proper development of a plant depends intrinsically on these molecules. DNA and RNA are needed particularly where plant cell division is taking place, that is within actively growing plant tissue. It is for this reason that when plants are chemically analysed phosphorus is found at higher concentrations in young plant tissue than in the older, less active parts. The same reason explains the fact that during the young seedling stage plants have a higher requirement for phosphorus than in the older established stages. In perennial ryegrass, the greater absorption of phosphorus by the plant has been shown to promote the tillering process.

The combination of phosphate with glucose and other sugars within the plant causes them to become 'activated', allowing them to form long chains of carbohydrate. These carbohydrate chains are required to produce strong cell walls and to manufacture energy reserves for dormant periods. It has been shown that where the phosphorus content of grass plants is low, they are less cold tolerant during the winter months as a result of their weak cell walls and poor reserves of energy.

In the soil, phosphorus is present in a variety of forms, both organic and inorganic. Soils of an alkaline nature have phosphorus present mainly as calcium phosphates, whereas if the soil is acidic it is generally in the form of iron and aluminium phosphates. All of these phosphates are rather insoluble in the soil. Some phosphorus is also held within the soil's organic matter and, although it is thought that it is not normally important for plant nutrition, if the content of inorganic phosphate is low, then the organic fraction may be useful in releasing phosphate to the plant root. As with the other plant nutrients, it is the phosphate in the soil solution which is the immediate source for the root. Because the inorganic forms of phosphate mentioned above are so insoluble, the amount of phosphate released into the soil solution is extremely low at any one time and would be inadequate to maintain plant growth for any period. Thus, as the root absorbs phosphate from the soil solution, it has to be replenished from phosphate in the solid compounds of iron, aluminium and calcium. The phosphate diffuses very slowly from these solid sources, through the soil solution, to the root surface. In order to make best use of this phosphate, the plant roots have to penetrate and explore a large volume of soil. Also, by increasing the surface area of the root, the quantity of soil phosphate which can be exploited becomes greater. Plants do this by the production of tiny hairs on the root surface which may only be one millimetre in length, but can potentially allow the plant to take four to five times the amount of phosphate absorbed without root hairs. Many plants also have fungi (mycorrhiza) attached to their roots. These mycorrhizal fungi obtain carbohydrate from the plant root, but in return may help the root to withdraw phosphate from the soil. This aid is of particular importance where the soil is low in the total amounts of phosphate held.

Even when the plant has used these various tactics to increase the amount of phosphate at the root surface, it still has an uphill task to move this phosphate inside the root for despatch to the leaves. This is because the concentration of phosphate at the exterior of the root is still considerably lower than the interior. The plant thus has to expend metabolic energy in order to pull phosphate into the root; this process being commonly known as active transport. It is for this reason that the uptake of phosphate from soil is dependent on soil temperature. At low soil temperatures the root's metabolism is sluggish and it is less able to actively pull in phosphate. During cold springs when the soil is slow to warm up, the growth of leaves may be restricted by the inability of the root system to supply them with adequate quantities of phosphate. Indeed, visual signs of deficiency have been observed under these conditions.

In some species of plant it has been observed that the root system appears to react to an inadequate phosphorus state within the plant. It does this by secreting mineral or organic acids, such as citric acid, into the soil causing the normally insoluble inorganic phosphate compounds in the immediate vicinity of the root to dissolve.

Plants differ in the amounts of phosphate which they need to take up for growth. Even within the limited number of grass species used for turf, differences are evident. For example, perennial ryegrass has a much greater requirement for phosphate than browntop bent or fine-leaved fescues and it is possible that even between different cultivars of the same grass species the requirements may vary.

Although the visual symptoms of phosphorus deficiency change from plant species to species, it has been seen to cause a general pattern of colour change in the leaves of turfgrasses. Initially, the older leaves turn a darker green and then the leaf edges become red-purple. Eventually the whole leaf turns dull red in colour. If the supply of phosphate to the plant continues to be deficient, then ultimately it will die.

Potassium

The word 'potash' refers to the alkaline substances obtained when the washings of burnt vegetable matter were dried in pots. The name was Latinised to 'potassium' which refers to the pure element. In plants the amounts of potassium can vary considerably, but it commonly makes up from one to 8% of the plant's dry weight. In fine turfgrasses the potassium content has been measured at 1.2% of the dry weight of the leaf blade. Its concentration tends to decrease as the plant matures.

Although potassium is the plant nutrient required in greatest quantity after nitrogen, there is still some mystery as to why plants need such large amounts. It does not form any part of the solid structures, but tends to stay soluble in the plant sap. One of its roles may be to neutralise the negative charge on organic acids produced in the plant and on the nitrate, sulphate and chloride absorbed by the root. However, other elements such as sodium could also carry out this role. Potassium's association with the functioning of plant enzymes has been well documented. Many enzymes use the element in order to fulfil their function in promoting biochemical reactions and in this function potassium is termed as an enzyme activator or cofactor. Synthesis of proteins from amino acids is particularly dependent on potassium activated enzymes at many stages of the process.

Another function in which it appears to be specifically required is for the control of the stomata on the leaf surface. These stomata are the openings through which the plant loses water vapour and transfers gases to and from the external atmosphere. The chloroplasts, where photosynthesis takes place within leaf cells, contain relatively large amounts of potassium and so it is assumed to be required for the photosynthetic process whereby plant carbohydrate is manufactured from carbon dioxide and water.

The rate at which potassium is taken up by a plant depends primarily on its concentration just outside the root surface. It is absorbed in solution within the water which the plant withdraws from the soil. In a soil with a high potassium status, this will be the prevalent method for the movement of the element in soil solution towards the root. However, where the total potassium concentration of the soil is very low, then diffusion to the root surface assumes greater importance. This is the process by which soil phosphate moves to the root. Potassium in the soil solution is normally quickly replenished from the fraction held by the negative electrical charge on the surfaces of clay and organic matter particles; known as the exchangeable fraction. It in turn is replenished from potassium bound within the mineral structure of the clay particles and from decomposing organic matter.

If there are extremely high concentrations of soil potassium available to the root, then its uptake becomes excessive to the quantity actually required by the plant. This is known as "luxury consumption". Although high levels of potassium within the plant may not be harmful, the absorption of magnesium may be reduced, eventually leading to magnesium deficiency.

Signs of potassium deficiency are normally seen first in the older leaves. In grasses, the leaves begin to droop, the areas between the leaf veins turn yellow and the tips wither. Eventually the yellow colour extends to the whole leaf apart from the mid-vein. Because of its association with so many plant enzymes, when the potassium concentration is low the plant may be physiologically impaired without showing any of the visual symptoms mentioned. For instance, because potassium is needed for the manufacture of carbohydrate, low potassium levels will cause insufficient quantities of carbohydrate to be produced. This leads to the formation of thin and weak cell walls which cause turfgrasses to be more prone to frost damage and fungal infection. The proneness to disease infection is enhanced by impaired protein synthesis in the plant leading to an accumulation of soluble nitrogen compounds. This produces extremely favourable conditions for the spread of fungal pathogens. A plant's tolerance to drought conditions is also reduced under conditions of low potassium. This results from its role in controlling the opening and closing of leaf stomata.

Calcium
Plants normally contain 1 to 3% of their dry weight as calcium. It is of extreme importance for the physical structure of the plant, particularly in the root. The formation of membranes within the plant cells requires calcium for their integrity and if these membranes disintegrate, then all the metabolic functions cease and the cell dies. High levels of calcium are also contained in the plant cell wall and here it forms chemical compounds with pectin substances which are required for cell wall stability. It is also found within plant cells as calcium carbonate or calcium oxalate. Calcium is present on the negatively charged sites on the surfaces of clay minerals, but in calcareous soils most of it is present as calcium carbonate. Normally, it is one of the predominant elements in soil solution and is only likely to be deficient in acid sandy soils.

The signs of deficiency are first observed in young leaves. In grasses, a reddish-brown discolouration occurs along the leaf margins which develops to a lighter red. Root tips are damaged by calcium deficiency and root growth may cease altogether when deficiency is severe.

Sulphur
The dry matter of plants contains around 0.1 to 0.2% of elemental sulphur. It is found within two essential amino acids: methionine and cysteine, both of which are components of most proteins. It is taken up by the plant from the soil solution as the sulphate molecule, but the principal reservoir of soil sulphur is the organic matter which, as it decomposes by microbial action, releases sulphate. As well as being present in the soil solution, it also becomes chemically bound to iron and aluminium oxides. The soil also obtains sulphur from the atmosphere as sulphur dioxide in gaseous form or dissolved in rainwater. This is particularly significant in industrial areas. Plants are able to absorb sulphur directly into their leaves from these atmospheric sources.

Deficiency of sulphur in turfgrasses is practically unknown in Britain as many fertilisers used on golf courses contain sulphate, but its visible symptoms are similar to those of nitrogen deficiency; i.e. the leaf blades turn pale green and then yellow.

Magnesium
Magnesium is best known in plant nutrition for its part within the chlorophyll molecule which absorbs incident sunlight and gives the leaf its green colour. About 10% of the plant's magnesium is taken up in chlorophyll; the whole plant normally containing between 0.2 to 1.2% of its dry weight as magnesium. It is essential also as an enzyme activator, particularly in the enzymes associated with photosynthesis. However, most plant magnesium is associated with ribosomes in the plant cell which are required for the synthesis of plant protein. The soil solution receives magnesium from the negatively charged sites on clay particles and organic matter. Uptake of magnesium by plant roots is adversely affected by the presence of high potassium concentrations. Absorption of phosphate by the root appears to be enhanced by high magnesium levels.

Deficiency of magnesium, which is most likely to occur on acid sandy soils, produces visual symptoms associated with the loss of chlorophyll from leaves. In addition, the leaf margins turn reddish-brown in the same way as for calcium deficiency.

Micronutrients
The micronutrients are those elements which are essential for plants, but only in minute quantities ranging from 0.1 to 200 parts per million of dry weight. In many cases if their concentration is too high above normal, then they become toxic. The elements iron, manganese, copper, zinc, boron, molybdenum and chlorine are all known to be required by plants.

Iron in soils is present in large quantities, but the amounts needed by plants are only small (100 to 200 parts per million of dry matter). It is needed as an activator for several plant enzymes and is required for the synthesis of chlorophyll. In soil, iron is present principally as iron oxide. Because these oxides are relatively soluble at low soil pH, there is generally sufficient iron available in acid or neutral soils. However, at high pH iron deficiency may be encountered, resulting from the insolubility of the oxide. This is most commonly observed in soils derived from chalk and limestone. The plant takes up most of its iron in the ferrous form. Deficiency symptoms appear as a yellowing between the leaf veins with the whole leaf becoming almost white in advanced stages. Iron is commonly used in greenkeeping, not as a plant nutrient, but to give swards an attractive dark colour, to scorch moss and to give some protection against fusarium patch disease.

Manganese acts as an activator for some plant enzymes, especially within the photo-synthesis system. In the soil it is present in solution; is held on the clay and organic matter by electrical attraction; and forms insoluble manganese oxides. Like most micronutrients, there is much less present in soil solution at high pH and so less is available to the plant root. At low pH the amount of available manganese may be so high as to become toxic to the plant. The deficiency symptoms of manganese are at first similar to those of iron, but there follows the development of small distinct lesions on the leaf and the leaves droop.

Boron appears to have a role in the metabolism of carbohydrate within plants. Soil boron is derived from weatherable rocks, particularly those laid down in the sea. It enters the soil solution as boric acid and this is the form taken up by plants, but in alkaline soils the boric acid becomes attached to aluminium and iron oxides, so becoming less available to the plant root. Grasses can grow in soils of low available boron content without showing any harmful effects. Where deficiency symptoms do occur, there is stunting of the growth point and the leaves become shortened. Discolouration of the leaf interveinal regions then takes place. Toxicity is normally seen as a blackening of the leaf margins and it often occurs where irrigation water contains high levels of boron.

Copper and Zinc are both needed by many plant enzymes as activating agents. In soils they are held by clay minerals, oxides and by the organic matter. Copper deficiency causes young leaves to become rolled or curled and often causes a bluish discolouration of the leaf tip in grasses. Deficiency in zinc results in the restriction of leaf development and causes them to become thin. There is also a darkening of leaf colour. Where either or both elements are present in toxic concentrations, then the uptake of iron becomes impaired and plants show symptoms of iron deficiency.

Molybdenum is required for the enzymatic conversion of nitrate–nitrogen in plants to ammonium before incorporation into amino acids. The element is also needed by leguminous plants such as clovers in order to fix nitrogen from the air through their root nodules. It is taken in by the plant root as molybdate from the soil solution, which in turn is replenished from molybdate bound to the iron oxides. It is interesting that at high soil pH more molybdate becomes detached from the oxides, so making it more available to the plant. Deficiency is more likely to occur in acid soils. Symptoms of deficiency are shown in most plant species by a bright yellow-green mottling before the leaf withers. This first shows in the older leaves.

Chlorine is required specifically for part of the photosynthesis pathway. It is taken up from the soil solution as the negatively charged chloride and, because plants normally take in more than is required for metabolic processes, deficiency is not normally a problem. Wilting damage may occur, however, to plants growing on soils with high chloride contents such as in coastal regions where there are high inputs of chloride from sea spray.

SOME PRINCIPLES FOR THE USE OF FERTILISERS ON GOLF COURSES

Introduction

A fertiliser programme for any turf area used for golf should be based upon a supply of nitrogen in sufficient quantity to gain optimum growth. Optimum growth means sufficient growth of both shoots and roots to produce the desired playing surface characteristics, without creating a need for more treatments than are absolutely necessary.

Supply of nitrogen by natural processes is very slow, so for most turf areas extra nitrogen is needed at intervals during the growing season to assist in producing a strong turf density and resistance to wear, amongst other factors. In comparison to the need for nitrogen, the requirement of turfgrasses for other nutrient elements is very small – often absent. Where there is a deficient level of these other elements, the purpose of applying them is to enable the grass plants to make best use of the nitrogen supplied. The need for nitrogen is best assessed visually while the need to supply minerals other than nitrogen should be determined by routine soil analysis at intervals (every 3 years for the average golf green) which take into account the likely rate of leaching on a particular site, in conjunction with an understanding of the type of turf required and its status as regards establishment.

Golf Greens and Tees

On golf greens and tees the fertiliser programme should be an integral part of the maintenance of a fine-textured sward of fescue and bent, the nutritional requirements of which are rather different to those of perennial ryegrass. There is the need for some nitrogen during the growing season to compensate for wear and clippings removed, and so to maintain a good turf texture. The frequency of application must, however, be strictly controlled. This strict control is just one aspect of maintenance which is necessary to avoid the development of the excess thatch and disease problems which result in a long term deterioration in turf quality and a dominance of annual meadow-grass *(Poa annua).*

To obtain an even effect on fine turf, fertiliser is applied as a powder or as mini-granules. A basic fertiliser will supply nitrogen-only from both organic (usually dried blood and hoof and horn meal) and inorganic (usually ammonium sulphate) sources, with a view to controlling factors such as weed, moss and worm invasion and drought susceptibility, as well as the growth rate and the period of response to a single dressing.

Should the condition of the turf, the nature of the rootzone and soil analysis indicate that a wider range of nutrients are needed by the turf on a particular site for the grasses to make best use of the nitrogen supplied, then it is usually sufficient to incorporate sources of these into the spring fertiliser dressing and subsequently to supply nitrogen as necessary thereafter during the growing season.

As fescues and bents require only very limited supplies of elements other than nitrogen, there should be caution in applying other sources of nutrients as this may lead to accumulations, particularly of phosphate, in the rootzone. Over-supply of supplementary nutrients is at best a waste of money and at worst could reduce the competitive edge of the desired grasses within a sward in favour of less desirable turfgrass species.

The best fertilisers for greens and tees are prepared on the basis of soil analysis by mixing together suitable sources of the nutrients required to promote healthy turf growth at each club. Where this is carried out on site a significant financial saving can be made over using an equivalent programme of commercial products (if, indeed, an equivalent programme using proprietary products can be devised).

The application rate of any one dressing should be based on the nitrogen content, with a maximum of 40 kg/ha of nitrogen per dressing. The frequency of application during the growing season should be aligned to the minimum consistent with providing a dense but not lush turf which will give a smooth surface under mowing.

Golf Fairways

Routine fertiliser treatment of fairways is not normally recommended. The slow growth required from such areas is usually promoted by the natural processes supplying nitrogen.

SLOW RELEASE FERTILISERS

The proper healthy growth of turfgrass requires a balanced uptake of mineral nutrients by the grass plant from the soil. Nitrogen (N), phosphorus (P) and potassium (K) are needed in greater quantities than other mineral nutrients and it is essential that ample supplies of these three elements are present in the soil. The grass root absorbs nutrients in a soluble form from the soil water and so when fertiliser is applied to turf the fertiliser components must dissolve in the soil solution before the plant can take them up. On the other hand, a surplus amount of mineral nutrient in the soil solution, above that required by the turf, can lead to large losses of nutrients into the drainage water. This is particularly true for freely drained, light, sandy soils.

A material which could release enough nutrients for grass growth without any losses by leaching would be highly desirable for turf cultivation. If nutrients were released only at the times of the year when grass was actively growing, this would be even more advantageous. Unfortunately, mineral fertilisers commonly used today do not have these properties. In fact, fertiliser application causes an immediate dramatic increase in the amounts of nitrogen and potassium in the soil solution. The turf takes up a proportion of these nutrients, causing a sudden flush in growth. The nitrogen is taken up mostly in the nitrate form although some ammonium-nitrogen is also absorbed. Excess ammonium is held at the surface of clay minerals or converted to nitrate by soil bacteria. Any surplus nitrate is easily leached out of the soil. Any potassium not absorbed by the grass roots may also be held by clay minerals or leached out.

Slow release fertilisers are materials which when applied to the soil can release plant nutrients slowly into the soil solution. This confers a more even pattern of grass growth, a reduction in leaching losses and a decrease in the frequency of fertiliser dressings. In fact, because the phosphate compounds in ordinary mineral fertilisers are rather insoluble, they release phosphate very slowly into the soil solution. Fertiliser potassium, on the other hand, tends to be very soluble in the soil. Nitrogen, which is the mineral element required in greatest abundance by plants, can form many compounds which are practically insoluble in soil solution and which slowly release plant-available nitrogen compounds. Because of this, there is a potential for the production of fertilisers containing slow release nitrogen.

Natural Organic Nitrogen Compounds
Greenkeepers have been using natural organic materials for many years. These include hoof and horn meal, dried blood and the compost in top dressings. In these materials the nitrogen forms compounds such as proteins which are gradually broken down by soil microorganisms to soluble ammonium and then to nitrate. Trials on turf have shown hoof and horn to have better slow release fertilizing properties than dried blood. However, both of these natural organic fertilisers have a rather unpredictable rate of ammonium release. They also tend to produce a turf which is more susceptible at certain times of the year to fusarium patch disease than fine turf treated with ammonium sulphate.

In response to the need for a fertiliser which will slowly release nutrients in a consistent and predictable fashion, fertiliser manufacturers have produced a variety of materials. These can be divided into three categories: synthetic organic nitrogen compounds; soluble fertiliser compounds treated to reduce their solubility and fertilisers containing chemicals which inhibit the conversion of ammonium–N to nitrate–N in the soil.

Synthetic Organic Nitrogen Compounds
Isobutylidene diurea (IBDU)
In the British Isles this is the synthetic organic compound most commonly used in slow release fertilisers. It contains 32% nitrogen. Its solubility in cold water is very low, but

when added to the soil it is broken down by microorganisms to soluble urea–N which itself is further decomposed to ammonium and nitrate. The grass plant may absorb some urea and ammonium, but will take up most of its nitrogen as nitrate. Because soil microorganisms become more active at higher temperatures, the rate at which IBDU is broken down to urea increases as soil temperature rises. As the amounts of soil moisture increase, the amount of IBDU decomposition increases also. The size of fertiliser granule is important. The larger the granule, the better are the slow release properties obtained.

During the winter months when the soil temperature is below about 10°C, the microbial breakdown of IBDU virtually ceases. However, there is still a very small release of soluble nitrogen. This results from a slow, purely chemical breakdown of the compound. Trials at Bingley have shown that the small release of soluble nitrogen during the winter months leads to a better turf colour and earlier spring growth than with ammonium sulphate treatments. The use of IBDU leads to less acidification than where turf is treated with ammonium sulphate.

There is a range of compound fertiliser products containing IBDU. They contain varying proportions of IBDU along with more soluble fertilisers such as ammonium nitrate and urea.

Crotonylidene diurea (CDU)
Although used as a slow release fertiliser in Japan and some European countries, this material is not readily available in the British Isles. It contains 32.5% N and the rate at which it releases plant-available nitrogen is dependent on the same factors as those described for IBDU. As with IBDU, there is very little decomposition of CDU to urea below 10°C. Tests at Bingley have shown CDU to produce an excessively high flush of grass growth when applied in spring, although good early spring growth was obtained by a carry-over effect from the previous autumn's application.

Ureaform
This is the oldest of the synthetic organic compounds used for fertiliser. It is now manufactured in the USA and is commonly used on the golf courses of that country. Ureaform is not a single chemical compound. In fact, it contains a range of different compounds which are formed when urea and formaldehyde react together. These compounds vary in their solubility and their speed of nitrogen release to the turf. The total nitrogen content is about 40% in most commercial products.

Ureaform releases soluble urea into the soil solution, the factors controlling this release being similar to those for IBDU and CDU. However, trials at STRI have shown that the more soluble fraction of the Ureaform quickly releases plant-available nitrogen in the soil whereas the rest is released so slowly that it has little fertilizing property. This may be due to the fact that the breakdown of Ureaform to urea is much reduced below 15°C. Its application tended to make the playing surface soften and produced a turf which was more susceptible to disease and invasion by weeds. A carry-over effect from autumn application to the spring was observed.

Fertilisers with Restricted Solubility
Magnesium ammonium phosphate
The chemical nature of this compound causes the ammonium to be only slightly soluble in the soil. Any release of ammonium is due to a chemical reaction and is not so dependent on microbial activity as with the organic compounds described above. The solubility depends largely on the size of the fertiliser granule. Unfortunately, the high phosphate content of magnesium ammonium phosphate (8 N : 40 P_2O_5) makes it rather unsuitable for turf unless it is supplemented with other nitrogen fertiliser.

Trials with this compound on fine turf have shown the granular form to produce more even grass growth during the summer than does the powdered form. A carry-over effect during winter has also been noted.

Resin coated fertiliser
With this type of product the soluble fertiliser salts are coated with a plastic resin through which they can slowly diffuse out into the soil solution. There is a range of products available which contain various ratios of N, P and K. A major advantage of these materials over other slow release fertilisers is that all of the contained nutrients are released slowly to the turf, not just nitrogen. As soil temperature increases, greater amounts of plant nutrient diffuse out into the soil solution. Their slow release properties have been found to be particularly suitable for seed bed applications.

Sulphur coated urea
The sulphur coated urea product most commonly available in the British Isles contains about 32% N. By coating water soluble urea with elemental sulphur its solubility in the soil is much decreased. The urea–N gets into the soil solution by diffusing through the coating or by the decomposition of the sulphur. The rate of urea–N release increases as soil temperature and soil moisture content increase and is also dependent on the thickness and uniformity of the sulphur coating.

Trials at STRI have shown sulphur coated urea to have fairly good slow release properties on turf, but its main drawback is that the coating may be damaged by mower blades. Over a two year test period the soil pH decreased to a greater extent with ammonium sulphate than with sulphur coated urea. Over a longer period of time the sulphur is likely to cause significant acidification in the soil.

Nitrification Inhibitors
The biological process by which ammonium is converted to nitrate is known as nitrification. If this process could be slowed down in the soil, the leaching of nitrate could be diminished with a consequent decrease in fertiliser application requirements. Smaller amounts of nitrate would then be available for plant uptake over a longer period of time. A number of chemicals can inhibit nitrification. Two of the most commonly used are Dicyandiamide and Nitrapyrin. Fertilisers containing nitrification inhibitors have only recently become available in the British Isles.

Conclusions
The slow release fertilisers available on the market are by no means perfect at their job. However, they do have particular qualities which may make them useful in particular situations, even though the costs of these materials are higher than conventional soluble mineral fertilisers. The use of slow release fertilisers can lead to reductions in the quantity of fertiliser used and frequency of application. This is particularly the case on very sandy soils where there is a large leaching loss of soluble nitrogen compounds. Slow release compounds can also give a more even pattern of grass growth during the summer in comparison to the application of a fertiliser like ammonium sulphate. However, the degree of consistency of growth will depend on the type of soil and situation.

Probably the greatest advantage of many slow release products is their ability to release some plant-available nitrogen during the winter period. The grass is able to use this nitrogen when milder temperatures allow growth. In addition, the grass is able to get off to a quick start in the early spring.

Manufacturers will no doubt introduce more products with slow release fertilizing properties in the future. With the increase in promotion for individual commercial products the need for independent research into their value for amenity turf becomes more essential.

THE VALUE OF SOIL TESTING

The nature and health of a particular soil are fairly apparent to the experienced eye by the examination of a sample in the hand and by looking at the quality of the associated turf. However, often these observations are not enough. In many situations laboratory testing of soil for its physical and chemical properties can supply the turf grower with precise information which can be used as a firm basis for decision making. For instance, from laboratory tests the relative merits of topsoils to be used in the construction of a golf green can be judged accurately; or the possible need for application of phosphate and potassium fertilisers to a green can be ascertained.

The soil tests commonly carried out fall into two categories: physical and chemical. The physical analysis of soil reveals its texture, the amount of organic matter present, the rate at which water moves through the soil and the size of pores within the soil. Chemical analysis produces information on soil acidity or alkalinity, the amounts of mineral nutrients available for the grass plant to take up and the presence of toxic substances which may be harmful to the turf. Some of the tests carried out at STRI are described briefly below. They are based on methods used in soil analytical laboratories throughout the world.

Physical Analysis
Particle size analysis
In order to measure the texture of a soil (that is the proportions of sand, silt and clay present) a particle size analysis is carried out. The soil mineral material is first dispersed in water and the sand size particles separated out by passing the liquid through sieves of varying mesh size. The coarse, medium and fine sands caught on the sieves are then separately weighed. Silt and clay particles, which pass through the sieves, are mixed in a vertical cylinder of water and allowed to sediment by gravity. By finding the quantities of material which have descended to a particular depth after a set time the weights of silt and clay can be determined. The proportions of sand, silt and clay present allow the soil to be designated a textural class such as 'clay-loam', 'sandy-clay' or 'silt'.

Organic matter content
The organic matter content of a soil is determined by igniting a soil sample at 400°C in a furnace and measuring the loss in weight. Other methods of destroying the organic matter employ oxidising chemicals.

Hydraulic conductivity
This is a measure of how potentially freely draining a soil is. It depends on the size of pores within the soil. Measurements are made by determining the rate at which water will descend through a sample of soil.

All of these physical tests are of particular value when samples of topsoil are being evaluated for their suitability in new constructions of golf greens or for top dressing mixes.

Chemical Analysis
Soil pH
The acidity or alkalinity of a soil is designated by its pH value. This is measured in a soil-water mixture using a pH meter equipped with a glass electrode. The actual conditions used vary slightly from laboratory to laboratory, so it is important that the specific method used is known when comparing results.

SOIL PHYSICAL ANALYSIS

SOIL SAMPLE RE: Nowhere Golf Club   DATE: 1992

BRIEF DESCRIPTION: Soil-Sand Mix for New Green   SOIL REF.NO: 001

CATEGORY	DIAMETER mm	%	
Stones	>8	0	SOIL TEXTURE
Coarse gravel	8–4	0	Sandy
Fine gravel	4–2	0	

Particle size distribution of mineral matter smaller than 2 mm

V. coarse sand	2–1	0	
Coarse sand	1.0–0.5	22	
Medium sand	0.50–0.25	61	
Fine sand	0.250–0.125	8	
V. fine sand	0.125–0.050	3	
Silt	0.050–0.002	4	
Clay	<0.002	2	
Loss on ignition (% of oven-dry fine earth)		3	
Calcium carbonate (% of air-dry fine earth)		0	
PH		5.3	
Phosphorus (P_2O_5) (mg/litre)		20	
Potassium (K_2O) (mg/litre)		50	

FIGURE 5: Typical Physical Analysis Results from a Well-Constructed Golf Green.

SOIL CHEMICAL ANALYSIS

SAMPLES RECEIVED FROM: Nowhere Golf Club

DATE SAMPLES RECEIVED: 1992   ADVISER: —

SOURCE	pH	PHOSPHATE P_2O_5: mg/litre	POTASH K_2O: mg/litre
Green No.1	5.2	14.0	62
Green No.2	5.2	12.0	65
Green No.3	5.3	13.0	70
Green No.4	5.2	16.0	72
Green No.5	5.4	15.0	65
Green No.6	5.3	14.0	69
Green No.7	5.3	14.0	62
Green No.8	5.1	13.0	63
Green No.9	5.4	12.0	67
Green No.10	5.3	11.0	59
Green No.11	5.4	13.0	61
Green No.12	5.2	15.0	65
Green No.13	5.3	15.0	63
Green No.14	5.2	16.0	63
Green No.15	5.1	11.0	74
Green No.16	5.6	9.0	72
Green No.17	5.4	10.0	79
Green No.18	5.4	15.0	79
Putting Green	5.3	15.0	78

FIGURE 6:   Typical Chemical Analysis Sheet from a Golf Course

The obtained pH value is interpreted using the pH scale which runs from 0 to 14. As pH values decrease from 7.0 it indicates greater acidity and, as they increase above 7.0, greater alkalinity. In fact, mineral soils generally have pH values ranging from 4.0 to 8.0 with most being around 6.0 to 6.5.

The pH of soil supporting fine turf to be held at an acid pH value of around 4.5 to 5.0, while ryegrass turf should have a more neutral soil pH of 6.0 to 6.5. However, the actual values of soil pH are probably not as important as the rate at which the value increases or decreases over a number of years. When a fast rise or fall in pH is observed it is usually advisable to take remedial action.

It is worthwhile noting that although the numerical difference between a soil pH of 6.0 and 5.0 appears small, a soil at pH 5.0 is ten times more acidic than one at 6.0, which in turn is ten times more acidic than a soil with a pH value of 7.0.

Extractable nutrients
The amounts of phosphate and potassium held by a soil, which are potentially available for the grass to take up, are measured by the technique of soil extraction. This simply involves shaking a sample of soil in a chemical solution for a standard time. The soil is then filtered off leaving a clear extract in which the concentrations of phosphate and potassium are subsequently measured. The actual chemical solutions used for soil extraction vary amongst laboratories and so, as in pH measurements, it is important to know the exact method used when interpreting results.

When the concentrations of phosphate and potassium extracted from the soil are found to be extremely low or extremely high, then advice can be given indicating that fertilization is, or is not, required. When the concentrations are found to be between these extremes, the advice given on fertilizing will take into account the particular situation at which the soil was sampled.

It was stated above that the technique of soil extraction indicates the amounts of soil phosphate and potassium *potentially* available for the grass to use. This is of some importance. By looking at grass growing healthily at the beginning of the season it would probably be assumed that there is an ample supply of nutrients in the soil. However, the plant nutrient reserves may, in fact, be rather low and later on in the growing season the turf could suffer from nutrient deficiency. The laboratory tests will show if there are indeed sufficient supplies of phosphate and potassium present for the whole growing season.

At the present time there is no generally used routine method which can quantify the amounts of plant-available nitrogen in soils. Because nitrogen is the soil nutrient required in greatest amount by turf, it is assumed that it should be regularly applied.

Tests can be carried out for other nutrients in soils such as magnesium and copper. In addition, the possibility of toxicities arising from the high concentrations of metals such as copper, nickel and zinc can be confirmed or denied by laboratory analysis of soils.

Soil Sampling
When taking soil samples for physical or chemical analysis the following points should be borne in mind:

(1) The sample should be representative of the whole area under examination. Thus, if a sample is being taken from a heap of topsoil then materials should be obtained from depth within the heap as well as from the surface. If the sample is being taken from beneath established turf, then small sub-samples should be obtained from the whole area of interest,

such as the golf green, and bulked together. The reason for this is that soil properties may vary quite markedly over even a small area, and so by taking a good representative sample these differences are evened out.

(2)   The depth to which the soil is sampled should be similar to the rooting depth of turf. This will normally be around 150–200 mm depth.

An ideal way to fulfil the above two requirements is to use the soil cores obtained from hollow tining in order to obtain a sample.

(3)   The time of year at which soil is sampled is important for chemical analysis. It should be obtained as late as possible after the previous fertiliser application, but early enough for analysis to be carried out and recommendations given prior to the next fertiliser application. This normally takes four to five weeks.

(4)   For chemical analysis on established turf, samples need to be sent for analysis every four to five years. However, where turf has been only recently established, and particularly where the soil is of a very sandy texture, samples should be analysed every one to two years. This is due to the fact that there are likely to be rapid changes in the chemical properties of the soil during the initial establishment period.

(5)   When sending samples for chemical analysis about 0.5 kg of soil is sufficient. This is also the case for physical analysis except that where a hydraulic conductivity measurement is requested, 5 kg is required.

If the sample of soil obtained is heavier than that required for analysis then the sample should be well mixed before a sub-sample of the appropriate weight is taken. This should then be wrapped securely in a strong polythene bag along with a label indicating the source of the soil. A covering letter should also be sent which outlines the analyses required.

RESEARCH ROUNDUP – PROJECTS SUPPORTED BY THE R&A

Since 1984 when the R&A first committed funds to research on agronomic matters related to golf a number of projects have been implemented. In the first phase of research, projects were carried out on: fertiliser nutrition of sand golf greens, the control of fairy rings, and the physical properties of golf greens in relation to playing quality. Further work which commenced in 1987-88 includes research on: irrigation, construction and nutrition of golf greens, and phosphorus and potassium requirements of bents and fescues. In 1990 the R&A funded a project on the phenomenon of 'dry patch' on greens.

The increased funding provided by the R&A has given well needed financial support to the Institute which was then better able to support other research projects related to golf. These include projects on: the playing quality and soil physical performance of sand/soil based rootzone materials for golf green construction, slow release and organic fertilisers for golf courses, fungicides for fusarium patch disease, together with the ongoing long-term programme of testing of bents and fescues for golf greens, fairways and rough.

Fertiliser Nutrition of Sand Golf Greens

Following our experiences in advisory work of architects installing pure sand greens and then leaving the greenkeeper to look after them, we decided that the fertiliser nutrition of sand greens was an area where knowledge was lacking and opinion unsupported by facts. As experimental sand green was constructed during 1985 using 250 mm rootzone sand overlying a gravel drainage carpet blinded with 50 mm coarse sand. The area was sown with an 80:20 fescue:bent mixture. In 1986 fertiliser treatments were started including three rates of nitrogen (100, 200 and 400 kg/ha of N per year), three rates of phosphate (0, 25 and 50 kg/ha per year) and three rates of potassium (0, 150 and 300 kg/ha per year). Lime treatments were either: [a] no lime or [b] limed at 1427 kg/ha per year of calcium carbonate. This rate was chosen to neutralise the predicted acidifying effects of the 200 kg/ha nitrogen treatment (using ammonium sulphate). These treatments, which were combined in all possible combinations to give 54 different treatments, were continued over the following years and up to and including 1989.

Data collected from the experiment included: grass cover and species composition including annual meadow-grass content, green 'speed', ball bounce, ball impacts and hardness, together with chemical analysis of soil and plants.

At first the high nitrogen plots gave the best cover and became dominated by bent at the expense of fescue. Playing quality tests started in 1987 showed interesting results which were not detected by botanical assessments. Green speed decreased with increasing nitrogen and with lime. Ball bounce also increased with nitrogen, potassium and with lime. Ball impact tests gave a longer bounce length after impact with increasing nitrogen. By 1988 significant effects of sand rootzone pH had started to develop, the ground cover of unlimed plots deteriorating because of the very acidic rootzone (less than pH 4.0 in some cases) and invasion by annual meadow-grass occurred in plots which had received lime. These also subsequently developed take-all patch disease. In May 1988 phosphorus deficiency developed in plots receiving the highest level of nitrogen and without lime. By October 1989 limed plots had an average of 30% annual meadow-grass whilst unlimed plots only had 1%. In winter 1989/90 fusarium patch disease occurred in 51 plots of which 49 had received lime.

In summary, sand greens represent a nutritional knife edge. All is well to start with then things start to go wrong. If no lime is used the turf eventually becomes too acidic and does not grow properly. If lime is used the result is annual meadow-grass, take-all patch and fusarium patch diseases.

Control of Fairy Rings
Fairy rings are a common problem on turf which are often intractable to control. Field experiments were carried out on a golf course fairway of methods of control using either: [a] a fungicide (oxycarboxin) drench; [b] fungicide applied using soil injection equipment; [c] fungicide drench and soil injection combined. The combination treatment of soil injection and drenching gave good control, the drench killing fungal mycelium near the surface and the soil injection killing deeper-lying fungal mycelium.

Physical Properties of Golf Greens in Relation to Playing Quality
Much commercial research has been done on the physical properties of clubs and golf balls but little on what happens when a ball hits the turf. As a first step, a project was started comprising two parts: [i] to develop apparatus and test methods for firing out golf balls with realistic speed and spin. The apparatus had to be transportable and usable outdoors on actual golf greens. A system also had to be devised to record the ball impacts. [ii] Field work was undertaken to fire balls into greens with standard configurations of speed and spin and observe the resulting ball behaviour particularly in relation to retention of, or loss of, backspin.

The apparatus for firing balls was developed from a baseball practice machine which was dismantled, modified and remounted on a transportation trolley in a manner which allowed backspin to be applied. Ball speeds over 70 mph (35 m/s) could be produced (if this seems low remember impact speed at the green is lower than speed off the clubface due to aerodynamic drag during flight) and spins of up to c. 4500 revs per second.

Tests in the field showed that firm greens led to a retention of backspin after initial impact allowing the ball to check on the second bounce. On soft, annual meadow-grass greens more energy was lost on first impact and, because of the longer contact time between the ball and pitch mark, back spin was completely converted to topspin after impact. The work was fully reported in a PhD thesis submitted to the University of Aston in Birmingham.

Irrigation, Construction and Fertiliser Nutrition of Golf Greens
Following the interesting results obtained from the trial on sand golf greens it was felt important to study the way in which green construction, watering and fertiliser input interacted together. Greens with different constructions have different water holding capacity with the consequent implications for water and nutrient retention. Also, over-watering is suspected to be partly responsible for sward deterioration characterised by ingress of annual meadow-grass. In 1988 an experimental area was constructed at the STRI experiment ground, including three types of green construction: [a] normal topsoil 'greens', [b] pure sand 'greens' and [c] a USGA type of construction (sand/soil/peat) forming a sand dominated rootzone. Three irrigation regimes were included representing over-watering, replacement of water lost by evapo-transpiration and under-watering.

Within each of the differently constructed 'greens' are plots receiving five different levels of fertiliser nitrogen with two phosphorus and potassium regimes, i.e. 'high' P and K or 'low' P and K. In addition, on each construction are two plots devoted to soil physical measurements, principally soil moisture content. For this purpose weighing lysimeters as they are termed, have been installed in each of the 'soil physics' plots. These lysimeters each consist of a

250 mm diameter heavy duty plastic cylinder filled with the rootzone material and fitting flush with the turf surface. Grass growing in the lysimeters is mown in the same manner as the rest of the experiment. The lysimeters were installed in such a way that they can be readily removed for weighing at weekly intervals. Changes in weight reflect changes in moisture content, this in turn can be used to check the water use and calculated evapotranspiration data. Each lysimeter also contains a collecting vessel underneath so that any nutrients leaching through the rootzone can be collected and amounts determined. This is especially important in relation to ill-informed concerns about golf courses causing nitrate pollution etc. In addition, botanical and playing quality data are being collected from the trial in a manner broadly similar to that used on the sand green trial mentioned above. Analysis of the results is presently ongoing.

Phosphorus and Potassium Nutrition of Bents and Fescues

Started in 1988, this trial aims to provide greater understanding of the phosphorus (P) and potassium (K) needs of bents and fescues grown in normal topsoil greens. In the past phosphorus has been implicated in annual meadow-grass ingress but the minimum requirements of both P and K for bents and fescues on normal soils is unknown. The trial contains 4 P levels and 4 K levels in combination, i.e. 16 treatment combinations. Leaf clippings and soil samples are removed from the plots at regular intervals for nutrient analysis. Also, control treatments, without P and K applications, are sampled on a monthly basis in order to measure natural variation in leaf P and K content. So far no effect of P and K on annual meadow-grass content has been observed but normally such changes take place over a number of years so this is not unexpected.

Dry Patch

Dry patch is a condition where areas of greens become hydrophobic (i.e. water repellent). These areas occur as localised patches over a green and whilst adjacent areas may be normal and healthy, the 'dry patch' areas become drought-stressed. The soil under the dry patches becomes snuff dry and almost impossible to re-wet. This condition was particularly noticeable in the dry summers of 1989 and 1990. The condition can be alleviated by application of wetting agents **before** the condition becomes established and even then extreme persistence on the part of the greenkeeper is required in continuing the treatments throughout the growing season to prevent a recurrence, and so far no real 'cure' exists. The possibility of a cure would be greatly increased if we understood the causes of the condition. In 1990, with R&A support, a project was started on the biology of dry patch, with the following aims: [1] to define the nature of dry patch; [2] to investigate two major implicated causes of dry patch; and [3] to develop methods for dry patch control.

During 1990 an extensive review of the literature has obtained background information on dry patch from studies in Australia, New Zealand and the USA. From these studies, experimental field and laboratory techniques for dry patch research, particularly for investigating the degree of water repellency in soils and the role of fungi in dry patch formation, have been developed. Two field sites, with severe dry patch problems in the North West of England have been selected for detailed investigations into the nature and characteristics of the dry patch and adjacent normal, unaffected turf. Initial tests, using a methanol droplet penetration technique, have compared the severity of dry patch present on these golf courses with published results from golf courses in other countries.

These tests have indicated that dry patch in the UK is at least equal in severity to that recorded anywhere else in the world to date. At both golf courses selected for this work, dry patch and adjacent normal turf areas are being compared and contrasted in their biological, physical and chemical properties to define the primary differences present.

At one course the greens have, for many years, been sites of considerable superficial fairy ring activity. Research on dry patch elsewhere has implicated superficial fairy ring fungi as primary causal factors in dry patch formation since the fungal material itself may be water-repellent and in addition, they may also deposit water-repellent waxy substances into turf which they colonise. Research to date has carefully monitored fairy ring activity and its association with dry patch formation. In conjunction with Liverpool Polytechnic, techniques have been developed for the study of fungi in turf affected by dry patch. These techniques include scanning electron microscopy for the direct high-magnification observation of fungi present and also biochemical analysis by mass absorption spectrophotometry and x-ray microanalysis to detect the presence of waxes of fungal origin.

To date the question of control has not been addressed since there is considerable further work to be done in understanding the fungal flora of golf greens and its role in dry patch formation. If further funds can be obtained it is hoped to extend this work for a further two years. (*This is now underway* : Ed.)

WEAR AND TEAR ON THE GOLF COURSE

In combating wear and tear on the golf course, prevention is always better than cure. Within any maintenance programme there should be preventative components, marrying in with operations to prepare playing surfaces. As a result of the effects of all year round foot traffic on the turf, wear and tear problems do develop on greens, surrounds, tees and fairways which require routine renovation to ensure the course will be brought back into prime condition as soon as steady growth starts in the spring.

Winter Work
Forward Planning
A big disadvantage in golf course maintenance is that there is no close season during which routine repairs can be effected as is the case with bowls or cricket. Repairs therefore are generally carried out in a staged process during the autumn and spring, fitting in treatments to greens, tees and fairways as can best be done around the demands of play. In order to develop a balanced routine in this respect, it is often necessary, for example, to build alternative tees, to reshape surrounds, to rebuild bunkers, and to put in drains, so the number of routine repairs which need doing annually in the future will be minimised, keeping each part of the course in play as much as possible. The identification of priorities for future amendments to course layout is generally best done in winter, when a golf course will show up in its worst light. Subsequently, there is plenty of time for planning the implementation of these jobs during the following autumn. With good forward planning, amendments to the course will take a minimum of time and effort.

Bare Ground
Large areas of bare ground should be returfed. When returfing, make sure that the turf being laid will match in with the surrounding grasses. Otherwise it will stick out like the proverbial sore thumb once growth returns and it can stay that way for many years. Also, take care that the soil being brought in at the turf base is not of a fine texture, i.e. not clayey or silty. When compacted, such soils will tend to prevent free drainage.

Finally on returfing, do provide a smooth finish for good presentation and subsequent smooth mowing once the turf has established. Returfing is a lot easier if the turf has been lifted to an even thickness.

Thin Turf
Where the turf has thinned on greens, tees and fairways is usually an area where the topsoil has become severely compacted. During the winter months, when ground conditions are moist but not saturated, it is very important to frequently aerate these areas. This may well involve doubling up with deep mechanical aeration on problem areas, and, on greens, carrying out local hand forking. It is necessary to do this so that as soon as growth weather returns in the spring the turf has the opportunity to grow away quickly and reknit.

On greens, thin areas are usually found to the front, on the line to the next tee, and around prime pin sites within the putting surfaces. To help avoid extra trampling of these areas when ground conditions tend to be wet for prolonged periods (which would result in further damage to the topsoil) careful pin positioning is required. Over the winter period it is essential to use second and third choice pin sites to give well used sections of greens a rest. So, do not just use forward pin positions during the winter, place the flag right around the margin and, to a sensible extent, on slight slopes too. When applying a longer winter cut, and when damper surfaces are prevalent, the greens will tend to be slow, so a ball will not tend to run on and away from less than ideal pin sites.

It may be possible with careful flag positioning to vary the routes taken by players on and off the greens. This will help to spread wear over surround areas.

Paths and Tracks

During the winter there is often a need to deal with muddy paths on a golf course. In helping to dry these up, the choice of material to be used is important as a material which will stay where it is placed is needed but at the same time it cannot be solid. Nor can it be so hard it will damage cylinders or bottom blades of mowing machinery if some of the material spreads out over adjacent mown turf.

Ash, cockleshells and bark are first choice materials for this purpose. Whilst coarse sand can also be effective, it does tend to be expensive and more easily lost into a muddy soil. Gravel will spread out and damage mowers.

Concrete and tarmac tend to be too expensive and ugly for widespread use on a golf course. They have other drawbacks too, in that concrete will not take a spike, so can be slippery, whilst tarmac could be ripped up by spikes if it softens in hot weather.

Bunkers

Many bunkers need routine topping up with fresh sand to replace losses due to wind blow, blast and mixing in with the underlying soil. A minimum of 100 mm firmed depth of sand is required over bunker floors, which represents 10 m³ sand per 100 m² surface area. A good bunker sand is a lime free material, predominantly in the medium to coarse particle size ranges, i.e. with the majority in the size range 0.25–1.0 mm in diameter. A laboratory test will be required to determine the sand quality.

Planning for Spring

In the Office

During January and February there are usually a number of days when the weather is not fit for work on the course, which gives the opportunity for looking through catalogues and preparing for a prompt start when spring arrives. Having all the necessary materials to hand for application as soon as signs of steady growth are evident will make it possible to put a summer finish on the course as quickly as the weather and conditions will permit.

Top Dressing

A primary spring treatment on greens, aprons and tees will be top dressing. The purpose of top dressing on greens will be first and foremost to smooth out putting surfaces disrupted by the pitch marking and foot printing which arises due to winter play. Nevertheless, the sandy mix to be applied for this purpose must be carefully chosen, with a view to matching, or indeed improving on, the quality of the underlying topsoil too. An amount in the order of 1 kg sandy compost per 1 m² of green should be provided for this spring dressing.

Tees too will need an overall top dressing in spring as growth begins, primarily to smooth out any superficial bumpiness. However, as a secondary benefit, the compost or soil used may also protect any seed broadcast in combination with the top dressing operation, with a view to encouraging a complete sward cover.

For tees without a means of irrigation a screened sandy soil, or a less sandy mix of sand and soil than would perhaps be used on greens, will be appropriate. Having said that, where grass winter tees have to be renovated, a good sand (e.g. again a medium to coarse, lime free material) will be the more appropriate top dressing to apply, aiming for maximum surface stability during future winter play. For each tee a rate similar to, or even slightly more than, that for greens suggested above should be applied.

Reseeding
While it is usually the case that spring oversowing is not required on greens and fairways, the opposite applies to tees. On main tees, select a seeds mix for this purpose which matches in well with the grasses that make up the turf. In the majority of cases this means using a seeds mixture of fescues and bents for oversowing purposes on tees.

Fertiliser
The spring fertiliser treatment is a key operation for all fine turf areas on a golf course. The need is to promote growth by careful applications of nitrogen to achieve a rapid progression to uniformity after mowing.

Over the winter soluble nitrogen will be leached from the soil and until natural breakdown of the organic content of the soil can start up as soil temperatures rise in spring, there is little if any nitrogen available to the grass plants for the promotion of growth. So, where such applications are cost-effective (i.e. mainly on greens and tees) it is necessary to provide a stimulus to growth by applying chemicals which supply nitrogen. Ammonium sulphate is the principal fertiliser used to encourage each grass plant to grow to mowing height and to encourage tillering, so that worn areas will fill in.

It can be taken as read that each green and tee will require a dressing of fertiliser in spring, but the need for fertiliser application on fairways is minimal. The fairways as a whole receive less intensive wear than greens and tees; the height of cut is not quite as close; and there is no removal of nutrients through boxing off when mowing. All these factors coming together mean that routine overall applications of fertiliser are unnecessary in nearly every case. However, this does not mean that an application of nitrogen on local worn areas will not be appropriate.

Waiting for Warmth
Even if the best overall renovation programme has been carried out during the winter and all is in hand for a prompt start in the spring, little can be done to bring the turf into summer condition until soil temperatures start to rise. The date at which this occurs tends to vary from year to year, depending upon the passing of night frosts.

This means that getting the best effect from spring renovation calls for careful timing, and this is where experience tells in effective golf course management.

GOLF GREEN RESEARCH

In any research programme, the ideal management programme for newly constructed golf greens may be arrived at by creating a range of surfaces using as many different combinations of turf management procedures as possible and establishing which combination produced the best surface. When the R&A approved research to be carried out into the interactions between construction, irrigation and fertiliser nutrition of golf greens, this form of approach was decided upon. Three types of golf green construction were investigated. These were two suspended water table constructions, consisting of a pure sand and a United States Golf Association (USGA) specification rootzone overlying a blinding layer and gravel carpet, and a simple topsoil with pipe drainage construction. The USGA specification rootzone was basically a selected sand with a little peat and soil to improve the moisture and nutrient retention capacity of the medium. Three different rates of irrigation were applied to the construction types, one rate representing adequate replacement of water losses, and two others representing 140% (over-watering) and 60% (under-watering) replacement. Five progressively increasing rates of nitrogen fertiliser were applied, with or without phosphate fertiliser, to ten subdivisions of each construction type. The whole design produced 90 different combinations of treatments, 30 on each construction.

The trial was constructed in the summer of 1988, and the irrigation and fertiliser treatments were imposed on established bent/fescue turf from April 1990. General management practices appropriate for the maintenance of fine turf were carried out and artificially simulated golf wear was applied.

Having produced the wide range of surfaces from the diverse treatment range applied, the means of identifying the "best" ones had to be devised. The concept of golf green turf quality may be divided into visual and playing quality aspects. The simplest means of finding out how the visual quality of the different turf types varied was to ask golfers, the "consumers", to score the turf according to their own subjective opinion – a sort of market research. When such a survey was carried out in May 1991, the general response to increasing nitrogen rate was an increase in turf merit until around 400 kg per hectare per annum nitrogen, after which merit declined. Phosphate fertiliser on the sand and USGA constructions produced consistently higher merit scores than untreated areas. Phosphate fertiliser did not alter the merit scores of the soil-based greens, but the response to nitrogen was considerably less pronounced on sand greens not treated with phosphate. Under the optimum conditions of nitrogen and phosphate input, the USGA constructions produced the finest looking surfaces, and the soils produced the worst.

The golfers were able to distinguish very clearly between the effects of different treatments. However, peoples opinions of what looks nice, like fashions, may alter with time. It is also difficult to obtain golfers who are prepared to do research work like this on a regular basis. As a result, this technique of visual quality evaluation couldn't become a standard method of golf green assessment. After measuring several different features of the turf it was found that no single measured characteristic was as sensitive or able to reproduce the general responses to the treatments as detected by the golfers. The closest was the measurement of reflectance ratio. This is a combined measure of the net effects of the total amount of live grass cover, the species present and and the overall greenness of the grass. In general, golfers were found to be unconcerned with the actual species present, but made their quality assessments on the basis of the total amount of live grass cover and its colour (greenness).

The abundance of bent in the swards varied with the fertility of the treatments received and of the rootzone media themselves. Bent cover increased with increasing nitrogen fertiliser rate and was highest on the soils and lowest on the sands. On sands, and to a lesser extent on the USGA constructions, the application of phosphate fertiliser also increased the abundance of bent. On soils it had little effect, although the swards in these cases were almost entirely composed of bent anyway. The amount of fescue in the swards generally behaved in an opposite manner to the bent, its abundance declining with increasing fertility of treatment. The irrigation treatments showed no effects in the first year, mainly because the treatments applied over this period were not severe enough and did not have sufficient time to take effect. In October 1991 however, it was found that under-watering, combined with high rates of nitrogen input, brought about the death of the turf on the sand-based rootzones, producing some extremely unsightly surfaces.

Annual meadow-grass (*Poa annua*) remained virtually absent from the sand and USGA rootzones. However, on the soils its abundance increased with increasing nitrogen rate. After two years of treatment, infestation had reached 35% of ground cover on the highest nitrogen, soil-based greens. No effects of phosphate fertiliser on annual meadow-grass were detected.

As a playing surface, the golf green has two roles to play with regard to the game. These are the provision of a surface over which the ball may be rolled during putting, and onto which balls may land after chips or drives. For putting, a set of green speed guidelines have already been developed by the United States Golf Association. Basically, when mowing at a cutting height of 5 mm, the faster the better. Assessment of the speed aspect of playing quality was therefore relatively straightforward. A rolling ramp was developed and the distance travelled by balls rolling across each green type was measured. These measurements showed that increasing nitrogen fertiliser rates slowed balls down. The application of phosphate fertiliser to the sand-based constructions also slowed down green speed. The sands produced the fastest and most consistent surfaces, but the effects of fertiliser rate were much more influential than construction type in governing roll speeds.

By firing golf balls onto the simulated greens with degrees of backspin, velocity and angle of approach comparable to those imparted by a 5-iron shot, the behaviour of golf balls after impact with the turf was studied. In October 1990, when the turf was generally quite moist, a maximum distance travelled by golf balls after impact was found at a nitrogen fertiliser application rate of around 250 kg per hectare per annum nitrogen. At rates above and below this the distances declined. Most of this distance was travelled during the first bounce of the ball. On sand-based greens, the balls tended to bounce further than on the soils. This contrasted with the pitchmark depths which were shallowest on the sands and increased with increasing nitrogen rate. The degree of "screw-back" after the ball had completed its first bounce was unaffected by fertilisers on USGA and soil greens. On sands however, there was some evidence to suggest that increasing the rate of nitrogen fertiliser brought about an increase in the degree of "screw-back" of the balls, suggesting a greater degree of backspin retention or holding power.

The work discussed here is largely descriptive. Over the period of the project, soil chemical analyses have been carried out, examining the rootzone pH, phosphorus, potassium and calcium content. In addition, the behaviour and effects of water in the construction types have been extensively studied in an attempt to provide explanations for the changes in turf quality which have been described. These results are not intended to be interpreted as advisory recommendations. It is hoped that by obtaining an improved understanding of the way in which turf responds to different treatments, as opposed to the unquestioning acceptance of dogma and commercial propaganda, management practices may be developed which lead more directly to better playing surfaces and happier golfers.

WINTER PLAY ON THE GOLF COURSE

A New Phenomenon?

Winter play on golf courses is nothing new. Ever since the game evolved on seaside links the winter period has been important – being close to towns where the native population are busy servicing holiday-makers through the summer, the winter being the locals playing season. The last 15-20 years of golf 'boom' has seen a dramatic increase in play right through the year and far more competitive winter golf. This can lead to conflicts of interest between a desire to protect the course through periods of adverse weather and the wishes of golfers who want to stay on the same measured course. A predetermined policy concerning play during the winter is a must to minimise conflict between Head Greenkeeper, Committee and golfer.

Year-Round Play?

The demand for year round play can only be met by good drainage. A dry turf and soil profile has a better chance of withstanding wear and tear by limiting compaction. Wet surfaces quickly churn to mud, reducing grass cover and playing quality. Greens are probably the most freely draining areas on golf courses these days. This, in itself, can cause problems when golfers see playable greens on their way to the Clubhouse only to find the 'Course closed' sign out to protect other areas of the course unfit for play. Heavy soils are, obviously, most prone to drainage difficulties. Improvements can be made to natural drainage though this may involve costly and disruptive redesign and the introduction of pipe drainage. In some circumstances employing intensive aeration operations and controlling traffic flow may be all that is necessary. Courses on freer draining land do not come through winters unscathed. These courses receive extra volume of play when other courses in the vicinity on heavier soils have to close, this additional traffic can cause significant wear damage.

Snow, Standing Water, Frost and the Potential for Damage

Snow cover and waterlogging are generally accepted as conditions unsuited to a continuation of play. The type of damage noted on different areas of the course will be similar under the same adverse conditions. The degree of damage will relate to soil condition (drainage potential and degree of compaction), height of cut – the tighter the cut the less resistant to wear, topography and amount of traffic. Design greatly influences the potential for winter disruption. Shaded areas will hold frost, snow and surface water longer than exposed ones. Saucer-shaped greens, or those containing low spots, low lying approaches and 'valley' fairways will pose drainage difficulties. Confined traffic routes will concentrate wear and exacerbate the difficulties posed by poor ground conditions, not only in green approaches and beside tees but also walkways from green to tee, tee to fairway and around carry features.

Snow cover is an obvious deterrent to play. Melting snow and prolonged heavy rain produces massive quantities of water and soft, wet surfaces. These must be allowed to dry out sufficiently as recommencing play too quickly onto saturated ground will promote churning up, resulting in the course resembling more a battle ground than a golfing arena. Warm rain in the summer stimulates strong growth, rain in winter allied to freezing temperatures produces exactly the opposite effect.

Play during and after frost can promote damage, the degree being related to the type of frost, timing and level of play, and the frequency of occurrence. Hoar frost is deemed to be insignificant and any slight bruising of brittle grass stems can recover relatively quickly. Penetrating frost is another matter. A solid frozen surface may seem playable but once the frost begins to thaw a wet surface can ride over deeper frozen ground when played upon, resulting in shearing of roots as well as muddying around pin positions and walk on/off points. Experience has shown that through periods of alternate freezing and thawing it is best to break the ice where frozen water lies to reduce potential damage. The greens are the area of the course most prone to damaging effects. The most obvious sign of damage will be discolouration of ground around pin positions and poor levels in these areas where golfers have stood near the hole to retrieve their ball. Longer term deterioration to sward quality is more serious and related to root shearing. Weakened root structure will detract from a rapid response to good growing conditions in the spring, delaying the availability of quality putting surfaces for the main competition season. Every winter golfers complain that greens are being closed due to frost when they "never were in the past with no sign of damage", and "the course down the road keeps their greens open". Playing on frost bound greens one or two days each winter may do no serious damage, particularly on lighter soils, but prolonged play – and once a precedent has been set it can be impossible to reverse – can delay strong growth in the spring. Comparisons between Clubs, even in very close proximity, must be avoided and the benefit of closing greens during periods of adverse weather will be noted by more rapid pick-up in their appearance and playing quality later in the year.

On the greens thinning grass cover affects trueness and a turf more susceptible to disease in spring. The damage caused by winter play can be even greater in surrounds and approaches which attract heavy wear as golfing traffic is drawn into narrow walk on/off routes. The placement of greenside bunkers and banks, together with severe contouring, can reduce the area over which traffic can be spread. If the same routes are used year round then compounded wear damage will result in thinning cover and soil erosion. Muddying up and grass loss are the most obvious signs of wear damage but possibly of greater potential disruption is the varying degrees of compaction induced in immediate approaches through heavy winter play. During the spring and summer golf balls landing short in such an approach will either hit a hard, compacted patch and run over the green or, alternatively, land softly. This 'unknown' can create impossible playing conditions for shots to the green, particularly on those courses where 'pitch and run' is an integral part of the game.

Tees are usually raised above ground height which can reduce drainage problems but congregation of golfing traffic is directed on and around tees, small teeing grounds and their surrounds being most prone to damage. The fact that the ladies do little damage to their own tees may permit them to remain on them right through the winter. "What's sauce for the goose ...". This can pose another conflict situation whereby the men want the same treatment. It usually only takes a week or two's play by the men through the wetter weather for them to realise the damage they will do to their tees and it is not difficult to encourage the taking off of play through the winter. By then the damage is done and up to one third of the summer teeing area may be lost.

Fairways will not escape from deterioration caused by playing during adverse weather, though the effects will be widespread and not as obvious. However, if the same routes to and from greens and tees are used year round the same picture is painted to the damage scenario on green and tee surrounds. Walkways, by their very nature, support concentrated traffic and, on a wholesale basis, fairways severely weakened by two years drought will greatly benefit from rest.

Unfortunately, golfers seem to need to see signs of physical damage through their activity to appreciate the reasons for taking play away from greens, tees and traffic routes utilised during the summer competition season. By then it is too late to repair the damage, winter is the time of minimal grass growth and any recovery response will be delayed to the spring or early summer. The idea behind preserving playing areas during periods of weather when wear damage will be severe is to provide greens and tees in the best condition for the longest possible duration.

Controlling Damage

In general, improving drainage capabilities will reduce the degree of damage produced by winter play. There are other ways and means of controlling excessive wear, e.g. confining damage to areas around the course where it is more acceptable, areas that rarely come into play through the summer and hence have a full growing season to recover. Prevention has to be preferable to cure.

The greens and surrounds are probably the main areas on the course where there will be little resistance to spending money if redesign or the introduction of drainage schemes are likely to provide benefit. Taking out or remodelling features that limit spread of play on the putting surface and in the approaches and surrounds can dramatically increase the traffic zone into and out from greens. The introduction of cut-off drains at the foot of surrounding banks or intensive aeration work in local wet patches may improve matters. Increasing the size of the putting surface to provide more room to spread pin placements and, hence, wear may be necessary. The practice of placing winter pin positions round the perimeter, concentrating on the area closest to the next tee, will reduce localised wear though the size of green plays an important factor. Concentrating pin positions to the front of greens is common practice but not necessarily a good one. This focuses traffic in green approaches and can produce weak aprons for the start of the summer season, poor grass cover giving bad lies for chip shots or putts and inconsistent bounce from hard, compacted ground.

When conditions dictate the main greens will have to close. There are no hard and fast rules as to the period over which they should remain closed, the duration of frost, snow or saturation will determine that. With the need to close greens at some point through the winter it should be part of the course management programme to prepare temporary greens well in advance. To provide an acceptable surface a level area of at least 200 m^2 should be maintained throughout the year, perhaps to the same standard as the green apron. Siting is very important, away from green approaches to take traffic on a different route, ideally to the side of the fairway nearest the next tee. To present these temporary greens in good condition they must be protected and considered "Ground Under Repair" when not in use, another good reason for placing them away from the approach to the main green. Some form of traffic control may be necessary; ropes, hoops, white line marker, signposts, to direct golfers around the course the way you want to take them. If there is additional land in the Clubs possession, inadequate for an extra 9 or 18 holes, the building of 2 or 3 extra holes which can be incorporated into the existing layout can enable the resting of a few holes each year, those which are most prone to winter damage. Where design allows changing the sequence of holes will take traffic on routes which may otherwise never see a single foot print.

Exceptionally large, well drained teeing grounds may be able to take year round play. These are few and far between and many Clubs are looking to long term tee building programmes to provide turf tees through the winter, a reaction to unfavourable comparisons between natural turf and artificial mats. Grass grows very slowly through the winter so play induced wear damage during the winter will be evident going into the growing season. It is preferable to provide separate tees to take traffic on different routes than have a single 'land mass' taking all the play. Adjacent level areas of fairway are often used for winter tees but are subject to drainage deficiencies and do little to re-locate traffic routes. On holes where there is simply no room to extend teeing area and undulating ground nearby a mat could provide the only answer. Mats should be sited away from main grassed tees, otherwise the same traffic routes and congregation areas will be used. Do not always site alternative tees forward of the main summer ones. In the colder winter golf balls travel shorter distances so forward tees encourage use of the same fairway landing areas. The idea of temporary marked out trolley parks can regulate traffic flow around tees, moving the parks from time to time. The introduction of pathways and additional drainage in tee surrounds may be necessary if there are no options for limiting wear in specific areas.

On fairways localised drainage schemes may be feasible in particular trouble spots. Physical barriers such as fencing or ropes may be essential to protect worn walkways and other weak areas. Encouraging golfers to walk down semi-rough can help restore fairway condition but with all re-routing fences or ropes should be moved once every 2–3 weeks or so to spread the load. 'Winter Rules' promotes placement as a means to providing golfers with acceptable lies, out of old divot marks and tyre tracks, but its value in retaining grass cover must be questioned and replacement of divots must be positively encouraged. On severely weakened fairways teeing up may be a better option.

Limiting Play
Trolley bans can be productive if implemented early enough – before worn 'paths' are produced. It is not just the weight of the trolley but the number and all the feet that go with them tracking along the same line. Electric trolleys also scuff turf when they start moving. Significantly less damage is produced when golfers play with fewer clubs in a lightweight bag enabling them to move away from the conventional traffic routes.

Design has a great influence on what can be achieved on small courses where there is limited capability to vary traffic routes. Where there is simply no opportunity to rest affected routes the introduction of artificial paths must be considered. Any such introduction must satisfy golfing, management and aesthetic criteria. The alternative is renovation of damaged turf by relieving compaction, relevelling and returfing – a costly and time consuming exercise. Only so much can be renovated in one year and if the degree of erosion is repeated each year such works are inappropriate and there is a necessity for stricter control measures or the introduction of pathways.

There is always consternation from within the Clubhouse when greens are closed through the winter. However, some Clubs have now reached a point where overplay through two exceptionally dry summers and mild winters is being recompensed by complete course closure for 2–3 months in winter. In addition to seasonal regulation of play thought may have to be given to a general reduction in the amount of year round play. Balancing the requirements of income to outlay may mean financial inducements to limit membership and reduce society play.

Summary
There is a general awareness that the majority of our courses are currently being overplayed. Permanent bare ground designates 'pathways' around many courses, particularly on entry and exit routes to greens and tees. This wear factor causes enough problems through the growing season; combined with minimal growth and winter conditions of snow, rain and frost could signal disaster for some of our courses - that is, of course, assuming that golfers still want to play on grass! The greenkeeper and agronomist appreciate that golfers want to play on the measured course right through the year and work towards that goal. However, we must all accept limitations imposed on us by poor draining sites, the weather, imposed management deficiencies and wear level. Unless far more appreciation is given to the desperate need to rest well worn areas, in addition to promoting drier surfaces, the future could see nothing but further deterioration and complaints about the condition of our courses.

TOURNAMENT PREPARATION

Organisation is the key word whether preparing for a major Championship or an important Club competition. There must be regular and effective communication between Head Greenkeeper, Committee and any overall Committee organising the event. The aim is to prepare a course with uniform conditions that are appropriate to the level of play expected.

There may be requirements from the overall organising Committee for additional size or length alteration at Championship tees, possibly alterations to bunkers, almost certainly some redefinition to tighten fairway lines, semi-rough and rough. Spectator car parking, pedestrian traffic routes through the course, and maintenance routes will all need planning in advance and marking out.

Where new tees and bunkers are involved, planning and construction may well have to start at the latest two years in advance of a major such as the 'Open'. At least one year in advance, adjustment should be made to fairway mowing lines, steps taken to encourage rough or semi-rough to grow in, and work on fairway bunkers completed.

An overall plan of the course with all the above marked on it is essential, together with checklist, timetable and progress chart.

Checklist
Greens
(1) Potentially disruptive aeration treatments such as Verti-Draining should be completed 18 months to two years in advance of a major Championship where needed. Avoid hollow coring in the spring prior to the event if possible.

(2) Top dress lightly, but frequently on three or four occasions in spring until satisfied with the smoothness of putting surfaces.

(3) Reduce any soft, thatchy build up at least a year in advance. Verticut lightly in spring prior to top dressing, and weekly with growth to within two or three days. Increase frequency of grooming to suit weather and growth.

(4) Apply a final feed ten days in advance so that growth flush is tailing off.

(5) Mow daily for several weeks in advance. Reduce the height of cut gradually over the final 14 days from 5 to 4 or 3.5 mm (bench setting) if using a triple mower. Double cut on the days of the competition, especially where using a triple mower.

(6) Avoid over-watering, aim to produce firm, true surfaces.

(7) Reserve pin positions which will be used during the event at least six weeks in advance. Allow for a balanced selection of placings over the course as a whole, e.g. six relatively hard, six moderate and six relatively easy. Anticipate walk-on and off wear patterns.

(8) Ensure that hole cutters are sharp and cut a perfectly circular hole 108 mm in diameter. The hole cup to be set 25 mm below the putting green surface. Paint the exposed soil white.

Green Surrounds
(1) Maintain surround at a height intermediate between that of putting green and fairway. Mow once or twice a week according to growth in the months prior to the tournament, every day during the event.

(2) Mow collars and aprons twice a week in the month beforehand, boxing off clippings. Verticut lightly, the last treatment being completed 10 to 14 days before the event.

Tees
(1) Top dress with appropriate sandy mixture to provide firm, true and level surfaces.

(2) Adjust use of water to maintain some growth, yet provide a firm stance.

(3) Reduce thatch and eliminate moss over the prior 12 months, especially on little used Championship tees.

(4) Reserve areas of Medal/Championship tees, protect a good part of par 3 tees during any practice days.

(5) During the event mow daily at need, boxing off cuttings.

Fairways
(1) Establish required fairway outlines a year in advance, especially on slow growing links.

(2) Carry out aeration, supplementary watering, renovation and weed control at need during the prior 12 months to provide a uniform and complete grass cover with finer, hardy bents and fescues predominating.

(3) In the run up to a major Championship there is some merit in protecting major landing zones, especially a short iron shot to the green during the prior winter and early spring. Divot repairs should be carried out daily during the tournament.

(4) Reduce height of cut to predetermined level through spring, mow daily during the competition.

(5) Eliminate spongy thatch during previous growing season(s). Light raking or brushing in the spring can be useful to reduce any soft, fluffy thatch.

Rough
(1) Establish required line of semi-rough and rough one year in advance and fertilize if necessary on infertile or very sandy soil to encourage adequate growth.

(2) Control weeds, particularly clover.

(3) Reduce heavy thatch or nap in semi-rough with verticuts or flail scarifiers a year in advance.

(4) Mow at designated heights for Championship at least a year in advance.

Bunkers
(1) Complete all major reconstruction and/or repairs to fairway bunkers two winters in advance. Finalise greenside bunker repair/rebuilding faces the winter before.

(2) Replenish sand, and top dress to provide 100 mm depth minimum over floor area and a skim up faces six months in advance.

Additional Points
(1) Decide on flag colour and that of flag sticks, purchase requirements and spares.

(2) Provide (coloured) boundary stakes, spray paint for definition of hazard boundaries, ground under repair.

(3) Arrange additional manpower for tidy-up jobs, emptying litter baskets, etc.

(4) Arrange back-up/loan of mowing equipment, water removal units. Locate source of mobile pumps for emergency use.

(5) Erect additional bridges as necessary at burns and ditches.

(6) Provide short range radio communication for key staff members.

(7) Arrange for care of greens and bunkers during play.

(8) Co-operate with installers of broadcasting equipment, hospitality tents, stands, temporary car parks and routes.

(9) Check provision of tables, chairs and public address system for awards.

(10) Install traffic route post and rope markers a week before, check daily during the competition.

SECTION 2

GOLF GREENS

THATCH ON THE GOLF GREEN

The accumulation of a layer of fibrous material is a natural feature of turf development and cannot be entirely prevented. Total prevention would in fact be most undesirable as a surface with no underlying fibre would lack resiliency and would easily become muddy in wet weather. However, when fibre builds up to an excessive degree it becomes a problem. About 15 mm of matted material would be acceptable on the golf greens, while a 25 mm layer would begin to prove troublesome. The 100–150 mm layers which are not infrequently seen make turf maintenance and the formation of good playing surfaces extremely difficult.

Most people who are experienced in turf management will realise that there is more than one form of thatch or fibre. In the past, words like mat, thatch or fibre have been used very loosely and more precise definition of terms would therefore be of value. The following classification could be a guide:

(a) *Litter*
A loose and fluffy accumulation of grass clippings and decaying leaf bases and sheaths in between the grass stems at the base of the sward. Litter is not usually seen on intensively used or well managed turf but is more characteristic of old and neglected lawns which are perhaps cut weekly without boxing off clippings and which receive very little additional treatment.

(b) *Fibre*
Fibre resembles coconut-matting, being tough and wiry in texture and brown in colour, and consists of old roots and other organic debris. Fibre usually overlies dry soil, the turf becoming very dry indeed and difficult to re-wet under drought conditions. Fibre is most commonly found under acidic conditions on fairways and semi-roughs where the sward is bent and fescue with a tendency to invasion by acid-loving weeds like sheep's sorrel, bedstraw and wood-rush.

(c) *Thatch*
Thatch is waterlogged throughout most of the year and smells strongly of decay and stagnation. It is yellow/brown in colour with black streaks showing the activity of anaerobic bacteria. The underlying soil is wet, compacted and usually of clay with restricted drainage. Annual meadow-grass invariably predominates in the sward with perhaps some surviving bent. Thatch can accumulate to layers several inches thick, particularly in water-collecting hollows on heavily played parts of golf greens, etc.

Accumulations of organic material of this kind are widespread in many plant communities. In any natural system, whether grassland or woodland, two processes may be traced – production and decomposition. Organic matter accumulation may therefore be caused either by excessive production or by insufficient decomposition. In the case of sports turf, fertiliser treatment increases production, sometimes excessively. The employment of fungicides and wormkillers together with maintenance of acidic conditions reduce decomposition so that there is a predisposition towards thatch formation.

Different grass species tend to produce thatch at different rates. The desirable fescue grasses, for example, tend to have leaf bases which are resistant to decomposition and are therefore prone to encourage fibre. The common weedgrass, annual meadow-grass, also tends to produce thatch probably because of fast growth under moist, fertile conditions.

Earthworms

It has been stated in the past that earthworms are primarily responsible for thatch breakdown and that the feature appears under golf greens as a result of eliminating earthworm populations. This view is probably over simplified or possibly totally false as it seems that earthworms may lack the capacity to digest thatch, although they do move soil around and may therefore slow the formation of distinct thatch layers. It seems more likely that microscopic fungi and bacteria in the soil tend to be the prime cause of underlying thatch breakdown and that the use of fungicides for controlling plant disease hence encourages thatch by limiting these useful organisms.

Fertility, particularly as far as nitrogen is concerned, plays an important part in plant production and decomposition. If the ratio of carbon to nitrogen becomes too high, organic matter breakdown is slow. This is why the addition of nitrogen to compost heaps fosters fast breakdown. Even when nitrogen is added to turf it may be rapidly leached out of the thatch layer and no longer available to the flora which cause decomposition. Acidity is equally important as there is less activity of soil organisms in very acid turf.

Moisture Effects

Temperature, moisture and aeration all affect soil biology and hence thatch. Very dry conditions will slow thatch breakdown because of lack of moisture limiting the growth of soil organisms. On the other hand, excessive moisture has the same effect as soil fungi and bacteria require air for their growth and air is very limited in waterlogged turf. Temperature also has some effect in that there is less soil microbial activity at a low temperature.

Thatch Control

As with many other problems, the prevention of fibre or thatch formation is more satisfactory and much less laborious than curing an established problem. In practical greenkeeping, it is possible to slant maintenance towards minimising the chances of serious thatch accumulation. Fungicidal applications should, for example, be kept to a minimum to avoid killing off useful soil fungi. Obviously, it is necessary to use fungicides to cure damaging diseases like fusarium but the damaging effects of fungicides should also be borne in mind.

Vertical mowing using rotary scarifiers is useful in preventing the accumulation of new thatch and, to some extent, in increasing the aeration of the very superficial layers. Frequent scarification using tools like the thatching reels or groomers on triple mowers is particularly important if carried out frequently, say every seven to ten days. It should be realised, however, that scarification can do little to remove thatch which is already accumulated, possibly to a depth of several inches. In the past, attempts have been made to remove such thatch by very severe scarification usually using pedestrian rotary scarifiers. Often this merely disrupts the putting surface and although considerable quantities of organic matter may be removed, the operation does nothing to attack the causes of thatch build up and so the material tends to accumulate again quite rapidly to its former level.

A more effective approach to thatch control involves the use of aeration equipment – conventional spikers fitted with flat or hollow tines, or more specialised sub-aeration machinery. Aeration is particularly useful in letting air down into waterlogged thatch layers, so increasing the activity of useful soil organisms. Its effect on drainage is also significant in that getting water away into lower soil layers also increases the air supply and fungal activity in the upper layers. Top dressing with sand compost is most desirable both in firming and diluting spongy thatch layers and in improving surface drainage. In some situations waterlogging of the surface may be caused by deeper compaction or poor drainage at lower levels than may be reached by surface aerating equipment and in such cases reconstruction of the green or the introduction of a better pipe drainage system may be the only answer.

Since annual meadow-grass swards seem particularly prone to spongy thatch formation, reducing the proportion of this grass in the green should be useful. Annual meadow-grass is, in any event, undesirable in a golf green from other points of view. Annual meadow-grass is encouraged by excessive nitrogen fertiliser treatment, and by the over-use of phosphate. It is also favoured by heavy summer watering which in itself tends to increase fibre by reducing soil air. Annual meadow-grass should therefore be discouraged by limiting fertiliser and by keeping swards as dry as possible each summer.

In the case of moorland golf greens where swards are naturally bent and fescue, hard brown layers of fibrous thatch are quite common. Here, there may be no waterlogging or slow surface drainage, indeed such fibrous thatch is often associated with dry conditions. Sometimes over-acidity is the cause and lime treatment cannot be entirely ruled out as a method of control. The use of lime on golf greens can, however, have many undesirable side effects and should only be undertaken after very careful thought and as a last resort. Moorland fibrous thatch layers often respond well to frequent scarification and aeration work and it is probable that such mechanical treatment is the best method of reducing the problem in these circumstances.

Really serious thatch problems have in the past sometimes been tackled by thinly stripping off the turf, physically removing the remaining thatch then cultivating the underlying soil and relaying the green. It should be realised, however, that unless the cause of the thatch is eliminated in this operation the thatch layer will merely tend to accumulate once again after the turf has been replaced. Certainly, soil cultivation may eliminate soil compaction and hence waterlogging, but unless this is the prime cause of the problem such work can be an expensive waste of time. It is better to see if the problem can be tackled by less extreme means before such measures are considered.

Associated with dry moorland thatch is the condition known as 'dry patch'. Here, the surface becomes very dry and difficult to re-wet with poor grass growth and moss activity. The problem is often associated with fungal growth. In such cases aeration work and treatment with wetting agents may be useful, together with elimination of surface high spots which tend to shed water.

THE SPEED OF GOLF GREENS

Some method of objectively assessing the speed of a golf green can be a valuable aid to maintenance. The relative speed of greens is a very important factor in summer course presentation, but it is something which can be very difficult to define. This is because an assessment of what is a fast, medium or slow green tends to be a subjective one, rather than something which is measured as routine, mainly because the recognised tool for the job, the Stimpmeter, has not been marketed in the UK. Those which have become available have been imported by individuals from the USA, where it is distributed by the United States Golf Association and is in common use.

The Stimpmeter was invented in the USA in 1935 by amateur golfer, E.S. Stimpson, "to achieve accurate, objective, statistically valid measurements of the speed of a putting surface" (USGA). It is a simple tool, which when used in a meaningful manner, gives a reflection of the rolling resistance of the turf surface, by rolling golf balls with a constant momentum over a level area in different directions and taking an average of the distance travelled.

It is an aluminium bar, 36 inches long with a V-shaped groove extending along its entire length. Thirty inches from one tapered end which rests on the ground is a notch which holds the ball. This notch is so designed that the ball will be released and roll down the groove when the bar is raised to an angle of about 20° from the horizontal. This ensures that the speed of the ball will always be the same when it reaches the lower end. To use the meter a level area of green must be selected, preferably at least 10 ft.sq. At least three balls are then rolled across the green using the meter and the distance that each travels should be measured. For accuracy, all three balls should come to rest not more than 8 inches apart. A further three balls should then be rolled across the green in the opposite direction. An average distance of travel should then be calculated. This distance can be compared with a series of figures produced by the USGA Green Section:–

Speeds for Regular Membership Play		Speeds for Tournament Play	
8' 6"	Fast	10' 6"	Fast
7' 6"	Medium-Fast	9' 6"	Medium-Fast
6' 6"	Medium	8' 6"	Medium
5' 6"	Medium-Slow	7' 6"	Medium-Slow
4' 6"	Slow	6' 6"	Slow

A set of figures should hence be obtained for each green and it should then be possible to produce more uniform conditions from green to green by management practices. Slow greens could perhaps be scarified or excessively hard greens watered.

As might be gathered, with this simple technology, once one has basic figures for greens at what is considered to be their best, it is then quite easy to see what effects have modifications to individual elements of the management programme, together with changing weather conditions, on the pace of putting surfaces. However, until Stimpmeters do come into common use in the UK, we have to rely on the subjective judgement of individual club memberships. The usual request is for faster greens.

If golf greens are shown to be excessively slow, then maintenance can be modified to improve matters. A layer of spongy thatch immediately below the surface is a common cause and reducing this by scarification can be effective, although it is often also necessary to attack the cause of thatch formation too. This may involve improving surface drainage and

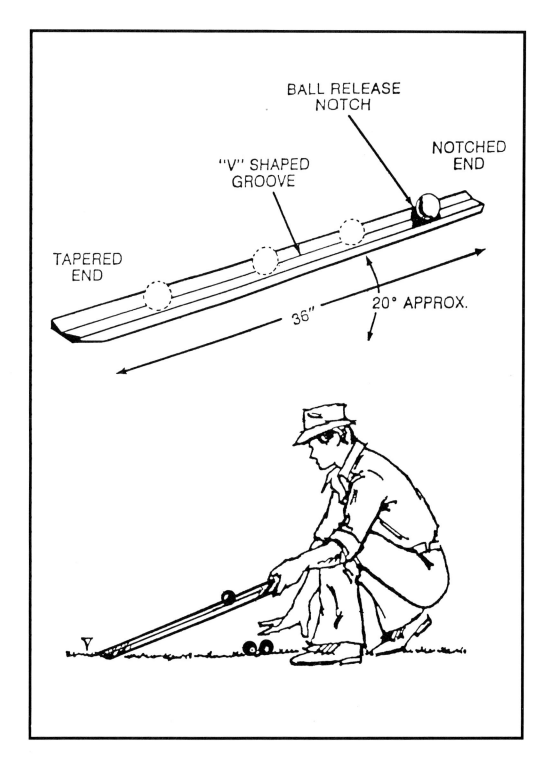

BALL RELEASE NOTCH

NOTCHED END

"V" SHAPED GROOVE

TAPERED END

20° APPROX.

36"

FIGURE 7: The Stimpmeter (Courtesy United States Golf Association).

55

soil conditions or reducing the annual meadow-grass content. Over-watering also produces soft, slow surfaces, as does the excessive use of fertiliser which give unnecessarily lush growth besides encouraging undesirable grass species. The use of soft or spongy top dressing materials like large quantities of peat may also encourage slow surfaces. Cutting too plays a part – greens cut too infrequently or at too high level would tend to be slow, although the significance of mowing height is often exaggerated by golfers.

The particular treatment which is usually referred to as affecting the speed of greens is height of cut, and certainly shaving greens close can have a significant result in this respect. However, this approach is short-term and **short-sighted**, in that over-close mowing in the long-term leads at best to soft surfaces dominated by the weedgrass *Poa annua* and at worst to dead patches and thin turf. Fast, bumpy greens are no use to anyone. Cutting with mowers set at 5 mm ($^3/_{16}$ in.) in the growing season and at 8 mm ($^5/_{16}$ in.) in winter is normal and acceptable in most circumstances.

To achieve a balanced approach, it is necessary to tailor virtually all the elements of the maintenance programme to the end of promoting green speed, with the most important operations being:

— the frequency of mowing
— the frequency of verticutting/turf grooming
— control in the use of nitrogen
— a delicate management of watering during dry spells
— the approach to top dressing and the materials used
— producing good surface drainage and maintaining a good access for light and air flow

Frequency of mowing is the key element. It does not necessarily mean that more grass is removed, but the more one cuts, the more polished the surface becomes and its rolling resistance falls. Similarly, verticutting or turf grooming to take out coarse, clumpy growth and eliminate any nap will also reduce rolling resistance. On the other hand, factors such as lush growth, soft surfaces, and a tendency to lay damp, all have a negative effect on the progress towards faster greens.

The whole object of treatment must be to produce firm, dry, very fine, slow-growing, uniform, and polished putting areas. Then greens will be fast. Even so, what is achieved ultimately will vary according to the turf type one is working with, changing weather conditions and with time. Fescue dominated turf will always be faster than annual meadow-grass. Greens will be faster in a dry year than in a wet one, and there can generally be a trend for greens to become progressively faster between June and September.

A final point to bear in mind is that greens can be made too fast, a situation in which putting is totally uncontrollable. Indeed, there is a current fashion in America to work to produce greens for club members which are up to 25% quicker than a standard which is considered fast for professional golf, and this must be considered a move which is going over the top. In the search for control of pace, it is far, far more important to aim to achieve a **consistent** speed from green to green over the whole course, including the putting green.

TURF GROOMERS

The search for pace on putting greens without the need to mow too closely was provided with a valuable aid some years ago with the introduction of turf groomers into this country. Close cutting of greens, to 3 mm or even lower, generally makes greens putt faster though long term weakening of the sward is the result if the practice is prolonged. This leads to deterioration in quality of sward by encouraging annual meadow-grass invasion, this species can seed below 3 mm! Moss and prostrate weeds are also likely to take advantage of a weak grass cover. Established bentgrass will grow quite happily at a 5 mm height of cut during the growing season, so will the fine fescues. Routine mowing at these heights means leaving more grass on the greens, producing a slower putting surface. The main advantage of implementing these sensible cutting heights is retention of ground cover and, long term, smoother putting surfaces. There is an added problem of lateral growth of shoots and leaves, promoting grain or nap, particularly with bentgrasses and annual meadow-grass which can produce a bumpier surface and thereby reduce pace. The use of turf groomers cuts down on lateral growth, stimulating vertical growth and a denser sward by the encouragement of more shoots, providing smaller and more plentiful leaves, over which the ball will travel smoothly and truly. Grooming units will also fine down patches of coarse grasses in the sward and pick up annual meadow-grass seed heads more efficiently than verticutters.

What are Turf Groomers?

Basically, turf groomers are a refinement of verticut reels. Verticutting has been around for many years as a routine treatment – vertical mowing cuts down into the turf surface to lift procumbent (flat) growth and organic debris, reducing the rate of thatch build up. On green triple mowers, verticutters are separate to the cutting units and are interchangeable with them. Changing over the units is not overly time-consuming, but this does produce a situation where the same mowing machine may have to carry out two functions, reducing its useful life through extra wear and tear and reducing the time it is available for its primary function of mowing the greens.

Turf groomers are reels that are fixed to the cutting unit, allowing the two operations to be carried out simultaneously. The original Turf Groomer was manufactured by Jacobsen, consisting of 71 blades providing 261 tempered steel knives mounted spirally on a powered roller set behind the front roller of the mowing unit. Each knife rotates through a groove of the front slotted roller. The 0.64 mm thick, 54.0 mm diameter blades are driven at 3000 rpm, slicing stolons and horizontal shoots which are lifted by the bevelled edges of the preceding roller. Jacobsen have now introduced a new groomer reel which has 85 blades, retaining the spiral mounting set into the front grooved roller to 11 mm. The next grooming reels to feature on a green triple were produced by Toro, working on a similar principle to the Jacobsen. The main differences are that the grooming reel on the Toro unit is set so that there is a gap between it and the front roller, and the grooming blades are individual rather than in a continuous spiral. With this arrangement, the Toro implement is not restricted to the use of a grooved Wiehle front roller, Swaged and Full roller options are available. The Toro unit also has variable blade spacing, 6 mm or 19 mm, whereas the Jacobsen is obviously confined to the gap between the grooves in the front roller. The reel with the closer spacing has 76 blades, whilst the wider spacing has 26. Each blade has six cutting teeth. The Toro blades are 0.71 mm thick and of 53.9 mm diameter, driven at 3200 rpm. The most recent grooming unit to come on to the market is the Ransomes Verti-Groom for their GT green triple mower, introduced in 1989. Ransomes have re-designed the original groomers by placing the grooming reel ahead of the front roller. This set up rather goes against the original principle, whereby the bevelled edges of the grooved roller lift trailing stems into the path of the groomer blades. Ransomes would argue that the speed of rotation of the groomer should ensure an efficient vertical cutting action while the following grooved roller lifts any remaining lateral growth into the cutting reel. The Ransomes Verti-Groom has 35 hardened steel blades each with five cutting teeth. The blades are of 60 mm diameter, spaced at 15 mm. The Jacobsen and Toro groomers are part of the free-floating cutting unit, whereas the Ransomes groomer is free-floating in a manner independent of the cutting unit. Groomers are also available on pedestrian cylinder mowers; the Jacobsen 19 and 22 in. Walking Greens Mowers, the LF 100 Lightweight Fairway Mower, the Ransomes 51 and 61 Super Certes, and the Toro Greenmaster 1000. The Bunton and John Deere pedestrian cylinder Greensmowers have a thatching attachment based on the groomer principle.

Using Turf Groomers

Turf groomers will complete the task they are designed for if set correctly and used as and when growing conditions permit. These implements were originally designed to work in conditions found in North America, where growing conditions tend to be more consistent. Grooming reels tend to be of variable depth and adjustment, 5 mm above front roller to 5 mm below front roller on the Ransomes. It is important to know the lower extreme setting for efficient use of this fine tuning implement, not too deep when it will serve as a verticutter which is not its intended purpose. Such treatment will not only be severe, but will reduce the working life of the groomers considerably. Settings of 1.6 mm above to 1.6 mm below the bottom blade will usually be appropriate, the exact setting being determined by the strength of the sward, growing conditions and the degree of lateral growth. Frequency of grooming must also relate to the prevailing growth and weather. During the first season of use it is suggested that groomers be used as little as once a fortnight, gradually working up to three or four operations per week. Remember that daily grooming, as practiced in the USA, may over-stress the grass in our variable, cooler climate. Reduce frequency and raise the setting when the green sward is under stress, say during drought conditions or when growth is less predictable in the spring and later autumn. Toro recommend using their reel with close spacing during periods of faster growth and the wider spaced reel when growth is slow, e.g. in the autumn. If grooming reels are set correctly, it should be possible to make the final perimeter cut with the units in action, though great care must be taken to regulate travelling speed to compensate for not travelling in a straight line, and also to lay off grooming in perimeter area which may weaken quickly, e.g. undulations in drought and main traffic routes on and off greens.

Dangers of Groomers

It must be stated that many of the early problems reported were a result of misuse, mainly incorrect setting – treating groomers like verticutters or, even worse, scarifiers – and too frequent use. If you are contemplating purchasing grooming units, make sure that your supplier provides full details of performance and use. In many instances it will be a case of trial and error to obtain the exact setting for your situation, the setting likely to vary with season, but you should be provided with sufficient information to ensure that your errors do no damage to the putting surface or the grooming blades. It is a good idea to carry out your tests on the practice putting green where any problems can be corrected before risking work on the main greens. With the necessity to regulate the use of the groomer, it is important that the grooming reel can be disengaged quickly and raised above the cutting height so as not to run along the turf when out of action. The Toro and Ransomes units have handwheels which quickly raise the reel 15 mm above the ground. Earlier groomers could be disengaged rapidly but could not be raised higher than the uppermost operating setting – clogging with grass clippings has been reported in this mode and the makers suggest keeping the groomer engaged after raising to its highest setting when not in use. The new Jacobsen groomer has a "quick height adjust knob" which allows for rapid raising of the implement.

As more and more grooming units have found their way on to golf courses, a few difficulties have arisen which are related to design rather than misuse. The use of coarse top dressing materials can create a problem with some units. Coarse sand or fine gravel particles can lodge in between the grooming blade and the roller into which it is set, possibly bending the knife or even snapping it off. Such damage not only means the cost of repair to the machine, but also to the turf which may be scalped, particularly on the perimeter cut. Our advice is not to use groomers after top dressing for at least four to five days, or as long as it takes for the majority of the dressing to migrate from the turf surface. If this procedure is not followed, you may not only risk damaging the groomer units but will also lift, and waste, a lot of top dressing.

The same principle applies to the application of fertilisers, particularly mini-granule or the larger granule slow release forms. On the Toro unit, setting the groomer away from the front roller has produced a wider roller base so the unit will not follow contours as closely. However, unless your greens have severe, tight contours, this should not be a problem except perhaps around green edges where undulations are often found, or on a severe Mackenzie two-tier green.

Summary

Turf groomers are here to stay and, if used sensibly and correctly, can be a valuable aid to producing smoother, faster greens. Jacobsen even go as far as to state that an immediate increase in green speed of up to 10 per cent or more can be achieved after just two passes, and that regular use can gradually increase green speed by as much as 25 per cent without lowering the height of cut. Whether these figures are applicable to the average British golf green has to be resolved scientifically, but there can be no doubt that groomers can have a noted positive effect on green speed, as well as helping to control annual meadow-grass by seed head removal and fining down patches of coarser perennial ryegrass or Yorkshire fog more efficiently than by verticutting. Groomers do not replace verticutting units, they should each have a role in greens management. Once a grooming programme is established, then the frequency of verticutting can be reduced. If you are thinking of purchasing grooming units for your current triple mower, then, in the majority of cases, we would support your decision. If you are looking to purchase a new triple, then we would recommend serious consideration be given to obtaining cutting reels with groomers. In such a situation arrange for demonstrations of all the market leaders to provide the best for your course, and a machine that your greenkeeping staff are happy to work with. Do not fall into the trap of believing that groomers are going to solve all of your problems, indeed there will be problems with the use of the units if you do not set them correctly or if they are over-used – grooming units are a conditioning tool and should be treated as such. Groomers are available to promote smoother and faster putting conditions without the need to sacrifice grass cover through over-close mowing, and we may soon see the day when Clubs that do not own grooming attachments for their greens mowers will be in the minority.

MOWING – HAND VERSUS TRIPLE

In the course of our advisory work during the past 10 to 15 years, a popular question at golf clubs, raised both by green committee members and by greenkeepers, has been "what do you think of triple mowers for greens"? Indeed, the question is still raised frequently but nowadays it is sometimes substituted by "is it true that some clubs are returning to using the small hand machines for cutting greens"? Concern at using the right equipment will always be uppermost in people's minds but differing outlooks and priorities, depending upon perhaps whether you are a greenkeeper or green committee member, can lead to different conclusions. Whichever camp you are from, however, there is no disputing facts and of these there are plenty to help decide whether triple or hand mowing is to be preferred in a particular instance.

Initial Considerations
Fine turf triple mowers are highly manoeuvrable and capable of turning within a very small area. Even so, the best is achieved from these triple mowers when fairly extensive areas such as 9 or 18 golf greens each of 500 m^2 or more have to be cut – very small areas of fine turf can be rather awkward to mow, particularly if the triple mower has to be turned on the actual putting surface due to surrounding banks or other obstructions. When mowing golf greens, the aim should always be to turn the large triple mower on the collar or surrounds if at all possible. Wet and soft fine turf can tend to mark due to regular turning with a triple mower within a confined area, although much depends on the care and skill of the operator – even small hand machines will mark a tender surface if care is not taken.

The size and shape of the area may also limit the number of directions in which one can mow with a large triple mower; remember that changing the direction of cut is considered an important aspect of mowing practice.

Advantages
Assuming there are greens of the right size and shape and that club finances are good enough to acquire a triple mower, then there are a great number of advantages to be obtained by using a triple machine. Time and labour saving are two major selling points with triple mowers and hopefully the time and labour that has been gained can be channelled into other aspects of management. It has been noticeable at some busy golf clubs with a small labour force that the introduction of triple mowers on both greens and tees in recent years has produced enormous course improvements and, with present demands upon staff, it is difficult to see how such clubs could manage otherwise.

Besides saving time and labour in relation to mowing, the fine turf triple mowers can, of course, be adapted to other purposes, i.e. machines are capable of light verticutting (vertical mowing) and also grooming. Indeed, the term mowers in the name should not be over-emphasised as these machines are multi-purpose. The verticutting units for the triple mower should always be considered a necessary purchase.

The Debatable Points
The narrow swaths produced with small hand machines often seem to be preferred on greens – the narrow bands on a green may psychologically help the aim!

On the question of actual finish, both the fine turf triple mowers and the best hand machines achieve an excellent cut. In the long term, however, the floating head principle of the fine turf triple mower *may* tend to produce a softer type of playing surface and use of the verticut units must not be neglected, particularly if there is a history of thatch and fibre troubles. Hand machines often seem to leave a firmer surface – maybe the rolling factor has some effect. The softer and perhaps occasionally slower putting surface sometimes found in the case of golf greens cut with triple mowers can also be attributed to the actual setting up of the cutting units. Experience has shown that with identical bench settings, fine turf triple mowers tend to leave a slightly longer grass cover than hand machines (again probably the difference of a cutting unit floating over the surface as compared to one that settles into the turf and drives through it). In other words, fine turf triple mowers will probably have to be set slightly lower than the hand machines to leave a similar length of grass. Setting up the three units on a triple mower so that they are all producing an identical finish is an important point that must receive close attention.

Some older triple mowers used on slightly coarser turf areas such as golf tees, surrounds and approaches, etc. do not have grass collection facilities and obviously this may be detrimental, particularly on tees. However, modern tee machines do have collecting boxes fitted. The larger hand machines used in these situations, besides having grass collection facilities, also produce a significant rolling effect which is often considered to be beneficial on areas such as tees.

On the question of maintenance costs, repairs will be expensive, irrespective of what type of mower is in use. It is really surprising how in the course of advisory work one sees such an enormous difference in machinery reliability and presentation. Some golf clubs seem to think that after three to four years a new triple mowing machine is the norm, but five miles down the road, the same type of machine doing similar work but receiving completely different attention can often look and perform in peak condition after six to seven years use.

Maybe a Compromise
After having had experience with both types of machine, i.e. triple and hand mowers, some golf clubs find circumstances have so developed in the last few years that the triple mower is the only machine which can cope with requirements. At other clubs, however, committee members, golfers and greenkeepers are finding that a combined approach of hand and triple mowing is perhaps the best answer, e.g. in the case of a golf green, cutting two or three times midweek with the small machines and then cutting Saturday and Sunday with the quicker, less labour demanding triple mowers. Similarly, on the tees, cutting every now and again (say one week out of every three or four) with a hand machine seems to reverse any detrimental effect resulting from constant use of the triple mowers.

WATERING GREENS – PRINCIPLES AND PERSPECTIVES

Principles
Is Watering Necessary?

Looking at this subject from a purist point of view, i.e. solely in terms of quality of grasses on greens, the answer is probably, "No". If one is lucky enough to have bent/fescue or even just bentgrass dominated greens, the turf will be sufficiently drought tolerant to survive most of the stretches of dry weather we (occasionally) experience in this country, if other maintenance practices are adapted to take account of minimising drought stress. Also, a measure of drought stress can give the most desirable turfgrass species a competitive edge over less tolerant grasses such as *Poa annua*.

However, taking a more realistic line, some ability to control moisture availability beneath greens is virtually essential if putting surfaces are to be produced to a consistently good standard to meet the demands of today's golfers. Indeed, it is not unrealistic to say that any course which is played more than moderately (say 30,000 rounds per year and above) really does need a sophisticated automatic irrigation system if necessary watering is to be carried out adequately without interrupting the through-put of play.

Losses of water from the soil due to evaporation and transpiration can be as much as 2.5 mm per day in a British summer. Watering becomes necessary when rainfall is inadequate to compensate for this and when soil moisture reserves are depleted to the point where the grass will start to show signs of drought stress. A small degree of stress, however, is not always undesirable. For example, if a slight moisture deficit is allowed to develop in the spring, this will encourage deeper rooting as the plants are forced to search below the top few inches for water. Such a sward would then be better prepared to withstand dry summer conditions than one with only a shallow root system. However, watering usually becomes necessary at some time during dry spells even when there is a fairly deep root system. There are various ways of determining just when to start watering. One technical approach is to use tensiometers installed in the soil to give an indication of the soil moisture tension (i.e. the amount of work which grass roots must do to extract water), but this method is not commonly used. Most experienced greenkeepers can judge when watering is necessary by probing the ground, examining soil cores and keeping a close watch on known drought sensitive areas which show signs of droughting before the rest of the turf.

Objectives of Watering

In an ideal world there would be two objectives to be gained from watering greens:

— to maintain a uniformity of surface characteristics between each and within each putting surface during spells of dry weather.
— to prevent a lack of moisture from restricting top growth during dry weather and leading to turf damage through management and wear.

These two points summarise the total need for water on golf greens, and it will be evident that there is no mention in the above of 'holding qualities' or 'speed' or 'colour'. This is because if control of watering is dependent on all or each of these three latter factors, the whole approach to watering is more likely than not causing actual long-term harm to the greens in respect of their year-round usability. In addition, inadvisable watering can cost the Club a lot of money too, from the aspects of creating a need for larger course budgets, together with the possibility of loss of revenue.

Perspectives
Dangers to be Avoided
There are two problems which can arise from routine watering of greens: over-watering; and under-watering. Remember that the former can be as damaging as the latter. Over-generous irrigation produces an environment in which only shallow-rooted grasses can survive, the result of which is:

— *Poa annua* dominated turf with the desired grasses precluded
— and heavy thatch build up at the base of the sward.

In playing terms, this does not mean a club cannot have satisfactory greens through the summer (once *Poa annua* seeding has ended) but for the remaining eight months of the year the club can be left with yellow, wet, soft, foot-printed, disease-riddled, mossy, weedy, pitch-marked, worn, muddy putting surfaces. Temporary greens will be the rule, not the exception, in such circumstances.

Providing a remedy to such problems is by no means as easy as creating them. A cure can take years of hard work and can cost a great deal of money. It should be noted too that working through a cure can also be a very painful process in terms of the loss of surface which can arise in summer as a result of trying to change the botanical composition of a green back to what it should be.

It must always be remembered that a green is not a 'static object', it is a living system, and what can be produced on the surface depends very much on the year-round quality of the sward's environment.

How to Avoid the Pitfalls
Correct policy for watering greens in spells of dry weather through the summer is to imitate frequent light summer showers (rather than frequent or even occasional tropical monsoons) simply to hold moisture (not free-running water) through the topsoil profile. So, watering needs to be done lightly but with sufficient frequency both overall and on drought-sensitive patches, to maintain a uniformity of moisture availability and a receptiveness to applied water over the whole of each green surface.

Saturating the soil and keeping it saturated creates the environment of the peat bog beneath the putting surface, while simply dampening the top while the soil underneath remains dry gives a competitive edge to shallow-rooted turfgrass species.

However, striking a balance to achieve the above criteria is easier said than done:

— What is happening on the surface in dry weather often bears no reflection of the moisture availability in the sub-surface.
— Even the most sophisticated pop-up watering systems cannot automatically put water just where it is needed,
— and where pop-ups are not available, there is the constant battle of trying to water greens carefully and adequately while a constant stream of players is either switching off the sprinklers or throwing them off the green.

Further factors which have to be taken into consideration when devising and managing a watering programme are:

— The soil type beneath greens, as some soils are more receptive to applied water than others.
— Variations in contouring, aspect, siting, shadiness, etc., of **each individual** green site.
— Constantly changing weather conditions affecting the rate of evaporation and transpiration.
— Whether or not moisture availability is a limiting factor to growth. (Could it be soil temperature instead?)
— Keeping an eye on the weather so that prolonged rain does not saturate greens which are already moist as a result of watering.

All the above call for constant checking and adjustment of watering practice.

Sprinklers

The size and shape of the area to be covered usually determines the choice of sprinkler. There are rotary, impact drive types which give a circular coverage and are suitable for use on golf greens. Pop-up sprinklers are permanently installed in the ground and only appear above the surface when in use. They give circular or part-circular coverage and systems can be designed for most sports areas. They are popular on golf courses where they can be used to irrigate tees and fairways as well as the greens. Pop-up systems are expensive but they have advantages as they save labour and they can be set to operate at night when there will be no interference with play.

Water Supplies

The commonest source of water for irrigation is the mains supply. This is perhaps the most convenient source, but the supply may be cut off or usage restricted when it is most needed. Bore holes, rivers, streams and ponds are also used but permission is usually needed from the catchment authority. With these sources it is important that sufficient quantities are available and that the water is free of injurious contaminants. Water from bore holes sometimes contains appreciable amounts of lime, whereas there are some cases of over-acid supplies from surface streams and ponds. A soft water is best and it is always a good idea to check the quality of any bore hole or surface water supply from time to time.

Irrigation Management

When irrigation is necessary the amount of water applied should be enough to maintain no more than a sufficiency of moisture at the rootzone, say the top 150 mm (6 in.) of soil. The irrigation system should have the capacity to supply the equivalent of about 25 mm of rain per week and the rate at which the water should be applied depends on the infiltration rate of the surface. Run-off should be avoided as it results in waste and causes over-watering of hollows, leaving high spots dry. On fine turf areas overall solid tine aeration is a useful preliminary to watering as this will aid penetration and help get the water through to the roots where it is needed. Round solid tines are recommended in preference to slit tines because with the latter the slits can dry out in the hot sun and open up, thus producing an uneven playing surface.

It is important that an adequate amount of water is applied – a minimum of 11 litres per m^2 on each occasion. There are two approaches to watering. One is to water quite heavily two or three times per week so that on each occasion the water gets well down to the roots and allowing the surface to dry in between. The alternative approach, which has become popular where there are pop-up systems also has merit. This involves very light watering (sometimes every night in dry weather) to maintain a moisture level at the roots which has never been allowed to get too low. This technique of more frequent watering is often necessary on areas with a very free draining sandy construction which tend to dry out rapidly. With both methods it is very important to make sure that the water applied actually gets down to the rootzone.

One problem with pop-up systems on golf courses has been over-watering. This is because the operation has been made so easy and also because decisions have been made to use the system frequently in attempts to justify its initial cost. Careful use of any irrigation system is important as there have been cases of annual meadow-grass/thatch build up where only light surface sprinklings have been given. If only the surface soil is kept moist this will encourage the shallow-rooted annual meadow-grass. This grass will produce thatch which will in turn hold more water at the surface and so the problem builds up. Most greenkeepers are aware of these problems now and there has been a change to more sensible use of irrigation systems.

As with many other aspects of turf management, irrigation is not always as straightforward as it first appears. Dry patches can develop during drought which do not respond to normal watering. These are caused by poor water infiltration and may be due to the presence of a dry fibre layer at the surface, raised features (on a golf green), compaction or the development of 'dry patch' which has been associated with fungal activity. Where such problems do occur, specialised local treatment should be provided. Carry out plenty of slit tine aeration at close centres using a hand fork. In addition to carrying out routine sprinkling, more often than not there will be a need to be making good use of spot watering techniques and plenty of wetting agent.

Wetting agents are detergents (materials which reduce the surface tension of water), the use of which assists the penetration of water into soil. There are proprietary turf wetting agents on the market, but some **non-ionic** commercial detergents can be used too. When using ordinary detergent over a protracted period, care must be taken to select a material which does not contain bleach and/or a high concentration of sodium. Wetting agents can be used on a routine basis on turf areas subject to dry patches, at intervals throughout the summer months. They can be of particular value as spot treatments on high areas or banks where water tends to run off. The point of using them is simply to make watering that much more effective in sustaining uniformity of the turf area.

Such an approach to watering is obviously labour-intensive, even where there is an automatic irrigation system installed. To be able to keep this labour input to a minimum, it is essential to have a well-designed watering system, but unfortunately many of the pop-up irrigation systems installed from the early days in the late 1960s and right through the 1970s do not meet the necessary criteria. The end result of inadequate design is poor distribution of water – local areas of greens getting drenched while the rest remain dry. With such systems, unless there is a good appreciation of their defects, and there is a high labour input to compensate for their deficiencies (nearly as much as if stand-pipe sprinklers were being used), then over-watering **and** under-watering problems are going to develop simultaneously.

There is ground swell within golf clubs to modernise out-dated pop-up systems, but up-grading is expensive and it is difficult to demonstrate the need for such improvements to committees and memberships in general. Nevertheless, if any club is to obtain full value from the insurance the installation of a watering system provides, and is to achieve the best from organisation of labour around the course as a whole, up-grading of watering systems to the minimum specification of the British Turf and Landscape Irrigation Association is vital.

As well as being needed for irrigation during dry spells, water is also needed for routine operations such as weed and worm control and the watering in of fertilisers for fine turf.

Finally, a note on maintenance. All irrigation systems should be regularly checked and any faults dealt with as they are found. Proper maintenance can eliminate many problems. Pumps and ancillary equipment should be serviced regularly and all pipes prone to frost damage should be drained before the winter.

THOUGHTS ON HAND WATERING

Demands for the perfect putting green at every hole become ever more exacting year by year. Running parallel with this is the weight of responsibility placed on the Course Manager in providing for the demands of Committees, whilst at the same time managing his greens in such a way as to obtain and maintain a technical base of high quality upon which to build presentation according to needs from week to week. From this a conflict arises in 'distance of vision': the golfer takes his assessment of greens on an average of day to day condition; while the Course Manager is aiming to balance this short term assessment against the longer term requirements of the course, looking months, or indeed years, ahead.

One of the flashpoints of this conflict of aims and ideas concerns use of water, that is whether or not water is over-used, or indeed under-used. Few involved in golf course management would argue that a high percentage of courses have not suffered some adverse effect from excess use of irrigation water on greens over the past 20 years, and the vast majority of Head Greenkeepers fight against over-watering. But those in the know are heavily out-numbered by others whose reaction to firmer putting surfaces and the odd brown patch is to apply more and more water to give lush greens and soft plugging (holding) surfaces.

Given that high capacity pop-up watering systems are here to stay, many courses have the potential for over-watering greens. So, what techniques can be applied to keep the pressure for damage to a minimum? The classic advice is always to pick out the 'hot spots' on greens – patches which drought early in dry weather – and as these dry out, start a watering programme. There is a lot to be said too for routine probing of greens to examine moisture availability within the top couple of inches of the profile. The use of a moisture meter to measure water availability within the rootzone can be valuable too. While the exact numbers may be meaningless, they are useful for comparison, and taking measurements or readings does give a good impression of professionalism.

There is no doubt anywhere that successful watering of greens depends upon starting early in a dry spell and keeping the moisture just topped up to nearly moist, but no more. This does run contrary to the conventional agronomic theory that occasional wetting and drying cycles favour the more desirable grasses and deeper rooting. But it has to be accepted too that theory does not always meet needs in practice.

One of the main objectives of golf green maintenance is to produce good uniformity in terms of density of grass cover, completeness of cover, and quick green speed both within each and between every green. When you have the typical situation of 18 greens with varying degrees of featuring, soil type and soil depth, and a constant risk of being caught out by unexpected heavy rain just after watering, no greenkeeper can really afford the luxury of a wetting and drying cycle approach to watering if he can possibly avoid it. Also, where the little-and-often practice is applied well, there seems to be little detriment to the production of good bentgrass turf.

It would therefore seem logical to be as flexible as possible in the capacity to put water on to greens, just when and where it is needed. Watering high spots whilst avoiding low hollows, or damping down areas and greens prone to baking, or selectively watering greens open to the sun (or worse still wind), whilst avoiding shady, sheltered, low lying places, before droughting problems set in, keeps back the need for a blanket approach until there is a general drying. When there is general drying one needs to use pop-up sprinklers, but hand hoses will be adequate beforehand.

It is important to stress that we do not advocate such watering with the aim of maintaining softer, easy to hold greens – quite the reverse. A flexible hand hosing programme helps to keep use of water to the minimum overall, whilst helping to keep the golfer satisfied. There are less likely to be complaints concerning hard greens if the development of brown patches can be kept to an absolute minimum, while at the same time the turf itself need not be lush green either.

Beyond the early stages of a dry spell there is a continuing need for hand-held hosing in that no pop-up system is automatic in the sense of being self-regulating. Again the shape, siting, aspect, featuring, soil type and soil depth of each green (and its apron), together with the quality of the design of the watering system itself and the effects of rain, mean results of pop-up watering can never be perfect. Minimum damage, with maximum benefit, calls for use of pop-ups as the lowest common denominator, i.e. watering those places well covered, which may well not be enough for individual areas of green, and these have to be topped up by hand hosing.

Judicious use of hose pipes has extra value too in getting maximum benefit from a wetting agent programme. To be effective in containing the major problem of dry patch, wetting agents have to be applied frequently (as often as every two to three weeks in serious cases), the programme of wetting agent application has to be started early in the year, and the detergents have to be washed in and backed up by ongoing watering. Allowing for spot treatments of wetting agent gets it just where it will have the best value, whilst keeping the costs to an essential minimum. The use of wetting agent applicators in conjunction with hand hosing is beneficial in controlling dry patch.

Lastly, in putting forward the case for hand-held hosing as part of the greens irrigation programme, the Institute is well aware that some course managers apply this technique already. Also, that it is very common at clubs which are using this technique just to use open hoses with the traditional thumb to break up the spray. Thumbs tend to get cold and/or tired. Then, open hosing jets water across the surface rather than encouraging it to sink in where it is needed. Some 'sophistication' can be achieved with a bent piece of copper pipe in the end of the hose, but why not large shower heads fitted with a tap – cheap technology!

DRY PATCHES ON GREENS

Most greenkeepers will have come across the condition known as 'dry patch' at some time during their working life. The typical symptoms occur as frequently on less intensively maintained areas like fairways as they do on the finer turf of golf greens, though perhaps not with the same dramatic effect on play and the sward.

Where management, particularly for greens, aims at uniformity of sward, a smooth, true surface and consistent speed, the occurrence of variably sized drier patches with a weakened turf cover can be a great inconvenience. Causes of dry patch are many and varied and some of them are considered below along with suggestions for tackling them or at least reducing their worst effects.

Induced Dry Patch
Drought created by compaction will cause weak, drier areas to develop on a green just as easily and quickly as they form on main traffic routes. On a golf green such areas develop at the edges often at the nearest convenient point where players walk off to collect their caddy carts en route for the next tee. There are two factors involved; the sheer weight of foot traffic moving on and off the playing surface and the effects of mowing. It is common mowing practice to make a final 'clean up' cut around the perimeter of a green and these areas then receive twice the mower traffic than other places. When using triple mowers on golf greens this can occur every day of the week at the height of the growing season. Naturally, the result is local compaction which lowers the infiltration rate of water into the soil and unless it is relieved by thorough and regular aeration, dry areas will develop. The type of aeration carried out is important and during autumn and winter thorough hollow tining of these areas, perhaps on a local basis, followed up by regular slitting can be satisfactory. During the summer solid tine aeration is often more appropriate despite the soil compaction that occurs around the tine hole as it is formed. Solid tine holes remain open to permit moisture penetration much longer than slits will on a traffic route and under a low watering regime they are much less likely to open up and so disfigure the turf and playing surface. Excessive irrigation to counter the latter problem or that of dry patches will always create more difficulties than it solves.

The formation of a surface mat of fibre can also be a factor in dry patch development. This is not quite the same as the thatch often seen as an excessive development of undecomposed organic remains below the sward, forming a soggy, yellowish layer that accepts and retains moisture, creating an entirely different surface problem. All turf will produce some mat or fibre and indeed a small amount is necessary to provide a degree of resilience at the playing surface. This acceptable type of fibre is often a brownish material showing decomposition and merging with the upper layers of soil. However, when such fibre becomes dried out it is extremely difficult to re-wet – very much like peat – and these places then show up locally as very dry areas. Prevention is always easier than specific curative treatment and regular aeration to keep the mat open and receptive to moisture helps considerably. If such patches do form, individual hand solid tining to supplement machine work followed up with an application of wetting agent solution and normal irrigation can correct matters. In severe cases it may be necessary to apply supplementary water to individual dry areas by hand sprinkler/hoses in order to re-wet them.

Development of dry patches on the lines described above could be hastened by the practice of treating individual mossy areas in turf with either a lawn sand dressing or frequently just calcined sulphate of iron and sand. Moss often invades turf that is weakened during summer droughts and controlling it with these types of mosskiller will lower the soil pH in the areas, creating more acid conditions that inhibit fibre breakdown and so the cycle continues.

Finally under this heading one must consider the higher mounds and sloping features within putting greens that nearly always cause this type of problem at some time. Fortunately nowadays the more acute featuring that is seen on older courses is less favoured by modern golf architects and with good reasons. Even slight discrepancies in height and slope can lead to surface run-off and thus create differential wetting and drying which no irrigation system can cope with properly. Excessive watering is highly detrimental to the production of good putting surfaces and to the desirable bents and fescue grasses which form the best type of turf. It is counter-productive to irrigate featured greens, especially using automatic watering systems to cater for the water requirements of higher features when inevitable surface run-off will result in gross over-watering of local hollows and flatter areas where most play occurs.

The best approach in this situation is to apply water to suit the needs of lower areas and ensure as far as possible that features are kept well aerated to aid moisture penetration using a wetting agent if necessary. Judicious supplementary watering of these features may also be helpful in a severe drought and, of course, with older manual watering systems the water can be applied only to features, leaving run-off to cater for low areas. Clearly, there is no easy answer to this problem and it is likely that some degree of droughting and discolouration will have to be accepted. In this situation, green is definitely not great.

Dry Patch of Fungal Origin

The classic example here is the dry bare patch or ring created by Type 1 fairy rings during the development of the fungus *Marasmius oreades*. This soil inhabiting fungus produces abundant mycelium which spreads through the soil beneath the turf making it impervious to the penetration of water. The grass dies out through drought and the characteristic bare zone of soil forms between a slowly advancing outer and inner ring of stimulated growth. The extent of the bare zone varies somewhat during the year with a little recovery of the turf around its edges in wetter months. The fungus can persist for many years very slowly extending outwards whilst the inner zone recovers as old mycelium decomposes and allows normal water penetration through the soil to support grass.

For many years excavation and soil sterilising was the only control method, but since this is laborious, disruptive and time-consuming, requiring meticulous attention to detail, it never found real favour. A simple method of control, after first spiking to open up the surface and treating with a wetting agent solution, is repeated soakings of the ring with water. Whilst in some instances this has proved effective where a number of rings occur, it can be as laborious as excavation.

Chemical control using fungicides based on oxycarboxin, benodanil and triforine has shown promise. The great difficulty with any underground mycelium that is also hydrophobic is in getting sufficient of the chemical into contact with the fungus. Control treatment should be carried out when the fungus is active after intensively spiking the affected zones including inner and outer rings, an application of wetting agent solution and thorough watering. This initial treatment is essential to moisten the affected soil properly before the use of the proprietary fungicide. Other forms of dry patch, often with a yellowish or bronzy ring though without any distinct zoning or bare soil areas, may also be associated with the development of hydrophobic fungi in the soil, preventing moisture penetration. In these instances treatment on the lines discussed above could be appropriate.

Hydrophobic Soil and Sands

Reports from New Zealand and the USA discuss hydrophobic or water repelling soils and particularly in relation to greens that are being modified by a sand top dressing programme. This treatment aims to improve surface drainage, sward and playing qualities of greens by very frequent light top dressings of a carefully chosen sand throughout the growing season. Various problems have been encountered, e.g. drainage and aeration at the interface where the sand lies over the original and usually heavy soil. Also as sand depth builds up, turf nutrition requires very close attention. In time, dry spots and patches appear where the sand has become hydrophobic.

The organic product which causes hydrophobic sand patches may be produced by the grass itself or by fungi which decay the grass. It has been found that the zone of maximum non-wettability in such patches is immediately below the fibre layer in the top inch of soil. No precise identification of the substances which produce the 'waxy' coating on the soil or sand particles from a dry patch area has been obtained. Photographs of sand particles from a dry patch area have been obtained at high magnification using an electron microscope and these clearly show the organic coating. It has been suggested that the substance is produced in limited amounts but that there is enough to coat the vast number of particles of clay or silt which collectively have a very large surface area in most normal soils. However, on sand there is enough present to coat a thin layer of sand grains which causes water to move over the repellent layer and enter cracks or pores where it channels down without wetting the surface soil. Hydrophobic dry spots occur commonly on sand top dressed greens and also on the naturally very sandy soil or links courses. It seems that when such a soil becomes dry, the molecules of the hydrophobic material align themselves on the surface of the sand grain so that water is repelled. In other words, if sand is not allowed to dry out completely it will not become water repellent. When dry spots do occur the best approach is to open up the immediate surface by spiking at close centres and shallow depth, following this with an application of wetting agent solution and thorough localised watering of the dry patches. Wetting agents frequently used in this country and quite widely available include Metapol HCR and Synperonic NDB. There are a number of commercial turf products on the market such as Aqua-Gro, Turfex, Wettasoil and Hydrowet.

DRY PATCH AND WETTING AGENTS

With the summers of 1989 and 1990 being the driest on record for many years, it is perhaps not surprising that dry patch is a major problem on many golf courses. Recent independent market surveys have indicated 84% of UK golf courses are affected by dry patch to some degree. These courses regularly use wetting agents, accumulating a financial cost to golf estimated between £1.5–2 million annually, which is further compounded by the high labour requirements for application. This section reflects on the experience of using wetting agents for the alleviation of severe dry patch, and recommends the most effective application strategies.

Dry patch, or localised dry spot as it is sometimes known, is where areas of turf dry out and become water-repellent (hydrophobic). Dry patch may be due to a physical cause such as high spots which selectively dry out, uneven watering systems or rootbreaks where shallow-rooted turf easily becomes drought-stressed. Also prone are sites where there is an excessive fibrous thatch layer. Of increasing concern is dry patch caused by fairy ring fungi which excrete waxy substances onto the surface of sand particles thus rendering the turf hydrophobic. Physical causes of dry patch may be avoided or prevented, e.g. by improving the turf coverage achieved by the irrigation system. In most cases, however, a programme of wetting agent applications to re-wet and keep moist turf affected by dry patch is necessary.

The choice of wetting agent, made according to its chemical structure, for use on turf is all important. In the 1930s soft soap solutions were used and in the 1950s mild detergents such as Teepol and ordinary washing up liquid were employed. In many cases these chemicals had adverse effects on both soil structure and grass tissue and consequently are no longer recommended. Fortunately, the wetting agents currently available are 'non-ionic', i.e. neutral in charge, which means they are able to persist in the soil and are the least phytotoxic type of wetting agent.

Currently, there are a number of products available for use on turf, the best known products are Aqua-gro, Hydrowet, Synperonic, Turfex and Wetta-Soil. Whatever wetting agent is chosen it is important to apply the product as detailed below to achieve the greatest alleviation of dry patch. When applying wetting agents, prevention is much more effective than cure. On greens prone to the development of dry patch, the routine use of wetting agents between late March (before the turf has dried out) and October is recommended. Curative applications of wetting agents are generally ineffective as the dry patch is extremely difficult to re-wet even with wetting agents. However, if this situation has been allowed to develop then spot treatment with Turfex will achieve initial re-wetting of water-repellent turf. After the initial application of wetting agent in the early spring, further applications should be made at 4-6 week intervals according to the severity of dry patch and climatic conditions. As well as blanket treatments to the entire green, more localised spot treatment of the worst areas using a watering can followed by selective irrigation using a hose is beneficial.

A dry 'spreadable' formulation of Aqua-gro is available which is well suited to spot application, especially when applied following hollow tining. Spreadable formulations of Aqua-gro and Hydrowet may also be applied after hollow tining to place the wetting agent in the most hydrophobic zone. In all cases wetting agent applications should be tied in with the routine or local aeration using slit or preferably chisel tines. Also, wetting agents should be thoroughly watered into the turf shortly after application to minimise the possibility of phytotoxicity.

To summarise, dry patch should be treated with wetting agents in the early season when the turf is still moist, and the application repeated as necessary through the growing season. Spot treatment of severe dry patch areas with a spreadable formulation or liquid followed by selective irrigation is also beneficial. A regular aeration programme will assist penetration of wetting agent through the turf surface and watering in after application is essential.

GOLF GREENS IN WINTER

The British climate is never kind to winter golf and the heavier the soil on which the course is built the more numerous the problems. With new courses, though the local soil may be clay, the actual greens are often built with light sandy topsoil mixes (the proportions pre-determined by laboratory tests) with special provision for under-drainage. Some are made almost entirely of sand. Sadly, though, there are greenkeepers still nursing along sets of golf greens built perhaps 50 or 60 years ago of heavy clay soil with no drainage layers and few drain pipes. There are plenty of such golf courses north of London (on the London clay) and elsewhere, providing golfers and management with many more headaches during the average winter than the courses on lighter soils, like the Bagshot sands in Surrey for instance.

Hole-Cutting

In wet weather the greenkeeper must have a regular programme so far as changing the pin holes is concerned. Never wait until the turf is starting to show wear before cutting a new hole. Use pin holes which are likely to be tolerated in winter to a greater degree than in the main golfing season. Here is a chance to put the pin nearer the edge where there is probably more spongy fibre, simply due to lack of wear. Moss and patches of Yorkshire fog do not like the concentrated traffic round the pin hole and cutting the hole in a mossy area can often be useful in reducing it.

The Value of Temporary Greens

Some golf clubs site the pins on the front of the greens all through the winter, keeping the rest of the green free from play until the spring, and never use temporary greens. This is certainly one of the options but, especially on the clay greens, there is a strong case for using the greens more or less in the normal way through the winter (though with more of the less favourite pin placements) but coming off the greens on to temporary greens when the surfaces are exceptionally wet and soft or when there is any frost either in or on the ground. For this to be done without an abnormal number of entries in the suggestions/complaints book, temporary greens must be available where putting surfaces are not vastly inferior to the main greens. They should be sited well to the right or left of the main greens where practicable (not directly in front as seems to be the case quite often) and should be carefully prepared, well in advance of use, by fertilizing, weedkilling, scarifying, spiking and top dressing – in fact, by similar management to that of the main greens.

The greatest harm is done following frost when a green is beginning to thaw out after a hard frost: this is when the grass roots suffer most.

Prevent the 'Beaten Tracks'!

Keep an eye on the surrounds for signs of undue stress caused by processions of trolleys. Be ready to re-route, possibly with the aid of real physical obstacles like hoops, or with plastic white strips inset in the turf or similar, depending on the degree of co-operation from the members. It would seem that rolls of barbed wire would be needed to turn some golfers from their usual route!

Breaking the Ice?

Some winters are bad for golf greens, especially 1979/80 and 1962/63 when many golf greens suffered severely, perhaps the worst affected being those in North West England. The difference between 1979/80 and 1962/63 lay in the fact that the turf was covered with snow for lengthy periods at a time in 1979/80. In 1962/63 there were alternate thawings and freezings which resulted in the complete destruction of the grass in the hollows where the frozen water lay. Wise after the event, we formed the impression that it was probably better to break the ice in the hollows than to adopt a policy of "laisser faire".

Mow When Needed

Grass growth does not stop completely in a normal winter, coarser grasses like Yorkshire fog and perennial ryegrass in particular growing away from the rest if allowed. Occasional topping of the turf with the mower on a relatively dry surface is good for both grass and golfer. Top at about 8 mm and use a single mower rather than one of the combination triples when the surface is at all inclined to be soft.

Spike When Dry Enough

Regular winter spiking, preferably with a machine fitted with sturdy long slit tines, whenever weather conditions permit, is always a great help in preserving good drainage and encouraging root growth. If possible, slitting should take place at weekly or two weekly intervals.

Sandy Top Dressings Useful

After spiking, a top dressing principally composed of a suitable medium lime-free sand (with a small admixture of sandy compost or topsoil to avoid the risk of producing a rootbreak at some future stage) can be most helpful in firming up a green which is soft in winter, although probably the chance has gone by this time; such dressings are better given in the autumn when the weather is more open and dry.

Don't Let the Trees Take Over!

Trees have a substantial contribution to make to the charm of many a golf course and to the character of the holes, but they *will* keep growing! Winter is the time to do some cutting back where necessary. A thick stand of trees to the side or behind a green will often shut off the sunlight entirely through the winter, keeping the green damp and soft, subject to diseases like fusarium patch and invasion by moss and algae. Rain dripping from overhanging branches will injure the grass directly by sheer physical impact (in some areas it also carries down pollution deposited on the tree). Tree roots enter the green and in summer rob the grass of its birthright of water and plant food. Winter is the time to assess the position objectively, rating turf first and trees a bad second, and to chop or trim where necessary for the green's sake. Where tree roots are a problem in the green, and several greens are affected, it might be worthwhile hiring one of the small trenching machines for a period and using it to cut a narrow slit round the greens, severing roots during the process. It is also useful to place a thick (500 gauge) polythene sheet in the trench wall to prevent further root invasion.

Compost Making

Winter is the time for building the new compost heaps which are needed to maintain continuity of supply, for turning over the heaps which are half-way to maturity (having already been standing out in the open for 12 months) and for breaking down the heaps which are mature (after standing for two years or so), bringing the compost under cover for drying, riddling and storage for eventual use as top dressing. Good natural compost derived from compost heaps made by stacking alternate layers of sandy topsoil and organic material (preferably farmyard manure or horse manure) is not seen around on golf courses these days as often as it should. There is really nothing to beat it, and greens where the basic treatment consists of plenty of sandy compost with the minimum of 'artificial' fertiliser are those, as a rule, with the best turf. In order to make good compost though, adequate weather-proof buildings are needed of suitable size for entry and exit with tractor and trailer, a hard floor for mixing and mechanical equipment for screening.

The Problem of Cold Springs

Good natural compost must be made on the golf course itself. The main top dressing is usually done in early autumn but it should not be forgotten that remarkable benefit can be obtained from a compost dressing applied about the end of February or the beginning of March to repair imperfections in putting surfaces caused by winter play and (perhaps more important still) to provide some early encouragement to growth. Early spring is a bad time for golf greens. Many greens in this country have a turf which is mainly a blend of bentgrass and annual meadow-grass. In March or April, before the soil has warmed up appreciably, there is often a period when there is uneven growth related to the mixed composition of the sward since some grasses start growth earlier than others. This gives rise to bumpy putting surfaces which persist until the annual meadow-grass catches up with the bent. An early compost dressing does wonders in helping the slower-growing grasses to catch up and also incidentally gives the grass a better colour – try top dressing just half a green with a good home-made compost in the early spring and the proof will be clearly seen.

Timely Fertiliser Application
Before the end of the winter thought should be given to the spring fertiliser and arrangements made to have it ready when required. Last spring many greenkeepers, waiting for the warmer weather which was so late in coming, left the spring fertiliser dressing too late. Whilst it is true that fertilisers may, up to a point, be wasted if they go on before the soil warms up sufficiently, to wait too long is just as bad and can leave the golfers to struggle with unfair putting surfaces right into June.

(Note: Home-production of compost has become increasingly rare in recent years, probably due to increasing labour and equipment costs, and to the fact that commercial top dressing materials are now available more freely and of better quality than in the past. Ed.)

EFFECTS OF PLAY ON GOLF GREENS UNDER ADVERSE WEATHER CONDITIONS

The aim of management is to keep play on the main greens for as near 12 months in the year as possible. However, this ideal has to be matched with the drainage qualities, soil type, aspect and elevation of the greens in question as well as prevailing weather conditions. An indication of the type of damage arising from play under adverse conditions is given below and, whilst appreciating that golfers expect winter play, these requirements must be kept in perspective. Most competitive golf and important fixtures take place outside the winter period. Winter golf is normally less competitive and if the minor inconvenience caused by playing to temporary greens of a satisfactory standard is accepted, when necessary, then the putting surfaces of the main greens are better preserved for when they are required and expected to be at their best. The use of temporary winter greens is of more benefit on heavy clay courses.

Wet Conditions

In wet conditions, the surface soil around the pin is likely to become severely compacted and regular solid/slit tine aeration will help minimise ill effects on drainage and the sward. Hole changes should be frequent, use being made of the outer regions of the greens as far as possible, although keeping towards the front in very wet spells. At short holes where plugging is severe under wet conditions, light applications of suitable sandy top dressing can help.

Frosty Conditions

Damage caused by play during frosty weather falls into two main categories.

Firstly, when frozen, plant tissues are easily bruised by players' feet. Following a thaw, it is often possible to see brown footmarks for several weeks, particularly around hole sites. The greater the weight of play in hard frost, obviously the greater becomes the extent of this damage. Affected areas remain thin for long periods, affecting the trueness of the putting surface, and are more susceptible to disease in spring.

Secondly, long term damage is caused when play takes place after a sudden thaw. In these conditions the top 13 mm or so becomes soft, whilst the underlying soil remains frozen. Root damage occurs from the shearing action as players' feet move the soft, unfrozen surface across the frozen sub-surface. This disrupts putting surfaces and creates weak areas that may not recover before the height of the competition season.

Temporary Greens

The best way to overcome these problems is to mow out separate temporary greens of good quality, perhaps 100–200 m^2 well clear of the major putting surfaces, and prepared in advance. It is important that these areas designated for temporary greens should be cut down well in advance of play, and these areas top dressed, scarified and fertilised well before the winter time. Many clubs do not wish to go to this trouble and put temporary holes on the approach, but damage may still be caused when retrieving balls which go through on to the actual green.

COMPACTION ON THE GOLF GREEN

It seems that in the last few years there has probably been more written words and discussion about golf green compaction than most other greenkeeping topics. As a result of such concentrated attention, compaction is a word that most green committee members are familiar with but unfortunately the mechanics of compaction problems are often still not fully understood by golfers. The more practical guardians of our golf courses, the greenkeepers, do however present a different story. There is no doubt that the great majority of greenkeepers understand most of what there is to know about compaction and its associated problems.

What are the Problems

Soil compaction occurs when a force (a moving weight), such as a machine or players' feet, pushes soil particles very closely together, thereby closing the pore spaces between the particles. With reduced soil pore space there is less oxygen available and any moisture from rainfall or irrigation may not flow through the soil. Compaction can occur in both the subsoil and in the topsoil. Where topsoil compaction is encountered there is usually a good chance of solving the problem with various management practices, such as hollow coring or slitting, but compaction in the subsoil is more difficult to correct and in these circumstances major reconstruction work may be needed.

Compaction on a golf green usually means slow drainage and impeded root action, and this results in a change in botanical composition and vigour of the grass cover. Annual meadow-grass with its shallow roots survives on a compacted turf surface, at the expense of the deeper rooting bents and fescues. The build up of thatchy material at the base of the turf is also another condition associated with golf green compaction and the secondary effects of thatch development are considerable not only as far as the turf is concerned but also the playing characteristics of the green.

Factors Affecting the Development of Compaction

Compaction problems on many of our golf greens today undoubtedly go back to the original construction. On very old courses the original constructional techniques were often entirely satisfactory at the time, bearing in mind comparatively light use and management, but with today's heavy usage and vastly different maintenance these old constructions are inadequate and compaction problems are often a consequence. Many of our old courses do not have efficient drainage within their greens. When the soil is moist the soil particles slide together much more easily and with an applied weight from feet or machinery, soil compaction often soon results. There is also another consideration that should not be forgotten, namely just the passage of time itself can lead to soil compaction, particularly in the lower levels of the topsoil or subsoil. Fine soil particles may collect together at a particular depth and then, maybe with the weight from just the soil above, compaction may result.

Sadly, in any discussion about compaction on newly constructed golf greens one has to say that often workmanship, particularly when using heavy equipment for levelling purposes, is frequently the cause of the problem. It is vital that where there is a possibility of compaction, especially in the subsoil, during the construction of new golf greens, that the Contractor undertakes subsoil cultivation at some suitable stage in the development.

Besides constructional work, design features can also have a significant influence on the development of soil compaction. Golf greens should have at least 70% available pin space to spread out the wear and thus avoid concentrated continual play on a relatively small area. Narrow entrances into greens or limited walk-off areas towards the next tee are other design features which may affect the development of compaction.

Mention was made earlier of how compaction is produced, i.e. the soil particles being pushed together, often with a significant reduction in pore space. Compacting processes proceed much easier and much more quickly with certain types of soil and, to generalise, one could say that soils with a high clay content are much more likely to compact as compared with sandy soils. To avoid possible compaction problems when constructing golf greens, great importance should therefore be given to a well drained base and a free draining sandy topsoil, preferably with a sand/soil mixture.

Curing Existing Problems
Poor drainage caused by subsoil compaction on an established green has in the past almost always required major remedial works which involved taking the green out of play for several months. In desperation, as an alternative to reconstruction it has not been unknown for some clubs to try something like deep mole ploughing, but the disruption to the playing surface was so great that this sort of work has been valueless. Nowadays however, with the introduction of the Verti-Drain machine and compressed air injection techniques, deep compaction can be relieved with little surface disturbance.

Where topsoil compaction is a problem there should be two objectives in view; relief of soil compaction by mechanical means, and the possible amendment of the topsoil characteristics.

Elimination of compaction by mechanical methods means aeration. Golf green aeration should be carried out frequently (once or twice per week) and as deep as possible, fitting tines appropriate to the time of year and bearing in mind playing commitments. Hollow tining in the autumn at the end of the main competition season is a good way of helping to relieve compaction – again the deeper the better, especially where there is compaction at depth. The frequent use of solid or slit tines is also invaluable for getting air into a compacted turf and soil, and there is no denying that the availability of machines such as the Sisis Hydromain and the Cushman System has been a great stride forward in enabling greenkeepers to aerate regularly up to 200 mm in the fight against compaction. If deep compaction is a problem, then the use of the Verti-Drain machine is most beneficial.

Besides the more conventional tine-type aeration equipment the development of mini-mole plough devices has been another welcomed development in recent years, enabling greenkeepers to form continuous aerating slits up to 175 mm below the surface without upsetting the playing surface significantly. Before leaving the subject of elimination of compaction by mechanical means, do not forget the hand fork. Localised compaction on golf greens is often just as much a problem as overall compaction and there is no denying limited localised hand forking still has a significant place in golf green management. Small and compacted dry patches which can be a problem on some courses in the hot summer weather are the ideal sort of areas for hand treatment.

Amending topsoil characteristics with the aim of producing a free draining growing medium will also more than likely be a necessity when dealing with compaction. The use of a very sandy compost, particularly after deep hollow tining, is an essential part of anti-compaction treatment, especially where the topsoil contains a large amount of clay.

Other Important Considerations
Heavy play on a moist soil and turf is more likely to produce compaction problems than play under drier conditions. Use of irrigation systems should therefore be closely controlled to avoid excessive applications of water, this being particularly true with automatic systems. Regular aeration should supplement any irrigation work, particularly if the soil on the greens tends to be rather slower draining than one would wish.

Winter play is another factor which unquestionably has contributed to compaction problems at some courses, particularly where drainage is not very efficient. At sites where wet conditions are quite common in wet weather, the preparation of temporary greens should be considered – these temporary greens being brought into play when very wet conditions occur on the main areas and when play under such conditions seems to be causing significant damage and likely compaction problems.

From time to time the point is raised about various pieces of maintenance equipment contributing towards golf green compaction. Triple mowers are favourites for this particular point of concern. It is unlikely that any piece of modern fine turf management equipment used in Britain today would encourage and produce compaction if the equipment is used under the right operating conditions. One should not forget that nothing produces more concentrated weight (and therefore more potential compaction) than players' feet.

Prevention Better Than Cure
This old proverb is certainly very applicable when considering compaction on golf greens as once you have the problem and its secondary effects the cure is not always straightforward. However, with the wide range of efficient deep aeration equipment available to greenkeepers at the present time, there is probably a greater chance of them winning the fight against compaction than ever before.

FURTHER OBSERVATIONS ON THE SUBJECT OF COMPACTION ON THE GOLF COURSE

Within our golf clubs attention has been focused on the problems associated with compaction due to increasing levels of play throughout the year. To define what we mean by compaction, it is basically a soil condition whereby the particles of soil are pushed together, primarily by the pressure exerted by the golfers on the turf surface above. Maintenance equipment also contributes to compaction but this is minimised by fitting low-ground-pressure tyres and is certainly not as significant as the concentrated weight imposed by players' feet, especially during wet weather. The weight of the topsoil alone may also result in the development of deeper-seated compaction over a prolonged period of time.

The direct consequences of the process of compaction are reduced soil pore space, impeded root growth and reduced drainage rates. The development of excessively soft, wet and thatchy playing surfaces dominated by annual meadow-grass testifies to the adverse effects of compaction on many of our golf courses and to a lack of remedial work in the past. Outbreaks of anthracnose (*Colletotrichum* basal rot) have become more prevalent in recent years and this is often indicative of the weak state of growth of the annual meadow-grass on highly compacted soils. Reinstating healthy grass growth by improving the supply of air to the roots will usually be sufficient to remedy the problem.

Compaction should not be seen as a difficulty confined to the golf green as all areas of the course are susceptible to a varying degree, especially traffic routes such as walk-off/walk-on to greens and tees. However, when formulating management strategies to minimise the adverse effects of compaction, the most vulnerable areas should have priority, notably the greens, tees, approaches and main traffic routes.

Combating Compaction

Having identified the problems associated with compaction, how can we best combat this undesirable condition on the golf course? The most effective answer would be to remove the golfer from the course, thereby eliminating the primary cause of soil compaction. This course of action is unlikely to receive universal approbation, but fortunately there are less radical methods of minimising compaction!

The philosophy of 'prevention is always better than cure' is certainly applicable on the golf course. Therefore, a system of 'traffic control' should be initiated to re-direct golfers away from heavily used routes and thereby spread the weight of golf traffic more evenly. The provision of **separate** winter tees, placed well away from the main summer tees, will help in this respect as the well-used spring/summer traffic routes from green to tee and tee to fairway will be rested. Temporary greens are never popular with the golfers but, if conditions dictate, should be employed to protect the main greens at critical times, e.g. when soil conditions are saturated and therefore most susceptible to compaction. To reduce the resistance of the golfers to the use of 'temporaries', putting surfaces comparable to the main greens must be prepared.

Good Drainage Helps

All soils are prone to compaction but heavy clay soils, which are inherently poor draining, are particularly susceptible. Many of our old established courses based on heavier soils were designed and constructed for much lighter use. Consequently, the efficiency of their drainage does not meet the demands of the game today. Indeed, golf greens were actually shaped to hold moisture, prior to the installation of modern automatic irrigation systems with their capacity to put on large quantities of water at any one time. To avoid possible compaction problems when constructing new greens, emphasis needs to be placed on introducing a free draining base, over which a sand/soil mixture is placed to ensure consistently high rates of drainage. Elevation of tees usually precludes the need for the introduction of a comparable drainage system to that advocated for greens. However, modifying the topsoil by ameliorating with an appropriate quantity of sand is usually necessary as the free draining topsoil produced will be less susceptible to the adverse effects of compaction. To circumvent poor drainage on fairway areas, additional drainage may also be necessary in the form of pipe drainage or ditches, perhaps augmented by slit drainage in situations where percolation through the topsoil is extremely slow.

Influence of Design
Design can have a significant influence on soil compaction. Golf greens should be formed so that at least 70% of the putting surface is available for pin positioning in order to avoid concentrating play, and thus compaction, on localised areas. The undesirability of creating narrow entrances into greens restricted walk-off areas or 'bottlenecks' (where many traffic routes converge) must also be taken into consideration when designing or modifying a course layout as these will also affect the development of soil compaction.

Aeration Treatments are of Fundamental Importance
To counteract existing compaction, aeration work should be seen as an ongoing process which must be carried out with modern, efficient equipment to achieve optimum benefits from individual treatments. At one time, hand forking performed once or twice a year was considered satisfactory, but this is totally inadequate on golf courses today which have to contend with 50,000 to 60,000 rounds of golf per year regardless of weather conditions.

The bulk of aeration work should be carried out during the autumn and winter months when soils are most susceptible to compaction. Deep penetration should be the objective (minimum 150 mm) to allow air in, facilitate water infiltration to lower levels and encourage deeper grass rooting. Without good gaseous exchange and movement of surplus water out of the system, excessively soft, thatch-ridden playing surfaces dominated by shallow-rooted annual meadow-grass will be perpetuated. On fairways, much deeper penetration is now possible with spiking units which operate on the tractor hydraulics, thereby forcing the tines into the ground to their optimum working depth.

Hollow tine aeration still has an important role to play in combating soil compaction within the top 75–100 mm of the soil profile – which is most susceptible to the condition. If hollow tining is followed by top dressing with a sandy top dressing mix, then more freely draining surfaces will result. In addition, hand forking should not be disregarded as this is particularly useful for treating localised, highly compacted areas.

Besides the more conventional aeration equipment, there are specialist forms of aeration which shatter the compacted soil and thereby restore freer draining, better aerated soil conditions. The vibratory mole plough – a development of the rigid mole plough – comes in this category which is designed to work in the depth range of between 125 and 175 mm. For alleviating deeper seated compaction (below the normal working depth of routine aeration equipment), Verti-Draining is invaluable and this operation has become an integral part of the aeration programme on many courses. If maximum benefit is to be derived from these particular treatments they must be applied before ground conditions are excessively wet, as in these circumstances the effect will be like passing a knife through butter – there will be little or no shattering of the compacted soil.

Spring/Summer Aeration Work

Although the importance of autumn/winter aeration work has been emphasised, spring and summer treatments should not be neglected, particularly on the slower draining sites. There is often resistance from within the golf club to applying aeration treatments to greens at these times, but the use of solid tines should minimise disturbance to the smoothness of the putting surfaces, particularly if conditions turn dry.

The development of drought-susceptible areas within greens can often be associated with highly compact soil conditions beneath. In these circumstances, localised spiking treatments of the affected areas are invaluable for aiding moisture penetration and thereby reinstating uniform turf conditions.

Irrigate with Discretion

Excessive irrigation can be implicated in the development of topsoil compaction, therefore close control must be exercised when using automatic watering systems. In addition, regular aeration should be seen as a complementary treatment to irrigation to ensure that water infiltration is not confined to the uppermost layers of soil as this feature will create, with the passage of play, an impervious 'cap' over the soil beneath.

WHY AERATE?

Compaction
Without doubt one of the commonest problems on sports turf areas is compaction caused largely by the very people the turf is there for – the players. There is nothing mysterious about compaction and all soils are vulnerable to it, though to varying degrees. Compaction is basically a soil condition resulting from forces of compression which create a breakdown in natural structure. As the soil structure deteriorates pore space is reduced and this has direct consequences on air and water movement and root growth. In a compacted soil, gaseous exchange will be poor, water movement slow and root growth restricted and such conditions are the very opposite to what we need for healthy turfgrass growth and good playability and surface performance. Nature provides earthworms to help maintain soil structure but the intensive pressures on sports turf areas are far from natural and create a situation which demands artificial assistance. This is obviously where aeration comes into play.

Soil is the very basis of any sports turf area and its characteristics are the single most important influence on the standard of provision. So, it must be kept in optimum condition if there is to be any chance of providing the optimum playing surface and without a good aeration programme the battle is lost right from the start.

Why All the Fuss?
Particularly at golf clubs, one question we are often asked is "Why all the fuss about aeration these days – it never used to be the case?" The people that put this to us are normally very quickly reminded that it never used to be the case that golf courses were expected to tolerate rounds of up to 60,000–80,000 per year and be in use 365 days of the year, hail, rain or shine. Going back 20 years or more, most greens were probably forked once or twice a year and that was that. It could well have proved sufficient then but greens with a similar programme these days just would not be capable of giving anything like adequate performance, and indeed even with all the 'fuss' about aeration there are cases where clubs to their cost are finding this out for themselves.

The Consequences
The consequences of compaction on golf greens are far-reaching and the annual meadow-grass dominated thatchy, slow surfaces (which are not too difficult to find) are clear testimony to this. As compaction increases, a downward spiral develops: bents and fescues diminish because of poor rooting conditions and annual meadow-grass (*Poa annua*) thrives; the rate of surface drainage decreases and greens get wetter in winter; waterlogged conditions create further problems for growth of the desirable species; and the whole situation culminates with the development of *Poa annua* dominated greens and thatch. So, the consequences are disastrous. Machinery for aerating golf greens has improved in recent years to meet the demands for the work and there is no excuse for not carrying out aeration frequently enough. The initial capital expenditure can be justified in every case.

Types of Aeration
Various types of tine are available and there do seem to be some differences of opinion on which should be used and when, although nobody doubts their general importance. The tine most effective at relieving compaction is clearly the hollow tine and for greens with thick thatch over a compacted soil, treatment with this type of equipment is essential and may well have to be repeated annually each autumn for several years and maybe in some cases in spring as well. The essence of hollow tining is that thatch and compacted soil within the top 75–100 mm are physically removed – subsequently to be replaced by freer draining top dressing, thereby effecting something of a surface exchange programme, taking out the problem or part of it and putting something better back. Roots then stand a far better chance

of producing a strong and deeper network and the infiltration of water is markedly assisted. Remember that hollow tining at 50 mm centres will remove almost 5% of the surface of a golf green and consequently you are removing 5% of your thatch in one operation.

However, where the depth of compacted soil extends below 100 mm mechanical hollow tining will not reach these depths but the work can, of course, be done by hand. Furthermore, there are sub-aeration machines specifically designed to relieve compaction at depth by a vibratory and fissuring action, along with the fine turf Verti-Drain unit which works on the deep forking/leverage principle, and these often have to be included in aeration programmes on greens with significant compaction problems.

Solid Versus Slit Tines

For more regular aeration work we have solid tines and slit tines of various shapes and sizes. Both types have their own particular application. Solid tines generally do not work any deeper than 100 mm and they are particularly useful for assisting the penetration of irrigation water into a dry, thatchy and compacted turf surface as they make direct channels through it – getting water in is sometimes just as important as getting water out. Slit tines on the other hand are able to penetrate much more deeply than this and recently developed equipment can get down as far as 225 mm, which is obviously extremely valuable where there is extensive compaction. Solid and slit tines allow air in, help to get water to lower levels and thereby generally greatly assist rooting and thatch breakdown. Without good gaseous exchange and the movement of excessive water out of the system, conditions simply stagnate and problems with poor rooting and thatch build up increase. One bone of contention is whether to use slit tines during the summer. Problems have been experienced with slits opening up in dry conditions. To some extent this can be overcome with irrigation, particularly where clubs have automatic systems, but one must not forget that simply putting water on to combat this type of problem is self-defeating when the reason for spiking in the first place is to improve *aeration*. Clubs without automatic irrigation are often best advised to use solid or chisel tines during the summer (as the tendency for surface disruption to occur with such tine patterns in dry conditions is far less) and to concentrate on a deeper slitting programme through the autumn, winter and early spring. Even where there is adequate irrigation, however, treatment during particularly dry weather must be suspended. Winter conditions do present difficulties too, e.g. when surfaces are frost-bound, but with these exceptions spiking should be regular and frequent throughout the year, say every seven to ten days with either solid or slit tines being used as considered appropriate. Sometimes an intensive programme of such work may still create some surface disruption but this has often to be tolerated if any progress is to be made.

Tees

Much of what has been said above applies to tees too, but it is a sad fact that the importance of regular aeration on these features of the course is often neglected and compaction remains, to the detriment of the turf and the surface generally. Regular slitting of tees from October to March each year is an important maintenance procedure – carrying out the work at least once a month.

Fairways

Similarly, on fairways aeration by and large is not done frequently enough. Good surface drainage and root growth is of no less importance on the fairways than on any other part of the course, where the requirement is for fine, wiry swards which do not turn to bogs in winter. Obviously, the degree of concentrated traffic on fairways is far less per unit area than on greens and tees but adequate aeration is still essential and in ideal circumstances slit tine spiking treatment once a fortnight from autumn through until spring is normally a good average, ground conditions permitting. On thatchy fairways spoon tining can be very useful done in the autumn or spring prior to harrowing and in some cases, particularly where there is compaction below, sub-aeration with a tractor-mounted unit such as the Twose Turf Conditioner or mechanical deep forking with a Verti-Drain unit might have to be considered too, especially on heavy traffic areas.

After Drought
Clubs tend to neglect spiking after a very dry summer, with the consequence that water penetration into the droughted fairway turf remains poor well into the autumn, producing weak growth. This is a consideration which requires far more attention being invaluable to the provision of better autumn playing conditions at many courses.

THE VALUE OF SUB-AERATION

The Problem

Test hole excavation into golf greens suffering from drainage problems often shows excessive compaction existing to a depth of several centimetres below the turf surface and this frequently accentuates the naturally slow drainage of soils with poor structure. The problem is most commonly found on older established inland greens where the hindrance to water penetration aggravates the problems caused by thatch where such exists. The slow infiltration of surface water to lower levels is a serious contributory factor in the development of thatch.

In more recent years the need for increased aeration has become much more accepted and modern equipment has speeded up and simplified the task of relieving compaction. Unfortunately, examination of soil profiles often shows that the depth of penetration obtained by orthodox aerating tines is not sufficient to fully penetrate the compacted region. Where this situation exists, deeper forms of aeration must be considered as a supplement to normal aeration, and not as an alternative.

The procedure found to be effective is to treat the green with a machine fitted with a mini-mole plough/subsoiling tine(s) and these can be either of the rigid or the vibration type. Within reason,the greater the depth of penetration that can be obtained the better, and with machinery presently available this means working at a depth of 128–177 mm. The tines should be drawn through the green at 230 mm, no more than 300 mm centres at an angle of some 20° across maximum fall. Wherever possible the tines should be drawn right through the putting area and drawn through the surround preferably on to land which falls away from the green. Where this is not possible the low end of the slits running through the putting area should be linked up by two or three additional slits cut on a line which will run out of downward sloping ground. If the maximum benefit is to be obtained from the sub-aeration, the work should be done in the very early autumn, e.g. September and before the soils become wet as a result of late autumn/winter rains. This is important as work done when the soils are wet has a similar effect to passing a knife through a block of spreading cheese and little or no shattering of the compaction is obtained. The appearance of the slit lines (i.e. brown lines) on the green's surface following the work may concern some golfers but they do not really affect putting and they can quickly cover up.

It should be realised that, unlike complete cultivation, the effects of the above-mentioned forms of aeration are only partial and therefore to gain real benefit some continuity of treatment from year to year is necessary. In many cases the use of the Verti-Drain machine would be preferable. Experience shows that quite considerable progress can be made in three years but the effectiveness of the green's under-drainage has some influence on the progress made. If the under-drainage is unsatisfactory due to the presence of a slow draining clay subsoil, the penetration of water draining to lower levels is again impeded and this could apply even where complete cultivation is carried out. In these cases the reconstruction of the green may have to be considered.

VERTI-DRAINING

Drainage and the Verti-Drain

An open, well aerated, free draining growing medium is of paramount importance in sports turf management and a package of aeration treatments is the major basic maintenance technique to help achieve these criteria. The Verti-Drain was first introduced from Holland in 1982 and its use is now well established throughout the British Isles. The Verti-Drain is a specialised tractor-mounted unit primarily designed to deal with deep-seated compaction which conventional aerators cannot penetrate down to. The operating principle is similar to hand forking where deep aeration of the soil profile is combined with breaking up of the compacted layers. Verti-Draining followed by top dressing also provides the opportunity to create vertical drainage channels which have a lasting effect.

About the Verti-Drain

There are currently four types of Verti-Drain available which are commonly referred to as the Popular, Greens and Sports Ground machines (two available widths). The former two units are predominantly employed on fine turf areas, the Sports Ground machine on winter games pitches, racecourses and golf course fairways. The availability of a variety of solid tine sizes, working depth (to a maximum of 400 mm), tine spacing and overall working width, enables a wide range of problem situations in different sports to be tackled. Hollow tines are also available to carry out a deeper soil exchange which cannot be achieved by the use of more conventional equipment. Many contractors now hire out the above units with an operator, although an increasing number of Verti-Drain machines are being purchased by individual clubs or local authorities who want freedom to choose the timing of operation and have the need to use it on a regular basis on a number of areas.

How to Achieve the Best Results....and Avoid Disasters!

As with other forms of aeration, the best result with the Verti-Drain occurs when the soil is no more than moist. A dry soil will hinder deep tine penetration and often result in tearing of the turf. To offset this condition, the application of an approved wetting agent can help to moisten the turf prior to the arrival of the Verti-Drain on site. Verti-Draining a wet soil will inevitably lead to smearing down the sides of tine holes and reduced fissuring of the soil.

The Verti-Drain must travel over the surface at the correct creeping speed (between 0.25 and 0.65 miles per hour) to achieve an even lift, otherwise surface rippling will occur – a condition difficult to remedy. The operator should be aware of any shallow pipe drainage or irrigation supply pipes. Worn tines will reduce the effectiveness of the unit and bent or wrongly aligned blocks of tines will invariably result in surface damage. Altering the angle at which the tines enter the soil decreases or increases the lifting effect of the unit.

The Verti-Drain will cope successfully with a limited number of small stones in the soil profile but areas with significant stone content and rock near to the surface should be avoided. Renovation work on localised areas of damage **must** be organised in advance and completed quickly and efficiently, removing obstructions and making good levels with sandy compost or equivalent. On fine turf a light rolling is given just to settle the surface before top dressing takes place.

Top Dressing

As well as relieving deep-seated compaction, Verti-Draining also provides an opportunity to give distinct, long lasting vertical drainage channels between the surface and (hopefully) freer draining layers below, i.e. a drainage carpet or free draining subsoil. These channels often act as a by-pass through more heavily compacted and destructured soil, allowing better movement of air and nutrients. Improved root growth and natural breakdown of thatch through bacterial action follow as a result of the above work. To maintain this connection it is therefore important to top dress either just before or just after Verti-Draining. However, on larger areas cost may well restrict the extent and amount of top dressing applied.

The most commonly applied material is sand, although it is better to use sandy compost on fine turf areas such as golf greens. For sand top dressing, a good quality medium/fine lime free material with a narrow particle size distribution range is recommended, although a similarly specified medium/coarse sand is often preferred on thatchy greens with deep-seated compaction in the soil profile. It is vital that as much sand as possible is worked down tine holes to make the connection between the surface and sub-base as well as avoiding a layering effect further down the profile in years to come (i.e. a sand rootbreak). Apply a dry sand to a dry surface and work in immediately, this makes the above desired aim much easier to achieve. Larger diameter solid tines or hollow tining further aid the working in of sand. In general, the Institute would prefer a sandier top dressing material to be used.

Applications on Golf Courses

On the golf course, the specialist use of the Verti-Drain on golf greens during the early autumn period is now well established but with the increasing levels of play, especially during the winter, and better standards expected by players, alleviating localised areas of heavy wear around the course has now become a routine necessity. This has extended the range for Verti-Drain use on the golf course as an integral part of the autumn/winter renovation programme with special emphasis on approaches, tees and traffic routes. Sections of, or whole fairways can also be Verti-Drained with advantage and a dressing of approved sand or sandy top dressing is advised prior to the treatment where surface drainage is poor or algal growth affects surface traction. To avoid disruption to play, top dressing with sandy compost or sand on golf greens is completed after Verti-Draining using in the order of 1.5 to 2 tonnes per green. Following settlement in the holes, a further light dressing may be required but care will have to be taken in respect of timing to avoid smothering the turf or encouraging disease. If in doubt, leave until the spring. The Greens Verti-Drain fitted with 12 or 18 mm ($^1/_2$ to $^3/_4$ in.) tines is used primarily on greens and tees, the Sports Ground unit fitted with 25 mm (1 in.) tines on approaches, traffic routes and fairways.

One word of caution – Clubs considering Verti-Draining should not gain the impression that the results are impressive in all situations, this is not necessarily the case. Taking a specific situation, where a limited depth of heavy loam soil overlies clay subsoil on a green, then if the profile is saturated Verti-Draining would have little benefit with no significant fissuring and with water backing up the holes from a saturated sub-base. In this situation where the green also has a uniform slope, a combination of hollow tining, deep slitting and Vibroslitting to a positive outlet could well be a better option although the real answer is fundamentally one of reconstruction, including installation of an under-drainage system.

HYDRAULIC OIL LEAKAGE

The advent of hydraulic systems on so many machines used on fine turf areas (and not only triple mowers although of course these are the major users) has inevitably led to an increase in the type of damage caused by hydraulic oil. Leaks occur in several ways, such as faulty valves, seals or hose failure. Clearly, regular pre-use checks of the equipment are essential and an annual maintenance overhaul is a 'must'. Operators must be fully aware of the damage likely to occur on fine turf from hydraulic oil and must be alert for the first signs of any leak. Damage is caused to the grass by ingredients in the oil but also due to the oil temperature. To minimise damage, the leaking unit should be driven off the most vulnerable areas, usually greens and approaches, as quickly as possible and into adjacent rough. Speedy follow up treatments can also help a lot, especially where only a smear or light mist of oil exists on the grass leaves. With a heavy leak, quite severe turf damage is likely, but even so treatment can aid recovery and reduce the extent of repair work ultimately needed.

Within 10 to 15 minutes of the leak occurring the affected area should be scrubbed for one to two minutes using a sponge and a solution of liquid non-ionic wetting agent or non-phosphate containing detergent diluted 1–10. Examples include Synperonic NDB, Aqua-Gro and Turfex, but other turf wetting agents can be used. Follow up by washing off the residue with a hand-held high pressure hose.

Normally scorch damage after a spill will be apparent in 48 hours and the maximum turf loss at about two weeks. If treatment has been prompt, some recovery should be noticed after three or four weeks of reasonable growing weather and an assessment of repairs needed can then be made. Where partial recovery has taken place indicating minimal oil contamination of the soil surface, the thin areas can be helped to thicken up by close shallow forking and light raking followed by rubbing in a mixture of sandy soil and fine grass seed. If the turf has been completely killed then oil has damaged the growing points of the plants and contaminated the soil to such an extent that seed is unlikely to be successful. In this case patching with turf in autumn is the only satisfactory answer.

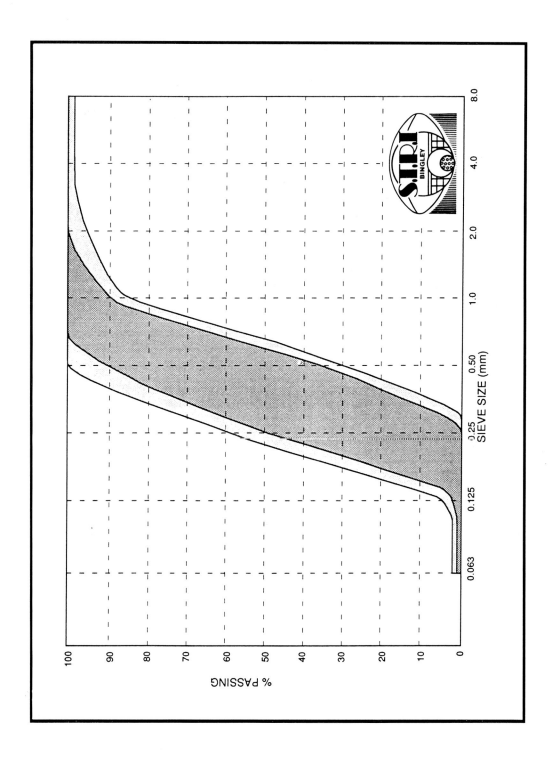

FIGURE 8: Grading curve defining recommended and acceptable limits of sand size for golf greens.

SANDS FOR TOP DRESSING GOLF GREENS

On areas of fine turf the main purpose of top dressing is to preserve a true and level surface and to dilute the build up of thatch. Ideally an annual application of 5-6 kg/m^2 of top dressing material will be used, with this quantity being divided into perhaps three applications to avoid excessive amounts of material on the surface at any one time. If the playing surface is on a heavy soil with poor drainage or has excess thatch, larger quantities should be applied in conjunction with a programme of hollow tining so that the drainage and aeration of the surface layer can be improved.

The composition of the top dressing material may vary depending on the type of construction and the availability of topsoil materials or composts for the top dressing. Where a green has been constructed with a special rootzone mix it is important to use a top dressing material which matches the mix in terms of the quantity of sand and the sand type. This will preserve a continuity in the profile of the green. In the extreme case of a pure sand construction the size and uniformity of the sand should match that of the rootzone sand.

Where a golf green has been developed from a native soil which may have a relatively high silt and clay content, it is sensible to use a relatively light (sandy) top dressing material in which the clay content has been diluted by sand to below 5% and the total silt and clay content should not exceed 10%. The use of a sand dominated by the medium or coarse sand size fraction (0.125–0.5 mm diameter or 0.25–1.0 mm diameter) is preferred for the preparation of this type of top dressing mix.

Sands with a high content of fine material should be avoided as these can clog the surface and excessively coarse sands are not popular as it is difficult to work sand grains above 2 mm in diameter into the turf and coarse particles such as these will damage mowers and are unpopular with golfers.

Consistency in the use of top dressing materials on fine turf is important and for instance, use of pure sand for perhaps a year followed by reversion to a sand-soil mix can form a root break. This thin layer of sand can have significant effects on the vertical movement of soil moisture and the penetration of grass roots will tend to reflect the moisture distribution within the soil.

In fine turf areas, the lime content of the top dressing material is critical. If the sand contains large quantities of shell or other calcareous material the pH of the surface layer will increase. This can have important effects on weed invasion, earthworm activity, turfgrass disease and the composition of grass species within the turf. In particular annual meadow-grass (*Poa annua*) will tend to invade the turf at the expense of the fescue (*Festuca*) and bent (*Agrostis*) species.

TOP DRESSING FOR GOLF

The general term 'top dressing' can be described as the application of a bulky material with a view to improving or maintaining the qualities of a playing surface. Top dressings should not be confused with fertiliser treatments, as the former may or may not have any plant food value.

The main reasons for applying a top dressing material are:

(i)   that it is an effective method of building up a true surface and thus improving the efficiency of mowing. This is a much more effective way of producing smooth levels than rolling, over-use of which induces compaction and subsequent drainage problems. This factor is of most importance to those sports that require a smooth running surface, such as golf;

(ii)   top dressing can also be of benefit by increasing the drought resistance of freely draining constructions. Conversely, applications of very sandy top dressings can assist surface drainage when carried out in conjunction with deep aeration treatments;

(iii)   in some cases application of appropriate top dressings can alter playing qualities, such as resiliency;

(iv)   newly seeded areas can be protected from the elements and also bird damage by covering them with suitable top dressings;

(v)   the top dressing which is applied to the turf surface may have a small plant food value, thus reducing the amount of artificial feeding required.

Top dressing work is generally confined to relatively small areas such as golf greens owing to the quantities of material involved. The timing of top dressing is important, as there should be some growth on the area to be dressed to avoid smothering the turf, and conditions should be reasonably dry.

Golf Greens

On fine turf areas such as golf greens the best material for top dressing purposes is usually a friable sandy compost. Proprietary composts are available for fine turf use, being made up from varying mixtures of sand, soil and fine grade peat. Some golf courses have their own compost-making facilities, thus enabling them to produce large quantities of top dressing material comprising a mixture of light topsoil, sand and some form of organic matter which will break down rapidly, forming an homogeneous 'soil', such as farmyard manure or grass clippings. Once a steady supply of home-made compost has been made available, then regular light applications should be possible throughout the main competition season, helping maintain smooth and uniform putting surfaces.

A major limiting factor with home-made composts (and also with the proprietary types) is the quality of the topsoil used in the mixture. If the soil contains a high proportion of fine silt and clay particles, then this can create further problems, particularly if used in high rainfall and poor drainage areas. Therefore, if the only available topsoil is of a heavy nature, then adequate amelioration with a suitable sand will be required in order to achieve the required drainage characteristics. In many cases heavy indigenous soils should not be used as top dressings, even when mixed with large quantities of sand. The quantities of sand and soil used in the final mix can be determined by laboratory tests carried out at the Institute.

As the supplies of good, light topsoils dwindle, there has been a trend in recent years towards the use of sand/organic matter mixtures. When used under appropriate conditions, these types of top dressings can have beneficial results, although their usefulness is also dependent on the qualities of the sand and peat used in them, which can be quite variable. The peat must be very finely ground so that it will become an integral part of the soil structure – fen peat can be an ideal component of a top dressing.

On golf courses, several top dressings may be given throughout the year, although the two main applications are made in the autumn after the main competition season and a lighter one in the early spring to help smooth out any unevenness in the surface caused by the winter frosts.

There has been some controversy over the use of pure sand on fine turf areas, particularly when the turf contains a deep thatch layer. There is no doubt that an application of sand will help to firm up a soft thatch turf, especially during a wet spring. However, if this practice is repeated, alternating this with normal compost top dressings, then problems will arise with the formation of root breaking layers in the soil profile. A soil component in the compost mixture is also a useful source of the microorganisms responsible for the breakdown of the thatch material. The problem of root breaking layers is not only confined to situations of irregular use of pure sand dressings. If the source, and type, of top dressing material is not consistent year in year out, then layering of top dressings may occur in the soil profile. Such a situation could not only restrict rooting depth, but may also impede drainage. Our basic advice would be: if you have a good source of a suitable top dressing, stick to it – do not chop and change your top dressing.

The exact proportions of each component of your top dressing should be determined by the soil already on site, and by what you are trying to achieve with the dressing. If the soil under the greens is sandy and naturally free-draining, then the top dressing should also be sandy in nature, with the majority of its particles lying in the same range as those of the soil on site. On the other hand, if the soil on site is rather heavy and relatively slow to drain, what is the point of adding more of the same? In this instance, we are looking to improve site conditions by applying a dressing of a sandy compost to facilitate freer drainage. For either situation the amount of organic material in the dressing needs to be closely monitored. Too great an organic matter input will tend to hold water at the surface – you will merely be adding to any organic thatch layer that already exists. In extremely free-draining situations, a small amount of organic matter can help increase drought resistance. Generally speaking, more than 10% organic matter in a top dressing is considered too much, and there is usually enough organic material in the soil constituent of a top dressing for the requirements of most situations.

In most instances a sand/soil mix with the proportions of 3 parts sand : 1 part topsoil or possibly 4 parts sand : 1 part topsoil could be used depending on the nature of the topsoil available. The type of sand used should be one of a fine to medium category, that is with the majority of its particles lying in the 0.125–0.5 mm range, and it should also be lime-free, except for links golf courses based on limy sands. For situations where thatch is a major problem, then sands with the majority of their particles lying in the 0.25–1.0 mm range can be used.

Summary
Clearly top dressing is an essential aspect of maintenance on golf greens. However, for this operation to be successful, a certain amount of skill is required in judging the appropriate material to use, adequately preparing the surface beforehand and choosing the correct weather and growing conditions in which to carry out the work. Tests on samples of top dressing materials in the soil physics laboratory at the Institute enables our Advisory Service to recommend the correct dressing for each individual situation, and greatly reduces the risk of applying a material that could turn out to be detrimental to the condition of the playing surface in the long term.

HOME-PRODUCE YOUR OWN COMPOST

The top dressing of today is the rooting medium for the grasses of tomorrow and its quality and texture dictate the characteristics of the playing surface on a putting green. This fact must never be forgotten. The playing surface should be free draining and not liable to become severely compacted under heavy play, but should have sufficient resiliency to assist the ball in stopping on the green when a short iron is used. The optimum top dressing should therefore contain a proportion of suitable sand to maintain the drainage capability and provide the desired firmness, and also some organic matter to help to maintain the required degree of resiliency.

The organic matter is probably the constituent which causes the greatest difficulty. It creates many of the problems on golf greens today. If it is omitted entirely from a top dressing and sand alone is used, there is danger of a rootbreak and subsequent shallow rooting and possible drought susceptibility. If too much organic matter is used, surfaces may become greasy, soft and lush, and other problems such as compaction may arise. If the wrong type of organic matter is used the tendency for thatch formation may be accelerated: for example, this often occurs when too much peat is used.

The most desirable source of organic material for top dressing is compost, obtained from a well constructed compost heap. For golf green use, 'compost' means organic material which has decomposed to such an extent that the original constituents are unrecognisable and which is still undergoing decomposition due to the activity of the micro-organisms present. The compost heap should therefore be built in such a way as to encourage the many living organisms which bring about decomposition. These organisms require heat, moisture, nitrogen and conditions which are not too acid.

Sources of Organic Matter
Useful ingredients for the compost heap include farmyard or stable manure, rotted leaves and well decomposed grass clippings. Other materials which have been used are spent hops, straw, sedge or moss peat, spent mushroom compost, and sewage sludge – in fact any organic material which will subsequently rot down. Some of these latter materials, however, can create problems which the user should be aware of before deciding to incorporate them in the heap. For example, some sewage wastes contain unacceptably high percentages of heavy metals which could cause toxicity, and many mushroom composts are too alkaline.

Straw can be used if chopped, thoroughly soaked and treated with nitrogenous fertiliser to accelerate decomposition beforehand. Many other coarse or woody materials also require added nitrogen to help microorganisms to break them down, and the process may often take quite a long time before it is complete. Seaweed is another useful source of organic matter, particularly on coastal areas, but also requires preliminary decomposition with the aid of nitrogen before being incorporated in the heap. Most peats are acid and are difficult to break down unless they are mixed with other rapidly decaying materials.

The Compost Heap
The compost heap should be constructed by laying down alternate layers of sandy soil and the materials discussed above, each layer being about 6 inches deep. The heap should be topped off with soil which should be extended down the sides. After about six months the heap should be turned over to allow oxygen to reach all parts and aid the process of rotting down. After a further 12–18 months the heap will probably be ready to bring indoors for breaking down and screening.

SIMPLE COMPOST SHED

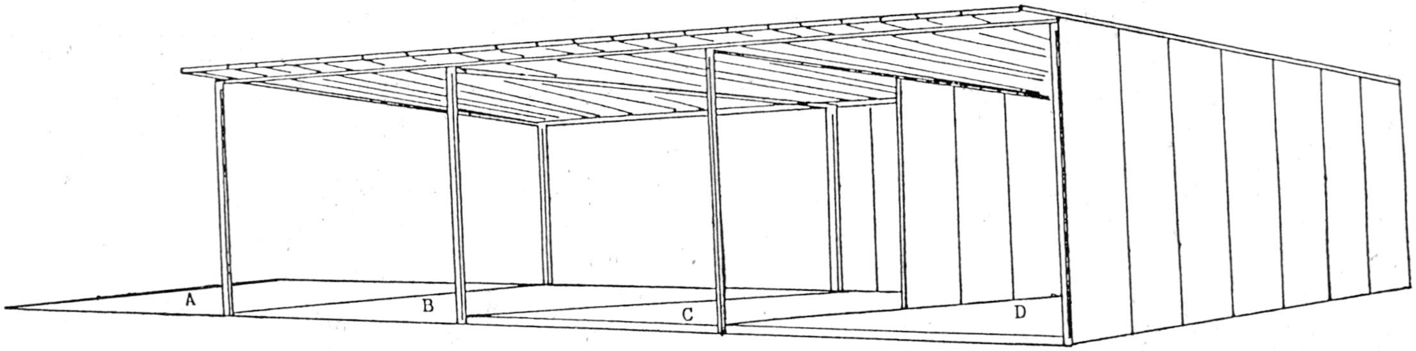

A. First year preliminary rotting heap built on hard ground in open.

B. Second year main compost heap, top cover only.

C. Screening and mixing section for compost.

D. Store for compost prepared for application.

DIMENSIONS

Height at front: 3.5 m (11 ft. 6 in.)

Height at back: 3.0 m (10 ft.)

Width (depth): 5.0 m (16 ft. 6 in.)

Length (B+C+D): 12.0 m (40 ft.)

NOTE:

1. Sections C and D protected on windward side and back.

2. Hard concrete base to Sections C and D - optional in Sections A and B.

3. Framework in round or squared timber with appropriate cladding, e.g. preserved timber or corrugated iron. Cladding, if of lightweight construction, may have to be fitted to inside the framework for adequate strength.

4. If required, allowance should be made for suitable gap between roof and top of back wall for aeration.

5. Dimensions depend on circumstances. Those given are the minimum for an 18 hole golf course.

FIGURE 9:   **Compost shed suitable for golf course purposes.**

The consistency and texture of the top dressing material based on the compost ought to be adjusted to the requirements of the golf greens and will be largely dictated by the nature of the soils on the greens; a very heavy clay soil would require a sandy consistency whereas a sandy soil prone to drought may require less sand and more organic material.

If the raw materials are available locally, the compost from your own 'factory' need not be too costly and yet it is perhaps the most valuable material you can obtain. It provides a natural source of nutrients for the grasses and if used judiciously can sustain reasonable growth without your having to use too much artificial fertiliser. It is not often appreciated that 1 tonne of good compost contains approximately the same amount of nitrogen as 50 kg of sulphate of ammonia.

It would be a tragedy if, as seems all too likely in these days of 'convenience packaging', the construction of compost heaps and home-processing of good quality **natural** compost for top dressing purposes were to become things of the past. Admittedly, substitutes are being supplied by the trade to fill the vacuum, and although many of these products are of great value, their cost prevents a golf club from purchasing enough to meet the annual requirements of the course, and their constituents cannot always be tailored to individual requirements.

The total annual requirement of compost for an 18-hole course varies, but if more top dressing of greens were to be done as we would like to see, i.e. say one main autumn dressing, a 'half rate' dressing in spring and two to three supplementary light summer dressings, a need of 60–70 tonnes per annum would not be excessive. Add to this your requirements for tees (divot filling, renovation and top dressing) and fairway divoting, not to mention approaches, temporary greens, etc., it is possible to utilise anything up to 100 tonnes in a year. Obviously, many golf clubs would not consider purchasing such large quantities of compost when costs can vary from £20 to £30 per ton and they usually limit their purchase to about 30–40 tonnes, i.e. sufficient for one autumn dressing to the greens only.

A golf club considering the development of a good home-made composting system from scratch is faced with a high initial expenditure, but if spread over, say, a ten year period the cost of the home-produced compost becomes lower and certainly the more compost produced, the cheaper it becomes. A reasonable sized shed of 12 x 5 metres in floor area (concreted) and 3.5 metres high, timber structured and clad with corrugated iron would be needed, and a good soil shredder and mechanical rotary screen. A large supply of suitable topsoil is often hard to find, however good sands can be obtained readily.

The purchase of proprietary composts, even possibly at slightly greater costs, is both labour saving and convenient and there is obviously a strong case for clubs to continue with this policy. However, it is always a matter of great regret to the Institute as we travel about the country from club to club in spring and summer to find that the annual compost was bought and applied in autumn and there is not so much as a bucketful on the premises for topping up the odd divot on a tee or smoothing over a piece of recent patching or even 'rubbing in' after hole changing. Compost is not just a 'once only' product but is in demand all year round to help put the finishing touch to many small tasks, and without it the general standards of greenkeeping must suffer.

FERTILISERS FOR FINE TURF

Of the three main plant nutrients for fine turf, nitrogen is the most important since it is the element primarily responsible for encouraging the growth of stem and leaf. Phosphate affects all plant growth processes and is particularly involved in root development. Potash rarely produces obvious benefits in turf though it is linked with the health and general functioning of the plant, and is said to encourage resistance to disease, to drought and to severe winter weather, particularly when there are high nitrogen levels.

Early Trials Demonstrate the Necessity for N and P

All three elements are therefore needed in the nutrition of turf, albeit at appropriate levels. None of them should be omitted completely. Some of the older readers of Institute publications will remember the famous 'Set D' trial at Bingley, now no longer with us unfortunately, since after some 40 years it had outlived its usefulness as an experiment and needed to yield place to trials of a different nature. Set D was a fertiliser trial set up in the early days of the Research Station and consisted of a whole series of fertilisers like sulphate of ammonia, superphosphate and sulphate of potash, alone and in all manner of combinations with other fertilisers both organic and inorganic. It was shown by the experiment that quite good turf could be maintained just by sulphate of ammonia alone, provided that periodic dressings of lime were given to counteract over-acidity. Better turf (still *Poa annua* free) was produced when superphosphate was added to the sulphate of ammonia, being more free from moss and having greater resistance to drought. The addition of potash made very little difference to the appearance of the turf except in drought (when the plots with potash were outstanding). We think a little is always useful in the main fertiliser mixtures for the reasons given above.

Sulphate of Iron

Apart from these N, P and K, there are other major and minor elements which are essential in plant nutrition, though it has been extremely rare to find any deficiency of any of them in turf. The situation needs watching however, particularly with regard to the new fashion for artificially produced sandy soils. Iron is one minor element which really is of definite value if included in fertilisers for most kinds of turf since it helps to give the grass a good dark green colour and to reduce weed, worm and disease troubles.

Avoid Alkaline Fertilisers

All fertilisers for regular use on fine turf should, as a rule, be slightly acidic or neutral in their effects. Alkaline materials like Nitro-chalk, if used regularly, will influence the botanical composition of the grasses in the sward for the worse and encourage weeds and worms.

The Value of 'Organics'

There is not the space here to describe detailed fertiliser programmes for the various types of golfing turf. Suffice it to say that a general complete fertiliser for spring application to fine turf might include sulphate of ammonia, superphosphate, sulphate of potash and sulphate of iron (in the calcined powder form) together with such suitable organic forms of nitrogen and phosphate as are available like dried blood, hoof and horn meal and bone meal. However, phosphate and potash fertilisers should only be used after chemical analysis of the soils on the greens. These organic forms help to produce a mixture which releases its nutrients more slowly and also have considerable 'conditioning value' in that they promote a greater friability and prevent the mixture caking too quickly.

A Variety of Fertiliser Needs

Follow-up dressings through the rest of the growing season might consist of nitrogen alone – a simple mixture of sulphate of ammonia, dried blood and/or hoof and horn meal. There is, however, a tremendous amount of variation in the fertiliser requirements of different golf courses. Some good golf greens receive virtually no fertiliser whatsoever, whilst other good greens, especially pure sand greens, may receive each year 14–28 g nitrogen per m^2 with corresponding amounts of phosphate and potash. On golf courses where there is a good supply of fertile home-made compost, actual fertiliser applications to the greens need to be minimal. The turf manager should always be interested in producing the correct results in terms of turf performance; yield of grass is not the aim.

Home-Mixing of Fertilisers

In the quantities normally required on golf courses the mixing process is not really difficult. The appropriate quantity of each fertiliser is spread out in turn on a hard, smooth surface such as a clean floor. The heap should be shovelled so as to turn and mix, the operation being carried out three times. In order to increase the accuracy of application, thus reducing the chances of scorch and to produce a fertiliser mixture which (subject to the compatibility of the ingredients) will keep under good storage for a considerable time without physical deterioration, it is good policy to mix the fertiliser thoroughly in turn with a carrier of screened dry soil or compost (at least twice as much carrier as fertiliser).

Choose Carefully Your Proprietary Fertiliser

Many turf managers these days prefer proprietary fertiliser mixtures to the home-mixed variety for the sake of convenience and despite the advantages of home-made mixes in terms of material cost and individual 'tailoring'. These fertilisers are commonly available in powder form but sometimes as small pellets (mini-granules or mini-crumbs). They are usually complete fertilisers and there is a wide range of nutrient contents, of plant food ratios and of constituents. Firms typically sell two products, one for spring/summer and one for autumn/winter use, the former being relatively high in nitrogen, the latter relatively low. When using proprietary products one is relying heavily on the background knowledge of the manufacturer, so it is important to buy the most reputable products and to use them generally in accordance with the manufacturer's recommendations. The Institute does not recommend the use of autumn/winter fertilisers.

Variation in Contents

It should be borne in mind that the ingredients used in proprietary fertilisers are not necessarily constant, being governed by market and other considerations. In view of the scarcity and price of organics, some manufacturers are now including a proportion of one of the newer slow release nitrogen fertilisers. Some contain sulphate of iron and some do not. Some products have magnesium compounds added and an odd one or two have added trace elements. Proprietary fertilisers are normally formulated so as to be suitable for application without dilution with compost or soil but there are still advantages to be gained by so diluting in order to facilitate spreading without scorch.

Fertiliser/Weedkiller Formulations

Several proprietary fertilisers contain selective weedkiller also. These are really of more interest to the home lawn owner than the professional turf manager.

Storage

Fertilisers should always be stored in dry conditions, but especially so if they are kept in containers other than polythene bags. Care should be taken to protect bags from sharp points or jagged edges and bags should be dropped flat rather than on their corners. To maintain dry conditions it is wise to have a platform of duckboard or similar between the floor and the bags and to ensure ventilation around the bags and in the building, though doors and windows

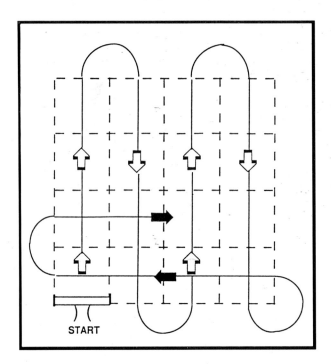

FIGURE 10: Using a linear type distributor.

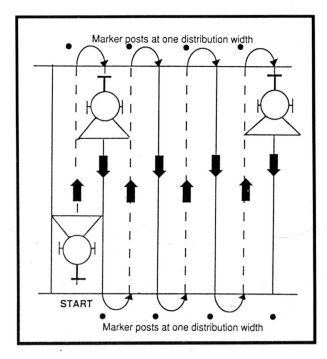

FIGURE 11: Using a spinner type distributor.

should be closed in damp weather. The most convenient arrangement is usually to have the bags stacked in a criss-cross manner, keeping the height down to about six bags and certainly not more than ten bags. Always close a part-used bag to conserve the remainder of the fertiliser in good condition.

Timing of Application
Good turf should be uniform, and even application of fertiliser is highly important. Uneven spreading results in uneven growth and colour, and excess application (such as caused by overlapping) may damage the turf severely. Fertiliser dressings should preferably be given during a dry spell in broken weather, when rain can be expected to fall shortly afterwards to wash in the fertiliser. If no rain falls within one or two days, generous watering should be undertaken where practicable to achieve the same end.

Application by Hand is Still the best Where Practicable
For relatively small areas like greens hand application is undoubtedly best, the fertiliser (suitably bulked out with the carrier referred to above) being divided into two and the two halves broadcast by hand in two directions at right angles to each other. Even on fine turf, fertiliser distributors are being increasingly used but it is a mistake to assume that these will automatically do a good job. Linear-type distributors spread fairly evenly within their width (subject to uniform fertiliser in good condition, evenness of ground, etc.) but great care is needed to achieve correct marrying of successive widths and to avoid difficulties at the ends of runs. It often pays to go off the site to turn, or to have at the ends polythene sheets on which to to this. For first-class work it is wise, even with good distributors of this type, to divide the fertiliser into halves and apply these in transverse directions at right angles. The small distributors of the spinner type used on fine turf commonly give more fertiliser in the middle of their spread than they do at the outside and so to improve the evenness of spread it is wise, once again, to divide the fertiliser into two but to work so that all the turf is treated twice **in the same direction**. This is achieved by making successive runs **half** a breadth away instead of a full breadth of the spread.

FERTILISER NUTRITION OF SAND GREENS

Summary of the first three years' results of an experiment funded by the R&A on the Fertiliser Nutrition of Sand Greens.

In the UK many golf courses are closed at some time during the year due to waterlogging. This problem has been compounded in recent years because of the increase in play, particularly during the winter. This has led increasingly to the use of sand-based constructions in an attempt to increase drainage rates and reduce the effects of compaction.

The use of pure sand in golf green construction has serious implications for fertiliser nutrition because:

(1) Sands are inherently low in available nutrients (particularly nitrogen).
(2) The potential for leaching is high because of the increase in water infiltration rates and lack of nutrient binding material such as clay particles and organic matter.

The experimental trial area was constructed in the summer of 1985 and consisted of 250 mm of medium/fine sand overlying 50 mm of coarse sand blinding layer over a 100 mm gravel base with drainage pipes. The area was sown in August 1985 with an 80/20 mixture of Frida Chewings fescue and Highland bent. The area was fully established by April 1986 when fertiliser treatments started. These consisted of three levels of the three main nutrients, nitrogen, potassium and phosphorus, with and without lime. The trial received a normal golf green management programme, i.e. regular mowing, verticutting and aeration and was subjected to artificial wear. The trial also received regular irrigation during dry weather in the summer and was subjected to simulated golf-type wear. Assessments were carried out once every three months and consisted of the more traditional analyses of botanical composition and ground cover. In addition, chemical analysis was carried out of the rootzone material to determine the nutrient status of the sand, together with some newer playing quality tests which included:

(1) Hardness using the Clegg Impact Soil Tester.
(2) Green speed using the Stimpmeter.
(3) Rebound resilience, whereby the rebound height of a golf ball dropped from 5 metres was recorded with a video camera located at approximately 10 metres from the impact at ground level.
(4) Holding power, whereby a golf ball was fired into each plot at a fixed speed, angle and back spin using a Juggs Baseball Pitch machine adapted to fire golf balls. The total horizontal distance of carry after pitching was measured.

Results
The results to date indicate that the two lowest levels of nitrogen (100 and 200 kg/ha per year) are insufficient to maintain ground cover. However, the highest rate of nitrogen (400 kg/ha per year) induced very lush summer growth which became susceptible to winter injury. The highest rate of nitrogen also favoured the growth of bentgrass at the expense of fescue. Wear treatments reduced the fescue content of all the plots.

In 1987 and 1988 the effects of lime became increasingly important. The ground cover of unlimed plots deteriorated particularly during the winters of 1987 and 1988. This was probably due to the decrease in pH induced by the regular application of sulphate of ammonia (used as source of nitrogen). Although liming improved the ground cover and general sward vigour, it also increased the invasion of the less desirable *Poa annua* (annual meadow-grass) due to the very rapid increase in surface pH. The bentgrass tolerated the more acidic, unlimed plots to a greater extent than the fescue.

Fescue responded to phosphorus and potassium application under its optimum growing conditions, i.e. low-nitrogen and suitable pH. Towards the end of the trial period there was a general response to phosphorus application. Phosphorus deficiency was identified in May 1988 and was particularly severe in those plots which received the highest rate of nitrogen, did not receive any phosphorus and were not limed. These plots gradually deteriorated during the summer so that the ground cover was reduced in the later assessments. The results suggest that some phosphorus is required to support bent/fescue turf, particularly when the turf is grown on an acidic sand rootzone requiring a large application of nitrogen. Although there was no response of ground cover to potassium fertiliser, the nutrient did affect the botanical composition towards the end of the trial period. The results of chemical analysis of the sand revealed that the sand potassium level was maintained in the plots that did not receive any fertiliser potassium. This probably means that potassium derived from the sand itself was sufficient to meet the plant's requirements, and explains the lack of any ground cover response.

Playing Quality
Hardness measurements decreased with increasing nitrogen and with lime, and probably reflected an increase in the ground cover and a general increase in growth on these plots. Green speed also decreased with nitrogen and lime, also because of the increase in growth on these plots. The results suggest that green speed can be controlled by the timing of fertiliser applications as well as mowing height reduction, e.g. fertiliser application could be delayed until after an important tournament. Rebound resilience increased with increasing nitrogen, lime and potassium. In other words, the golf balls bounced higher on the lusher plots, due to a 'springiness' effect of the turf. The response of potassium was particularly surprising because of the lack of response in the ground cover analysis, and indicates a more subtle response to potassium. Holding power increased with nitrogen and lime, i.e. the balls stopped more quickly in the plots which contained the higher ground cover.

Conclusions
The playing quality tests should provide a platform for future golf green research as they are both relevant to golf ball/green interactions and proved to be sensitive indicators of turfgrass vigour differences. The ground cover results have provided some useful information on the optimum level of nitrogen required to sustain golf green turf grown on a sand rootzone. They should also provide a useful indication of the phosphorus and potassium requirements as the trial is to be continued after this initial three-year establishment period.

GREEN SURROUNDS

To define to some extent what is meant by surrounds, these are areas with an intermediate height of cut between putting surface and fairway. The immediate surround is a collar, usually the width of one or two passes with a mower, which encircles the putting surface. In addition, features around the green such as mounds and banks are sometimes mown as surround. In front of a green, i.e. looking back towards the tee, the collar may be increased in width to form an apron or fore-green on the approach. Normal practice is to cut these areas as for tees.

No exact dimensions can be recommended for surrounds and aprons because the size and shape will vary according to the landform of the site, the positioning of bunkers, mounds, banks and water hazards, along with the length of the hole and how it is designed to be played. The size and quality of the machinery used, and time taken to cut and maintain these areas has also to be taken into consideration.

While surrounds help to provide a visual blend between putting surface and fairway, more important is their value in playing the game of golf. If carefully designed they can reward, be usefully employed in, or to some extent penalise the approach shot to the green as appropriate. For example, a reasonable shot which just trickles to the edge of the putting surface will be held on the collar and the player should still be able to take his putter. On the other hand, an over-hit shot into a bank behind a green should not be rewarded by the ball running back into the middle of the putting surface, and a well shaped surround at the toe of the bank could help to hold the ball at the margin. Similarly, an over-hit ball running through the green should not be held up by fairway length grass or mounds or a bank which falls away and could be allowed to run on, according to its momentum, across a wide surround area.

Hence, the design of the surrounds should be allied to the way each hole *should* be played.

The Right Surface?
To be useful in play, the turf and the surface developed on the surrounds has to be right. Much has been written in recent years about what is right for putting, that is a firm, fast surface composed primarily of fine grass species (bents and fescues). These criteria of species present, the texture of the turf, its density, the firmness underfoot and smoothness apply also to the surrounds. The only difference between the surrounds and the putting surface should be the length of cut. In general therefore, maintenance work on collars and aprons should be along similar lines to that applied on the actual putting surface.

Obtaining the ideal can often be a much simpler process on the surrounds than it is on the putting surface, as the former seems to get somewhat less abused. Frequently a soggy, thatch-ridden, annual meadow-grass green is surrounded by firm turf composed of fescues and bents.

Maintenance
All the major items of greens maintenance should be applied to the surrounds. The need for regular mowing at a level intermediate to the putting surface and fairway is an obvious point, but cuttings must be boxed off to help keep the surface firm. Sit-on triple mowers are very useful for these areas. Also, this will help to keep down weeds and worms, and hence reduce expensive spraying.

On collar and apron, occasional light treatments with verticut units or a pedestrian-operated scarifier should be considered during the growing season.

But, of course, just keeping these areas trimmed is not the end of maintenance. As with all turf areas, fundamental and regular aeration must be carried out throughout the year to encourage strong, dense turf and as an aid to surface drainage. Particular attention must be paid to the apron, on to which traffic from the fairway will be funnelled, and the line of walk-offs to the next tee. However, watch out for sprinkler heads when spiking – a tine through a cap can cause expensive damage, especially to the gear-driven type.

Top dressing must not be neglected on collars and aprons which have to be smooth enough for putting, while no-one will be encouraged to pitch in front of a green if the ball kicks badly instead of running on. Compost applied to the putting surface can be dragged into the surrounds when matting in, allow for extra material on a green where the apron is wide.

As to fertiliser treatment, the emphasis should be on supplying nitrogen if needed and being cautious about frequency of application.

By watering during a dry spell the aim should be to maintain an evenly moist topsoil without over-watering. Watering systems should be well designed to apply water routinely to aprons, and can be adjusted to cover surrounds.

Traffic management is also a vital part of surround maintenance and appropriate guidance to players, such as hoops or white lines, have to be carefully positioned to spread wear (and that guidance must be enforced).

Drainage
The drainage qualities of the approach and surround must be good to maintain the right quality of turf and to provide a satisfactory surface for play. If the natural drainage through the subsoil is not good, then a drainage system to cover the whole area of the green site will be needed. The immediate surrounds should be incorporated within such a drainage system, extending this as appropriate to ensure the apron or approach is well covered. Trapping surface or sub-surface flow of ground water onto the surrounds by means of catchwater drains is often required on hillside courses.

In Conclusion
It can be seen from the above that a great deal of thought needs to be given to the design (construction) and maintenance of the surrounds to a golf green, but it is evident up and down the country that this attention to detail is lacking on many courses. So, why not stand back and look at your greens – could a bit of artistry in surrounds make yours a better golf course?

REGULATION OF GOLF TROLLEY USAGE

With the rapid expansion of golf and the increasing demands of play there has been a corresponding increase in the number of trolleys on our courses. Although of potential benefit to the golfer, their impact on the golf course must be carefully considered and, if necessary, restrictions enforced.

Their primary drawback can be related to the constant attrition of the same 'paths', notably around the main playing areas of greens and tees. Very often the same routes are exploited through the entry and exit areas – with worn turf surfaces and compacted soils the inevitable consequence where the weight of golf traffic is focussed. In contrast, golfers who prefer to carry their clubs can circumvent obstacles with greater ease and traverse the putting surfaces, thus adopting a much wider range of traffic routes.

The pressures imposed by golf trolleys are particularly acute during the late autumn and winter months when the decline is aggravated by the lack of natural turf recovery and vulnerability of the 'wet' soils to compaction forces. The advent of wide-wheeled trolleys (to replace the narrow-wheeled versions) has eased the pressure to a degree, but the emergence of heavier electrically-driven trolleys has increased the 'scouring effect' on the turf – notably under wet surface conditions.

An appropriate course of action should be formulated in accordance with the individual site conditions, but the following factors should be taken into consideration:

(1) The drainage potential of the course.
(2) Course layout and design, eg. compact or expansive, flat or undulating.
(3) The aspect of the course, ie. exposed or protected.
(4) The prevailing ground and weather conditions.
(5) The intensity of play and its distribution throughout the year.

Undoubtedly, atemporary winter suspension of the use of golf trolleys will, in most instances, have a marked influence on the viability and quality of the turf surfaces. Enforcing a local rule that clubs must be carried will help to 'break the pattern' and spread the 'load' of golf traffic more evenly. The majority of golfers should be sufficiently fit to carry a 'pencil' golf bag (and reduced number of clubs in winter) without significantly diminishing their enjoyment of the game. There may be mitigating circumstances on the grounds of ill health, but doctors' certificates must be carefully scrutinised so that the rule is not abused.

A ban on trolleys will prove most effective through the winter months (eg. December to February inclusive) when surfaces are most vulnerable, although this needs to be tailored to each site's requirements. This should encompass both the pulled and powered trolleys, as this will prove simpler and less devisive. Where good channels of communication are established and co-operation of the golfers assured, then temporary suspensions – in accordance with prevailing ground and weather conditions – may be a workable compromise. However, this strategy is usually less effective due to the difficulties of decision-making, monitoring and enforcement within the structure of course management.

The use of trolleys is inextricably linked with the need for adequate traffic control directives. These can take several forms including ropes, hoops and white lines; backed up by clear, strategically-placed signs. By such means, vulnerable areas can be protected and different traffic routes are brought into use. The designation of 'trolley parks' may serve a similar purpose and dictate an alternative route from fairway to green and green to the next tee. The introduction of purpose-built paths, to take the weight of trolley traffic, may be warranted in certain situations, eg. alongside tees, but they **must** satisfy golfing, management and aesthetic criteria.

Where course layout and space allow, consider building separate 'alternative' tees, which will be mainly used in winter but could, at need, take some summer play. They should be sited so that traffic will naturally follow a different route to that used in summer.

The above measures should not be regarded as a substitute for a temporary trolley ban, but rather as being **complementary** with the objective of countering the increasing pressures of our golf courses and maintaining optimum playing conditions year-round!

CONTROLLING TRAFFIC ON HEAVILY WORN AREAS

Prevention Before Cure

Prevention before cure is a good maxim for many problems encountered in management and this certainly applies to combating wear and tear on the golf course. Indeed, every Head Greenkeeper should have a preventative component built into the maintenance programme when developing playing surfaces.

Nevertheless, in recent years there has been an ever-increasing level of course usage on all fronts from visitors, parties, competitions and winter play to the general membership playing more often. The nett result of all this year-round foot traffic is the development of worn areas on greens, surrounds, tees and fairways, which necessitates a routine renovation programme each year to ensure the course will be brought back into good condition for the start of the main competition season. The difficulty with repair work is that for golf there is no close season when quick repairs can be completed and seeded or turfed areas given time to fully recover. It is a question of phasing them in over the autumn to spring period around the demands that play imposes.

Influence of Design

Design plays an important part in spreading traffic flow over a larger area and hence reducing wear. On existing greens, this may involve increasing available putting area by developing aprons, removing unnecessary surround mounding and trees or softening existing contours. Widening entrances by rebuilding bunkers, increasing exit points, raising hollows and introducing drains are all factors which could reduce wear. In addition, this point highlights the importance of achieving good green design on any new construction projects.

Extending and relevelling existing tees also helps to spread wear by providing extra area and, when associated with an increase in width, allows for additional lateral movement of tee markers. Where space allows, the provision of alternative tees off-line to existing areas has many advantages in not only allowing the main tees to be rested and renovated, but also the traffic routes from green to tee and tee to fairway. If the alternative tee is situated off-line and in front or behind the existing tee, then an additional benefit is gained by spreading wear on landing zones on fairways. Where a path is mown out through carry to the fairway, it is good policy to change the line during the winter and thereby alternate traffic flow.

Maintenance and Renovation

General maintenance practices are also vital in preventing wear and aiding recovery, and maintaining a dense, healthy turf is always a sound base from which to start. On greens, using second and third choice pin sites helps to spread wear uniformly over the putting surface, an essential requisite for consistency, and it may also be possible to vary the routes taken by golfers on and off greens with careful flag positioning. This will help to spread wear over surround areas.

A renovation programme on greens, tees, surrounds and particularly traffic routes is now an annual requirement; a process which starts with re-routing through the use of hoops or ropes. It is always sound politics to keep the membership informed of work on the course as they are then more likely to abide by the instructions rather than flaunt them. Communication is especially important at the present time, as we are seeing an increasing need for renovation work on all areas. Many golfers believe the Head Greenkeeper makes them walk further by re-routing simply out of spite. Thin and bare areas do not fully recover without renovation work, principally involving forms of deep aeration, turfing/seeding and localised application of fertiliser in the spring.

Taking the re-routing theme a stage further, a number of Clubs are now changing the sequence of holes and hence traffic routes in winter where design allows. The availability of an additional green or hole is a distinct advantage here.

Tractors and Paths

How many Clubs mow around the side and back of greens with tractors and gang mowers and find that in adverse weather conditions this leads to an increase in compaction, rutting and loss of turf cover? Mowing with a triple surround cylinder mower cuts out the compacting effects of tractor-mounted equipment and minimises surface damage. Likewise, tractor routes can be re-directed from fairways to semi-rough and restrictions placed on the use of trolleys, especially the electric ones, in periods of adverse weather conditions. The use of golf buggies should be kept to the absolute minimum as they can significantly aggravate wear problems on traffic routes.

Many Committees consider the introduction of non-turf paths as an easy answer to wear problems in a number of areas, but it should always be remembered they have a number of disadvantages. Apart from not being aesthetically pleasing, non-turf paths only transfer wear to the end of the path and can affect play, particularly when placed near to greens or tees. In addition, there is no real satisfactory material, with ash and cockle-shells about the best choice. Using the correct grade of bark can be more pleasing to the eye, but can be moisture retentive in wet weather. Coarse sand can be very effective, although it is expensive and tends to become lost in muddy soil. Gravel spills out on to surrounding ground and inevitably damages mowers. Concrete and tarmac are also expensive, with concrete areas not taking a spike, as well as being slippery in wet weather. On the other hand, tarmac can be ripped by spikes if it becomes soft in hot summer weather. Non-turf paths should be regarded as a last resort when all other options have failed and all we are left with is a muddy path year-round.

Limiting Usage

Even with a full programme to spread traffic flow more evenly, a number of golf courses still have serious wear problems, and here consideration is now being given to reducing the number of rounds played per year. This involves cutting down on visiting parties, increasing the green fee and limiting new membership. This can, of course, be an unpopular course of action as it often involves raising annual subscriptions to compensate for loss of revenue. However, the average golfer is now becoming more aware of the general problem of wear and the price that has to be paid to reduce it on the golf course.

Conclusion

A good standard of maintenance and design will help keep traffic flow evenly spread over the maximum area and enable each part of the course to be played as much as possible, as well as reducing the amount of future routine repairs to a minimum. Where these methods fail, an annual renovation programme is essential to restore a full sward cover for the start of the growing season.

With the advent of milder winters, a higher standard expected by golfers and an increasing autumn to spring level of play, the time is fast approaching when Clubs must seriously consider cutting down on the number of rounds played per year and compensate the loss of revenue through alternative means.

THE USE OF SULPHATE OF IRON

Sulphate of iron has been used for well over half a century as a turfgrass treatment. During this time the benefits of applying this chemical to turf, either alone or in fertiliser or lawn sand mixtures, have been recognised and consequently its role in turf management is now well established. This section describes how sulphate of iron may be used to discourage moss, algae and weed invasion, earthworm casting and certain diseases.

Effects of Sulphate of Iron on Moss, Algae and Weeds

Sulphate of iron applied at 10 g/m^2 is a traditional treatment for moss control, applied alone or in conjunction with sulphate of ammonia and a carrier such as sand. Moss is killed very quickly by sulphate of iron although duration of control is generally short. However, as it is very cheap to purchase it is probably the most cost-effective pesticide for moss control available. Sulphate of iron applied at the moss killing rate may also be effective against algae in turf. However, whilst some suppression of algae may be achieved by repeated application, long lasting control will only be achieved by correcting the cultural conditions (shade, poor drainage etc.) which favour algal growth. Additional benefits of regular sulphate of iron application may be gained in the control of broad-leaved weeds, especially when used in conjunction with sulphate of ammonia as a fertiliser treatment.

Effects on Earthworm Casting

Earthworms cannot tolerate acidic turf, so applying an acidic material such as sulphate of iron will keep earthworms away from the turf surface and thus keep casting to a minimum. Thus, the problem of earthworm casts providing seedbeds for weeds, creating muddy conditions and interfering with play may be reduced. In a current trial at STRI applying sulphate of iron at rates between 4 and 8 g/m^2 in the early winter months has inhibited earthworm casting for 2 to 3 weeks. Termination of approvals for the use of chlordane (the most effective earthworm killer) have now been introduced for large areas of turf and from 31 December 1992 the use of chlordane will no longer be permitted on any type of turf. It is possible that sulphate of iron may play an increasing role in earthworm management programmes in the future.

Effects on Disease

During cool wet weather, fusarium patch disease may cause serious damage to fine turf. The fungal pathogen which causes fusarium patch, *M. nivale* is most active under neutral or alkaline conditions at the turf surface where the fungus is active. Consequently, sulphate of iron by acidifying plant tissues and thatch to which it comes into contact will help control the disease. Although not as effective as a fungicide spray, regular use of sulphate of iron will help minimise incidence and severity of fusarium patch and thus reduce the need for fungicide application. As well as fusarium patch another disease namely take-all patch is favoured by an alkaline turf surface. Re-acidifying the turf surface with sulphate of iron may limit the spread of take-all patch disease.

Other Uses for Sulphate of Iron

Sulphate of iron is widely known for its darkening effect on turf colour, thus producing a more attractive sward. The greening effect is mainly due to a darkening of dead material at the base of the sward which makes thin or bare areas less noticeable to the sportsman. Several liquid formulations of iron combined with sulphur and urea are now available which are designed specifically to have a cosmetic effect on the turf. Initial tests at STRI have indicated that these liquid iron products may darken the turf colour very rapidly and also give some reduction of fusarium patch disease and earthworm casting.

SECTION 3

GOLF TEES

MANAGEMENT OF GOLF TEES

Mowing

Tees should preferably always be cut with a cylinder type of mower which will give a finer finish. On average, weekly cutting is necessary during the growing season with perhaps more frequent mowing during intervals of spring and summer growth. The cutting level should be 6–13 mm as appropriate. As a general rule, clippings should always be boxed off as allowing them to fly always encourages worms and weeds and can lead to an accumulation of matted material which will not withstand wear. Such soft, spongy surfaces should be avoided. In view of this, it is not a good idea to cut tees using fairway gang mowers even if tees are large enough to make this possible. The time saved by such practices is appreciated, but it is only gained at the expense of the finish of the playing surface. For larger tees, speedy machines such as triple mowers are now available which allow mowing to be carried out rapidly but with the added facility of clipping removal.

For banks and surrounding areas hand mowers of the hover type are frequently used, or newer machines which depend on a rotating nylon cord. Many steep, small banks can only be cut with these types of machine but it is an advantage to avoid such features during initial construction so that larger sit-on machines can be used, so saving valuable time.

Fertiliser

For the average tee, a spring fertiliser dressing giving balanced quantities of nitrogen, phosphate and potash can be sufficient to maintain good growth through the year. The application of phosphate and potash may not be necessary and should be based on chemical analysis. If growth slackens off during the summer or early autumn, a booster dressing of nitrogen can, however, be given in order to maintain sufficient levels of growth and help in the rapid regeneration of worn areas. Autumn compost treatment can also be a valuable source of plant nutrient.

Weeds, Pests and Diseases

Adequate weed control is essential to maintain an even and attractive playing surface on tees and when required this work should not be neglected. Weedkilling should be carried out during a period good growth, preferably in the early summer using a 2,4-D/mecoprop weedkiller which should prove adequate for the usual spectrum of weeds encountered in such situations – daisies, dandelions, clover, etc. Worm control is another essential if good teeing surfaces are to be provided as worms can cause very muddy conditions, particularly during moist weather in the autumn and spring. It is at these times of year that control should be carried out when the worms are working actively near the surface. The most effective wormkiller of recent times, chlordane, is now banned on environmental and health grounds, but carbaryl can be recommended as a safer (although shorter-lived) alternative. Clearing worm casts makes for cleaner and neater mowing as well as improving the playing surface.

Turf diseases are seldom of great significance on tees which are not as intensively maintained as greens. Perhaps the most common disease is Corticium (red thread) which produces mottled patches during the summer. This disease is associated with low levels of nitrogen and nitrogenous fertiliser is generally sufficient to control the disease by improving the grass's

109

ability to combat it. Occasionally, fusarium patch disease may also be troublesome on tees and needs treating with fungicide.

Renovation

Divot repair work should be regarded as a continuous process from spring to autumn, a weekly round of repair work by the greenkeeping staff being the ideal to aim for. Some Clubs opt for leaving a suitable supply of soil/seed mix at each tee for members to use as appropriate, but this approach seldom proves really successful. Again, non-ryegrass seed should be employed, mixed with a good quality soil. A 50/50 sand/soil mix can be usefully substituted where tees have heavy topsoil surfaces but very sandy divot filling mixes tend to blow out of place in dry or windy conditions. As with fairways, healthy tee swards composed of the desirable grasses show good natural recovery and minimise the problem of continuous repair.

Seeding after mid-September is rarely successful in the North, though may be worth risking up to the end of the month further South. Since seeding is far and away the easiest and cheapest method of renovation, clubs wishing to play off well grassed tees during spring and summer should consider closing down damaged general tees in September to allow timely renovation and a recovery period from the wear and tear of hectic summer use. If the Medal tees are kept in play, then their damaged areas will have to be repaired by turfing later on during the winter. It is usually only links courses that have to resort to extensive turf patching in autumn and winter to repair damage.

Autumn Work

On most golf courses, summer tees come out of play at some point in the autumn, play being transferred to winter tees or tee mats. The main tees should then be renovated as promptly as possible in order to ensure complete recovery by the time they come into play next spring. Thorough spiking is frequently useful at this time to relieve any compaction caused by the season's play. The flat slitting type of tine is usually adequate, although deep hollow tine aeration may occasionally be required. After spiking, surfaces should be trued up by top dressing, preferably using a light sandy compost, and reseeded or returfed. Returfing establishes the surface more quickly than reseeding but adequate supplies of good quality turf suitable for the purpose are obviously required. A turf nursery for tee renovation purposes is always a useful feature on golf courses, although at a pinch an area to the side of one fairway, adequately mown and receiving some attention such as weedkilling, etc. during the summer can serve for tee repair. In addition to the main annual top dressing, tees can benefit from supplementary sandy dressings during the rest of the year, aimed at maintaining firm, dry and level surfaces.

Although greens should be considered top priority on golf courses, it should not be forgotten that we are looking for similar conditions on tees, i.e. level, firm and free draining. Indeed, top dressing tees is a most important operation, especially those on par 3 holes which tend to receive most wear. The same materials that are used for top dressing greens should be used on tees. Annual overall top dressing can be sufficient with regular divoting work through the main competition season.

As levels on tees are usually poorer than on greens at the end of the main competition season, then a valuable 'additional' source of dressing can be found by hollow tining tees and working the cores back on to the tee along with the sandy top dressing material that has been bought in.

After autumn renovation work, tees should be rested until fully established, play continuing on alternative winter locations. Similarly, winter tees, if used, should be renovated in the spring at the end of their period of use so that they will be once again ready for play the following autumn.

Another autumn job required is tree pruning as tees are often surrounded by trees and can become heavily shaded. Heavy shade is a common cause of wet teeing surfaces and poor grass growth, so trees should therefore be pruned regularly, all over-hanging branches being removed. Thinning surrounding shrubberies increases air flow and reduces surface dampness.

Tees Are Important

Given good initial construction, adequate size and regular attention, tees can be a credit to any golf course. Inevitably, they take second place to the greens in the greenkeeper's mind but one cannot claim to have a first-class golf course without first-class tees.

TEES – WINTER AND SUMMER

In the early days of golf there were never any formally-built teeing grounds – the rules merely stated that the ball should be teed within a certain number of club lengths of the previous hole. The first written record of purpose-built teeing areas appeared during the last years of the 19th Century. Their position, size, construction and use have been subjects for contention ever since. Clearly, where play is concentrated on to a strip of grass barely 16 m² at the start of each hole, there are the beginnings of a problem. Since tees were often the 'poor relation' in new constructions, constructed with existing soil having slow natural drainage qualities and often mishandled and compacted into the bargain, with inadequate provision for drainage and, above all, limitation in size, the seeds of today's disaster areas of many courses were sown right at the start.

Areas that could support 10,000 rounds per annum or less in the early years – when minimal winter play was of no consequence, have not the slightest chance of surviving the summer on today's thronged courses, busy from dawn till dusk and perhaps averaging 50,000 rounds per year, let alone take winter play as well.

The successful tee must be slightly elevated, allowing a view of the fairway at 200 metres, not overhung by trees nor with exaggerated slopes. Its surface should be firm, level and adequately drained at all seasons with a uniform cover of turf.

Size
To achieve this aim, the first requirement is adequate size for the amount of play that the course takes. If you are embarking on a new construction, make sure you build to cope with any projected increase in play. Many existing tees like Topsy "just growed", the original 5 x 5 had an extra piece stuck on the side one year with an extension on the rear the next, each piece with different soils and turf. Through differential settlement the whole aspect can become displeasing, to say nothing of vital areas being lost to use. Yet again there is the situation where a multiplicity of pocket handkerchief size tees have sprung up over the years, each with banks requiring tedious, labour-intensive 'hover' mowing and surfaces unfit for cutting with anything other than an 450 mm hand mower.

In these situations committees must develop a planned programme of tee construction to meet the needs of today's golf and spread over, say, five years with a clearly defined order of priorities. They must address the following aspects relating to each site: route to and from tee (including a separate route for winter tees wherever practicable); size; drainage; soil improvement; access to surface and banks for easy maintenance with modern triples and the need for irrigation.

At par 3 holes it is generally most satisfactory to have one large tee accommodating Ladies, General and Medal play. Aim for at least 400 m² with sufficient width for three or four shifts of the tee boxes. There may well be amalgamation of two or even three separate teeing areas to achieve this. At longer holes it is preferable to retain separate tees, aiming for, say, 350 m², possibly divided up as 50 m² Ladies, 200 m² Mens, 100 m² Medal.

Position
Tees will have been originally sited by the Architect to make best use of the immediate topography, to allow the drop from the tee shot to be seen and to suit natural or man-made fairway levels, features and bunkers, as well as green design. Changing the actual position of a tee should therefore never be made lightly – the usual need is for a greater surface area to accommodate increased play.

Aim to provide at least sufficient width to allow two shifts of the tee boxes, i.e. 14–20 metres, so that wear can be spread more evenly over the surface, minimising traffic over repaired places. This is especially important for medal tees where the measured length of a hole at the distance marker governs where tee boxes may be set. In general, go for width rather than length which also helps overcome problems of sight lines for landing zones. These are often obscured from the rear of long, narrow tees, especially where the ground in front falls away sharply.

Shape
Far too often tees stick out like sore thumbs – they may serve architectural and golfing requirements but by no stretch of the imagination can they be said to blend into the natural landscape. The elevated rectangular tee with sharply sloping banks has been the standard for many years. It looks unnatural, is difficult to maintain with modern-day equipment and often banks are so steep as to require expensive, laborious hand Flymo-ing.

On flat ground there is no need for excessive elevation, a mere 230 mm above surrounding level is ample for drainage purposes with banks eased out to gradients no more than 1 in 3, corners well rounded off for easy mowing of the surface with wider machines and no sharp angles along the edges that will scalp. Above all, the tees and their banks should blend into the natural ground contours around them.

At some sites, of course, elevation or the need for quantities of fill are dictated by the terrain and the chances of achieving a natural look are much reduced. On a descending slope, cut and fill minimises cost but always looks unnatural and certainly needs careful handling to create a durable and useful tee. Be particular to provide an adequate depth of soil on the 'cut' side, proper internal drainage and the essential catchwater drains at the rear and sides where slopes shed surface water towards the playing surfaces. Do not neglect the approach paths to such tees either, protecting these from excess water can be just as important as the tee itself. The use of additional imported fill will help to avoid excessive cut into a hillside and similarly a slight gradient of 1 in 80 back to front is imperceptible and helps drainage, as well as reducing the quantity of fill needed.

Tees sited on rising ground will benefit from an upward slope back to front and it is surprising how strong a slope can be acceptable to golfers on a sharp rise.

Layout
For years the standard tee has been of rectangular shape, very often with sharp edges that are frequently scalped, pointing roughly at the green or fairway landing zone. Although this type of tee allows maximum use of the maintained area, its angular corners are more easily kept with hand mowers than triples. The shape does not blend into any landscape and edges and corners must be well rounded off if they are not to be mangled by mowing. To save critical comment from golfers, its alignment to the hole or landing zone must be perfect.

The less formally shaped tee is something of a rarity, possibly less easy to execute well but it can blend far better into the natural landscape. The easy curves and gentle gradients look right as well as being easier to negotiate and cut tidily with a triple. However, do not over-emphasise softened edges otherwise too high a proportion of the flatter, useful area will be lost. Even the random informal tee shape should not be taken too far, golfers still require of their tees a sense of orientation and the more successful informal ones are shapes based on overlapping circles and an implicit rectangle.

Winter Tees

There is no doubt that given a choice every golfer will opt for playing the year round off grass. There is equally no doubt that no municipal courses and very few private ones have such low levels of winter play that the standard summer tees can cope with 12 months' use. One could argue that if tees were made large enough this objection would be overcome, but this is rarely feasible and, in any case, routes between green and tee would be sadly over-used, requiring unsightly hard surface paths everywhere.

The best compromise is undoubtedly to provide separate winter tees on the opposite side of the green to the summer tees and with their own separate access. This takes wear off summer traffic routes for the worst part of the year, giving them chance to recover or to be repaired. The smaller winter tees and their access tracks can be repaired in April and have a full summer's growth to recover.

At short holes there may not be sufficient space to allow this strategy to be adopted, in which case an artificial tee, temporary or permanent, within the grass tee may have to be accepted as a last resort. Many clubs, already adopt these tactics, moving off summer tees, preferably in early October, so that they have some chance of making recovery growth. Selected areas of fairway or carry are used in winter but too often length is a sacred cow that cannot be sacrificed and some of the potential of separate winter tees is lost by sticking them immediately in front or, worse still, to one side of the summer areas. How much better to give their placing a little thought, selecting a flatter area of rough or semi-rough that must be reasonably free draining and chosen to move traffic off routes so often disrupted by summer play. If you must have the same length, go forward a little at some holes, back at others – you may even attain greater benefit with different landing zones coming into play.

There are as yet no really satisfactory artificial tee surfaces. Those based on nylon or polypropylene bristle become clogged with mud, the pile abrades quickly or becomes severely flattened in use and difficult to get tee pegs into. Such tees must be large enough to provide a firm, dry standing area as well as the teeing surface which must, of course, be capable of taking and holding a tee peg firmly. The rubber link type of mat is, to some extent, self-cleaning and when set in a solid wooden base with a slatted base over a free draining area with a short section of artificial grass tee in either end (easily replaced when worn out), can be quite successful. Artificial tees must be set near a well-drained access path.

Presentation

The good Head Greenkeeper always has something of the showman in his make-up. Directed into the proper channels, this ability can set off a good course to perfection and will always enhance the mediocre. It does not encompass the provision of bedding out plants or exotic shrubs around tees or on their embankments – such unnatural excrescences should be confined to their proper place, in the environs of the club house.

Nowhere does presentation count for more than at the opening and closing holes of a course. Size of the 1st tee is vital – wear must be well distributed and divot repairs kept fully up-to-date so that the surface is irreproachable. Levels must be smooth and true, the soil sandy and free draining to provide a firm, dry stance in all weathers, and supporting the dwarf, hard-wearing, fine-leaved bent and fescue grasses that blend so well together. Near to the club house a permanent path will be in keeping with traffic, regulated further by a neat fence and all notices sited neatly and logically. Always strive to get the players off to a good start and in the right frame of mind to enjoy the game.

TRAFFIC ON GOLF TURF

With the ever increasing congestion on golf courses these days, there may come a time when traffic flow around the holes needs to become controlled in a similar manner to that applied to our roadways. Indeed, Clubs are already finding it more and more necessary for example to determine starting times, to encourage early and late starts, to use both the 1st and 10th as opening holes and to discourage slow play as much as possible, simply to get players around with the minimum of hindrance to each other. The effect of all these metal and rubber studded feet trampling the same paths, scrambling up banks and on the course as a whole in wet weather can be devastating to turf and is a constant source of problems (and complaints) to the course manager and green committee alike. So, the provision of means to keep this damage to a minimum on all courses must be an on-going priority if the appeal of the site is not to deteriorate on a par with the condition of many of the roads in this country.

The 'bare, brown and battered' syndrome is particularly associated with the areas on and around tees, plus the pathways from the previous green (or club house), and on to the fairway. These are golf course bottlenecks and the solution to such problems can again parallel road traffic control which, in such situations, may mean the provision of more appropriate and wider surfaces, dual or multi-carriageways or bypasses.

The condition of pathways is nearly always a bugbear on golf courses. The most direct route from green to tee is invariably the one chosen by golfers unless there is some really insurmountable obstacle in the way. Even then there may well be the odd adventurous soul who will leap a chasm or slash through the dense undergrowth with the club which has recently topped his ball. But it is the trunk route on inland courses which is characterised as the brown, often sludge-filled streak which fans out to a patch close to the tee.

Some Clubs are fortunate in that the landform and space available makes it possible for the definition of alternative routes from green to tee over which wear can be spread but there are very few courses where this capacity is present at every hole. Where alternative routes can be provided they must be well thought out and maintained, and players must be persuaded to use them as directed if the aim of easy walking over a clean surface is to be achieved.

However, more and more Clubs are having to install well-constructed, hard pathways over such sections of the course – in hilly areas this may be the only means of getting golfers around safely – and choice of material for surfacing is important in such cases. Concrete and tarmac paths are not suitable, they do not blend into the environment and metal spiked shoes will slide over them. But the material used must bind to minimise spread out on to mown areas of turf and consequent damage to machinery – so gravel is out too. Hoggin and crushed stone, well compacted, can be suitable materials at reasonable cost. Also, in certain parts of the country sea-shells are available which form an attractive and quite stable surface, although some find the crunching noise disturbing when putting out.

Hard paths have their place over carries too, for example to circumvent a feature played over at a short hole, or to reach the fairway from an elevated tee on a steep down slope. A well conceived, hard path can be attractive in the right circumstances but it is preferable to adopt the more natural, dual or multi-carriage system if it is practical.

However, to return to tees: the persistent damage which can be caused on the line to the tees often fans out on reaching the teeing grounds and may well spread over the banks and surface of the tee too. The design of the tees is often at fault in such situations by leading players to one spot every time, or perhaps, due to elevation, causing a need to scramble up banks to reach the markers. Hard paths alongside tees may be helpful in certain situations.

Wherever possible the slopes on banks to tees should be relatively gentle, e.g. 1 in 4 or 1 in 3. Where steeper banks are necessary, steps are often provided and while this will reduce damage to the banks it does mean constant trampling and constant damage to one area of the tee surface at the top of the stairs. A final resort to eliminate this latter problem, if it cannot be achieved by better design at that site, may be the incorporation of a hard path along one edge of the tee so that players can walk along then step off at the point of the day's markers.

The current fashion when improvements are made to tees (in order to create extra space in which to move tee markers), is to build one large tee to incorporate back, day and ladies' markers. Such a design does have its place, particularly at the first hole and it does make maintenance easier, but such a form does not necessarily provide the ideal tee. In many respects having a single tee at each hole tends to aggravate the traffic problems outlined above. A useful alternative for increasing tee area to the single tee principle is to have a selection of tees which need not be grouped together. Separation of tees where space can be made available not only allows for reduction of wear on one traffic route but also, when well thought out, introduces variety into play as each can alter the aspect of a hole.

These factors of separation are of prime importance when siting of winter tees is considered. To get the best out of the main tees on a course, the careful use of winter tees is vital. Most traffic damage is caused during the winter, so winter tees should be well away from summer tees to protect the main areas and the route or routes to them. Often the space available for siting winter tees is quite limited and in these situations winter mats have to be used. These are not the most popular surfaces but their acceptability can be improved through the care in which the site is prepared and through the variety this siting can introduce into playing the course.

The areas around the tees are not the only parts of a course subject to damage due to concentrated foot traffic. Problems can arise on fairways, green approaches and on the putting surfaces themselves.

The most common feature causing traffic problems on fairways and approaches is the presence of large or closely grouped bunkers which narrow the routes through which players can pass. This is something which clubs may have to live with unless it is intended to change the nature of a particular hole or holes through route widening schemes. If such changes are necessary on a large scale, it is usually profitable to seek the advice of a reputable golf course architect (preferably a member of the British Association of Golf Course Architects) rather than to go it alone.

On the putting surface it is primarily the walk-off area which can suffer so we have come full circle and return to the line from pin to tee. Control of trolley flow may help to spread the load on the green as the position at which trolleys can be left while putting out may be used to dictate the walk-off point (then the line to the next tee). So, clear and discrete marking of carefully considered routes around the golf course, changed regularly, may help to spread the load on the putting surface, could dictate the line to the tee selected as the starting point for the next hole where markers have been set so that the hole will be played in a particular way, all to the best advantage of minimum wear on the course as a whole. The co-operation of players is needed too or a stage may yet be reached where a knowledge of the highway code has to supersede course etiquette.

GRASS IN SHADE

Turfgrass persistence in shade depends not only on the amount and quality of such light as there is, but on the height and frequency of cut, the available moisture (especially if there is competition from tree roots), and the microclimate of the shaded area, particularly insofar as it may encourage disease. Moderation is the watchword – in mowing, nitrogen application and wear.

The selection of grasses for shade usually implies the aim of producing something as near ordinary turf as possible in spite of adverse conditions. The need is not for shade grasses, but for turfgrasses that will tolerate shade. Typical shade grasses would be wavy hair-grass (*Deschampsia flexuosa*), wood meadow-grass (*Poa nemoralis*) or wood millet (*Milium effusum*). These are well adapted to tolerate stress in shaded habitats and would obviously be suitable for the creation of a woodland flora, but they will not form a turf or stand up to wear. Therefore, they are not recommended for golf tees or greens.

Philip Grime, in "Plant strategies and vegetation processes" states that "in response to shade, the majority of plants produce less dry matter, retain photosynthate in the shoot at the expense of root growth, develop longer internodes and petioles, and produce larger, thinner leaves." This is fairly widely known, but he goes on, "However, when the responses of different ecological groups of plants are compared, a paradox becomes apparent. This arises from the fact that the capacity to maximise dry matter production in shade through modification of the phenotype is most apparent in species characteristic of unshaded or lightly shaded environments whilst plants associated with deep shade tend to grow slowly and to show much less pronounced morphogenetic responses to shade treatment."

In other words, the natural shade grasses like wavy hair-grass are basically slow growing plants, and nothing will alter this. So they have no potential to produce turf for normal use. Wood meadow-grass is likewise only suitable for areas to be mown very seldom, if at all. It should be thought of as the most readily available natural grass for shade, rather than as a turfgrass. Instead, for the dry and difficult conditions, one must look to the turfgrasses which have some ability to withstand stress; or, for conditions which are more favourable for growth, to the opportunistic species. Bakker & Vos in the Netherlands in 1976 explained well the two kinds of shade, for which the most appropriate grasses are indicated in the following Table.

GRASSES ADAPTED TO VARIOUS SHADE CONDITIONS

No mowing	Infrequent mowing	
	Dry shade	Moist shade
Red and fine fescues, esp. strong creeping red fescue. Wood meadow-grass. Wavy hair-grass.	Chewings fescue. Slender creeping red fescue. Strong creeping red fescue. Possibly other fine fescues in moderate shade.	Bentgrasses. Red fescues, as for dry shade. Rough-stalked meadow-grass.

For **dry shade** in UK conditions, typically under trees where there is competition from tree roots for moisture and nutrients, the most useful grasses are the various forms of red fescue (*F. rubra*), including Chewings fescue. They are suitable both for severe shade (5–10% of daylight) where mowing is best avoided altogether if possible, and moderate shade (20–30% of daylight) where infrequent mowing, say three to five times a year at about 50 mm, is reasonable.

In **moist shade**, where rain falls even though light is restricted, as for example against a wall or building, fine fescues are also valuable but in addition bentgrasses will grow well once they have come through their slow establishment phase and provided that disease is controlled. The most shade-tolerant bent is generally considered to be velvet bent, but there seems to be little difference between it and the other species of bent, and 'Highland' browntop or a creeping bent could be expected to establish and develop faster. Rough-stalked meadow-grass and annual meadow-grass are also well adapted to moist conditions. The fast establishment of rough-stalked meadow-grass is advantageous.

Even with the fescues and bents, the degree of wear which they will tolerate will depend on how vigorously they grow and how full a cover is maintained. The responses to shade described by Grime – less dry matter, reduced root development, and longer and weaker leaves – all diminish wear tolerance. The most wear-tolerant UK turfgrasses – smooth-stalked meadow-grass, perennial ryegrass and timothy – are not really suited to shade conditions, although it is possible for the two former to survive to some extent. In the USA there is considerable emphasis on testing for shade tolerance, and some cultivars of smooth-stalked meadow-grass in particular are advertised for shade tolerance. Nevertheless, smooth-stalked meadow-grass is generally less well adapted to UK conditions than perennial ryegrass, red fescue or bentgrasses, and therefore even the most shade-tolerant cultivar of smooth-stalked meadow-grass is not likely to do very well.

Some of the cultivar differences in shade tolerance are bound up with resistance to various diseases. For example, powdery mildew (*Erysiphe graminis*) has been shown to be very important on smooth-stalked meadow-grass, and leaf spots on fescues and rough-stalked meadow-grass. In UK conditions several diseases, particularly fusarium patch disease, are made worse by the absence of sunlight and the humid conditions of some shaded areas, and this is an additional factor to bear n mind with shaded situations, especially where bentgrasses and annual meadow-grass are growing.

TEE CONSTRUCTION

Tee construction should be a very straightforward process about which very little that is new could be said. Nevertheless, poor results from such work are not all that uncommon, and given that many clubs are in the throes of a tee rebuilding programme, a resume of ideas on design, construction techniques, and the materials required, could well be of benefit to the majority.

The Concept

When thinking about the building of tees, the point at which to start must be the concept, ie. what we are actually looking for as a result. This comes down to: clean, firm, even stances; plenty of space over which to spread wear patterns; high quality turf – if not actually putting surface standard, then at least good apron quality; the potential for rapid management; and allowance for the free and safe movement of play from the previous green, through the tee and off to the next fairway. So, there are several constraints to be met in tee construction which may not necessarily be served by building as big a rectangular platform as can be afforded.

Design Criteria

Normally, the best design features for a set of teeing grounds encompass best use of the available space, giving adequate provision for Championship, Medal, Day and Ladies tees, without there being unwanted "dead" areas still in need of maintenance between the separate courses. The shorter the hole, the more tee area is needed, especially width as opposed to length of teeing ground, to avoid shortening of a course, and indeed to provide more moves of tee boxes over any total area.

The total area of teeing grounds to be aimed for at individual holes will depend upon the shot to be played from the proposed tee. If this is to be played with a mid to short iron, then up to 300 m^2 total teeing ground should be aimed for, while if a long iron or a wood will be taken, then 250 m^2 total space will be more than enough.

Tees need not be square, they can be of any shape. Neither is it always desirable to build one big tee at each hole. Indeed, so long as ease of maintenance with largish equipment is borne in mind, there is much to be said for having two or three alternative tees at each hole, especially for the tee of the day course, so that repairs can be easily effected and there is a measured course specifically for winter play.

The elevation of new tees must be kept to the absolute minimum. Time spent managing excessive banks is time wasted, while the more banking which needs to be provided often means a loss of platform area. To be considered too is the requirement for easy access for players, ideally along the full length of each tee so that players only have to walk a short distance to the box of the day, avoiding wear patterns at a gate or at the top of steps. Then, one should look at flow of play from hole to hole, aiming to bring play to the tees from the rear, and away to the front, with the option of using either side for access, to avoid toing and froing along a single line. Most problems in this latter respect are caused by jamming tees into awkward corners. This can not always be avoided, but if it can it should.

When it comes to siting tees, it cannot be repeated often enough that tees and trees do not mix. Tees butted up to specimen trees, tees surrounded by hedges, and tees in woodland glades, all perform badly. While these features look pretty at the outset, they will cause disappointment and cost money in the longer term.

Building Up a Base

Some form of fill is generally required to build up the base of the tees. What is used varies according to what is easily available and is relatively cheap. Subsoil fill from an out-of-the-way area of the course is the most common material used, with builders' rubble coming in second. If builders rubble is used, it has to be remembered that this still has to be capped off to prevent future settlement into the voids and an adequate depth of subsoil capping is needed, say 300–350 mm minimum, so as to be able to carry out subsoil cultivation works if required. With any fill it is vital that it is adequately firmed by trucking or wheeling in comparatively thin layers, and that anything which will rot or rust to create a void is kept out of the construction.

Other than on very wet land, it is usually unnecessary to install drainage beneath tees. However, subsoil cultivation is usually very worthwhile after topsoil spread to ensure that water can penetrate the ground and enter the formation build up, ideally making two passes. Such work is of special importance on large tees.

Once a base has been built up using subsoil fill or rubble covered with subsoil fill, the stage has been reached where a formation surface needs to be created. On the tee platform, this means trimming and smoothing to provide a slight fall from front to back, eg. 1 in 70 to 1 in 100, to an elevation which is 150 mm below planned finished levels. Water-collecting hollows must be eliminated at this stage. The banks should be shaped too for an easy step up on to the tee, and for easy mowing with a triple mower – maximum gradient 1 in 3.

Selecting Topsoil

Choice of topsoil or topsoil mix will depend upon the circumstances of individual clubs. Such selection is conditioned by, for example, the weight of play, the availability of watering and in what form, the average rainfall of the area, the degree of exposure of individual tee sites, and so on. Generally speaking though, the likelihood of being able to use neat topsoil off the course is very low. Indeed, in the vast majority of instances it will be a case for using a sand and soil mix, either bought in ready-made, or the components bought in for on-course mixing.

There is no set mix for tee use. The proportions of sand and soil employed should be varied according to the considerations set out above, and according to the nature of the soil itself, to control the amounts of very fine sand, silt and clay in the final product. It is important too that the sand used matches up with the soil. Having lab tests carried out on materials well in advance of the implementation of a project adds a little to costs, but certainly eliminates some of the problems which can be encountered along the way.

When calculating volumes of sand and soil mix required, allow for a loose depth of 200 mm to cover the platforms evenly. Less is required for banks, say 100 to 150 mm loose depth, depending upon the likelihood of routine trampling, and how important is the level of ongoing presentation.

The Grass Cover

Whether a new tee is seeded or turfed depends upon the time available for establishment. The vast majority will be turfed, although this can be costly. Even so, the better the quality of turf bought (from a reputable supplier, purpose-grown), the better will be the establishment and the better will be the long term results.

Whether seeding or turfing, choose a fine grass mixture without perennial ryegrass, a species which is still not suited to a good standard of tee presentation. Select species from Chewings fescue, slender creeping red fescue, smooth-stalked meadow-grass and browntop bent (turf of this type is readily available). However, do not just look at the grass species when choosing turf, look too for a little bit of fibre mat at the base of the grasses, and at the quality of the underlying soil which will be lifted. A thin layer of fibre mat suggests the turf is a shade more mature than average and will establish and be ready for play more quickly. While heavy soil at the base of the turf must be avoided, as this will not integrate well with the soil on the turf bed, it will become smeared and compacted in wet weather, or it will bake out hard and lift when it is dry.

Finishing Touches
The turf must be laid firmly on the soil bed, and it does help establishment if a pre-turfing fertiliser has been raked in. Ensure the turf is in good contact with the underlying soil by lightly rolling afterwards. Remember the smoother the surface is at this stage, the more quickly the tee will be able to be played.

Once the tee starts to grow, start top dressing to perfect surface levels, ideally using a material similar to that used for the rootzone mix. The tee can be brought into play when the turf is well rooted, and the surface is smooth enough for close mowing. It is useful to allow for at least two dressings of organic spring and summer fertiliser during the first growing season.

SECTION 4

GOLF FAIRWAYS, SEMI-ROUGH AND ROUGH

FAIRWAY, SEMI-ROUGH AND ROUGH MANAGEMENT

Fairways

The fairway is usually considered to be the turfed area between the tee and the putting green which is mown at a lower height of cut than the surrounding rough. To produce good quality fairways where golfers' judgement and control are tested to the full, certain criteria have to be met. The main desirable characteristics are smoothness, grass density, uniformity and being firm yet resilient. The management programme is therefore tailored to develop these qualities in the playing surfaces and goes hand in hand with favouring conditions that encourage the best grass species, namely bents and fescues.

Mowing

An important part of summer maintenance is to develop uniformity and the formation of a dense, upright turf which is firm yet resilient to the well struck shot. Fairways are mown relatively close to promote these qualities, but not cutting too close to cause scalping. Indeed, height of cut is critical in achieving proper ball positioning on the turf and control in hitting the shots. The preferred height of cut is 13–19 mm, although deviations from this range will occur depending on the state of growth and prevailing weather conditions. Frequency may well fluctuate between three times a week on lush, green fairway to once a fortnight – an average would be weekly during the growing season.

The delineation between fairway and semi-rough should never be mown in a straight line, mow in an undulating contour pattern that will give shape and character, especially on holes where all the fairway is visible from the tee.

Divots

Minimising the extent of divot damage by cultural means is the primary policy to adopt, followed by efficient repair work. A soft, lush, spongy turf is associated with larger divots; a situation that can be reversed with management practices, including improving drainage and root growth by aeration, verticutting to remove thatch accumulation and cutting out fertiliser applications. Smaller divots will then be produced on a firmer surface, assuming the same basic stroke type. Divot repair should be confined primarily to the growing season, employing a mixture of screened sandy compost and a suitable fescue/bent seeds mixture. Aim for a seeding rate in the order to 17–35 g/m². The best results will be achieved under good growing conditions during moist spells of weather.

A useful tip in the early spring before gang mowing starts is to sweep up all the dead turves and debris left from winter play and follow up with a divoting party. This leaves a clean surface and encourages recovery as growth starts to pick up.

Weed Control

The cultivation of a dense, healthy fescue/bent turf is one of the soundest means of preventing weed invasion. Other beneficial cultural practices include worm control and avoiding application of lime and fertiliser. Worms bring up dormant weed seed to the surface, and a smeared cast is an ideal seed bed for weedgrass invasion. Lime and fertiliser invariably encourage worm and weed activity.

If chemical control is warranted, use an appropriate selective herbicide and apply strictly at the manufacturer's recommended rate. Timing should ideally coincide with a calm, dry, overcast day during a period of good growth.

Fertiliser
Maintenance of a bent/fescue sward is dependent on low fertility, so fertiliser should not be warranted. In fact, fertiliser application will only increase mowing requirements, a distinct disadvantage when time is so important in the summer months. However, there are instances where compaction, poor drainage and soil poverty result in thinning of the sward, moss invasion and the formation of bare areas. Here, a combination of aeration and careful fertiliser treatment (based on nitrogen) is recommended on selected localised trouble spots.

Aeration
With the ever increasing levels of play on golf courses, particularly during the winter, soil compaction and impeded surface drainage are becoming real problems. This condition is highlighted on areas where traffic is funnelled into confined sections, such as the entrance to the fairway from the tee.

Aeration is vital in combating compaction and impeded surface drainage, but it also has numerous other benefits. These include encouraging root growth, the natural breakdown of thatch and, in the long term, the finer grasses, fescue and bent. There is now certainly a need to increase the frequency and intensity of aeration treatments to combat compaction brought about through play. Regular deep slit tine aeration is therefore essential during autumn to spring on a two to three weekly basis. In fact, this work can be extended to any time when the ground is firm enough to take the tractor without rutting yet the soil is moist enough to gain good tine penetration. Aim to give all traffic routes and other concentrated areas of wear a double pass with the aerator whenever the fairways are slit.

Improvements in tractor-mounted aerators now allow deep penetrating tines to be fitted (225–300 mm) and with the facility of hydraulics for enhancing tine penetration. Verti-Drain machines are extensively used on fairways and, despite being an expensive unit to hire or buy for large scale fairway aeration, there are real benefits to be gained by breaking up compaction to a depth of 400 mm and improving surface drainage. The use of Verti-Drain machines is most useful on traffic routes and compacted areas.

Drainage
On clay sites, aeration alone may not be sufficient to overcome compaction and poor drainage imposed by the nature of the soil profile. In these cases drainage in the form of ditches and/or a piped drainage scheme may be required to alleviate the problem. Mole ploughing has also proved to be a useful exercise in providing temporary drainage channels running into the drainage aggregate of a main drain or connecting laterals within a system.

Verticutting
One management treatment that has become more prevalent in recent years is verticutting. The practice is widely carried out on greens using verticut reels on the triple mower; it is simply a question of extending the work to approaches and fairways to gain the same benefits yet using different machinery. Time the operation for periods of good growth and, bearing in mind the limited time available to implement fairway work during the summer months, it is recommended a spring and autumn treatment be undertaken. A number of tractor-mounted or trailed units are available. All arisings should be picked up with a large tractor-mounted leaf sweeper or similar if the verticut unit does not possess a collecting facility.

Worm Casting

Worm casting can be particularly troublesome on parkland type courses where the casts create a messy, unsightly surface which is disruptive to winter play and efficient gang mowing. Casts also encourage moles, effect surface levels and smother turfgrasses which, in turn, provides a seed bed for weeds. Worm activity can be discouraged by avoiding creating limy conditions and using excessive amounts of fertiliser and organic materials. When cultural methods fail and casting is prolific, chemical control becomes a necessity.

A number of wormkillers are available on the market, the most common products being those based on carbaryl. Alternative wormkillers are available, e.g. those based on carbendazim and thiophanate-methyl, but these are not as long lasting. Strict adherence to the manufacturer's recommended rate is vital if successful control of large areas is to be achieved. Remember the cost of treating fairways will be expensive whatever the product chosen.

The Rough

The rough is not specifically defined in the Rules of Golf but is included in "through the green" as follows:

> *"Through the green is the whole area of the course except: (a) the teeing ground and putting green of the hole being played; and (b) all hazards on the course."*

In terms of management, the rough is the area of the course surrounding the green, the tee and the fairway of each hole. Like many aspects of golf course maintenance, the management of the rough consists of achieving a balance. In this case, it involves striking a balance between virtually the whole course being mown at fairway height – the wide open prairie syndrome – to deep jungle-type rough extending right up to the fairway edge. The former creates a situation where the golfer can hook or slice a drive with little fear of stroke penalty, the latter extracts maximum stroke penalty, but creates the major problems of losing golf balls and slowing up play, a very pertinent point when considering high levels of play, e.g. public courses.

There is also variation in the types of rough encountered, from the semi-open with tall-growing grasses, e.g. links, to heather, ling/grass mixtures, e.g. moorland/heathland, and pastureland, lush, dense, spongy, e.g. parkland. Since no hard and fast standards exist, it is up to those responsible for golf course management to balance the speed of play desired and the ease of finding golf balls with the degree of difficulty sought and the desirability for a low maintenance regime. This can be largely achieved by variation in cutting height and grading of the rough from deep rough to perimeter fairway.

Semi-Rough

Breaking up the rough into component parts, the semi-rough is that band of rough immediately surrounding a fairway and lying between the fairway and the most distant rough. If space permits, an intermediate band can be introduced between the semi-rough and fairway to extract different degrees of stroke penalty, as well as providing shot variety. In a similar fashion to developing definition between putting surfaces and fairway, by introducing a collar, the semi-rough fulfils the same function between fairway and deep rough, only in this instance is virtually created by mowing alone.

The mowing height, contouring, frequency and width of cut depend on the degree of difficulty and rapidity of play desired, but there are ground rules. Firstly, a common height of cut would be in the order of 37–63 mm with a typical mowing frequency of weekly or fortnightly, depending on the state of growth. An important point to stress here is that the semi-rough is mown with gang mowers on a regular basis to maintain a clear definition between fairway and deep rough.

There is still a distinct tendency for operatives to mow in straight lines because it is easier and quicker, but for presentation, the semi-rough and fairway should be contoured to the terrain of the land and graduated to provide more of a challenge to the better golfer, e.g. increase the semi-rough width to give fairways 30 m wide at the 230 m mark compared with 40 m at the 140 m mark. (A useful average to take for fairway width is 32–35 m.) The width of the semi-rough would generally be between 3–5 m, although on municipal courses this figure is often increased to speed up play.

On large acreage courses, a further refinement would involve introducing another band of semi-rough mown at an intermediate height between fairway and semi-rough height, i.e. 25–37 mm, and to a width of 1.5–2.5 m. This band of semi-rough would be mown more frequently, say every five to ten days.

Other Maintenance
Whilst maintenance of rough areas needs to be kept to a minimum, this does not mean neglect. Apart from mowing, slit tine aeration with a tractor-mounted aerator is recommended for the semi-rough, as well as verticutting or raking to remove dead growth that can often build up to form a mat.

Weed control may be necessary to prevent infection of the fairways, but as there is a movement towards conservation of the rough and promoting native flora and fauna, caution should be exercised before chemical control is implemented.

It is most unlikely that the semi-rough will have any fertiliser requirement.

Leatherjackets can cause considerable damage in the semi-rough where the turf is soft and spongy and, therefore, control using an appropriate insecticide is advisable. However, cultural practices should not be forgotten, the aim is to improve the uniformity and density of the turf and firmness of the surface, i.e. through aeration and verticutting.

On golf courses with deciduous trees it is essential in the autumn to pick up leaves and thereby keep play flowing and prevent unnecessary problems to turf growth. A large tractor-mounted leaf sweeper is the most common means of quick and efficient leaf removal.

Deep Rough
On parkland courses the rough adjacent to semi-rough is usually mown at a height of 100 mm for presentation and speeding up play. Depending on the height of cut, gang mowers or rotary trailed mowers are employed, the latter are useful for cutting heather on heathland or moorland courses. In the case of heather, a yearly late autumn mowing prevents heather becoming too 'leggy' and instead encourages the formation of young, new shoots.

In the sometimes obsessive quest for presentation, manicuring of courses has developed to such an extent that there are often few natural areas where the grass is allowed to grow in its natural state. Besides cutting down maintenance costs, there are advantages in allowing the deep rough to grow without mowing, especially where golf shots seldom stray. There is a good case for bringing grassy mounds in the semi-rough into this category of rough, as well as carry areas from tee to fairway.

Desirable grasses will be allowed to seed, leading to colonisation of adjacent areas. Existing or sown wild flowers provide colour and the deep rough can be a cover and food source for wildlife. These all enhance the aesthetic value and interest of the golf course to golfers.

A word of caution, natural areas require careful planning and effort as there is a thin dividing line between a natural setting and an unkempt one which appears to have been forgotten. In this respect, a yearly mowing regime would be appropriate, as well as grubbing out saplings, e.g. hawthorn, to prevent scrub forming.

Some Other Factors
Moles
It is worth mentioning that mole problems can coincide with a large worm population, as worms from a major part of the mole's diet. If the mole infestation is severe, then some form of trapping, poisoning or gassing will be necessary. Various mechanical mole traps are available. They are carefully placed in the mole runs and have to be checked daily. Baits containing strychnine or warfarin have also been used to poison the pests. Gassing can be carried out using gas or smoke generators which fill the mole tunnels with cyanide or hydrogen phosphide gas. Once the moles have been eliminated it is worthwhile carrying out worm control to deter further re-invasion by moles from neighbouring land.

Trees
Apart from on some links courses, trees are an important feature on the golf course and they do require attention from time to time. The majority of trees on the golf course are found around the tees, greens and between the fairways. Group plantings on the fairways are not often found but individual specimen trees are sometimes used to create additional interest. An annual inspection will usually show which trees require attention and if any major branches need lopping due to disease or some other hazard, then it is wise to employ the services of a competent tree surgeon. A planting programme is needed to maintain an even distribution of younger and mature trees. Deciduous trees can be planted from October to March, but evergreens are usually most successful if planted in autumn or early spring. With these, you should avoid planting in the winter months of December, January and February. There are many possible pitfalls when it comes to buying and planting trees and it pays to thoroughly read up on the subject or seek the advice of an arboriculturist before going ahead.

Spreading the Wear
The practice of only allowing wide-wheel trolleys on the course is common at many clubs – particularly during the winter. This sort of restriction will help to reduce wheelmarking on wet fairways. Muddy tracks can often be seen on regularly used areas whatever type of trolley is being used and it is a good idea to try and spread the wear evenly. This can be achieved by means of temporarily fencing or roping areas off to guide the traffic in a particular direction away from tees, etc. The fence or rope guides should be moved every week or two to ensure that maximum use is made of the space available. Without this sort of friendly persuasion the golfers are likely to continue using the same old paths and boggy conditions can soon result.

It is clear from the above that the fairways should not just be neglected through the winter. Regular aeration work to help relieve compaction is perhaps the most important operation, but it must be emphasised that the tractor should only be used when ground conditions are suitable.

DEALING WITH DIVOTS

Scarred areas of fairway, strewn with divots, are not only unsightly but also provide unsatisfactory and unfair playing surfaces, often giving a player a poor lie after a good previous shot. Even in cases where most fairway areas provide perfectly acceptable surfaces, concentrated divoting can occur on areas where most tee shots tend to land and the layout of some holes unfortunately tends to encourage the development of such localised problem patches.

The problem of divots on fairways can be approached in two ways – prevention by minimising the chance of serious scarring developing, and cure by efficient repair work. As with most other problems, prevention is undoubtedly better than cure.

Preventative Treatments

In the case of some holes, the widening of a particular section of fairway, the elimination of surplus bunkers or mounds, or more frequent changing of tee markers can do much to prevent the deterioration of small areas where concentrated play has occurred. Spreading wear over larger areas helps considerably.

The correct basic maintenance of fairways is also of importance. In the past there has unfortunately been a tendency to try to reduce the divot problem by encouraging lush and vigorous grass growth with the idea that strongly growing swards will recover from scarring more rapidly. Such mistaken attempts to improve grass growth by the liberal use of fertilisers and by liming can be disastrous in the long term. Such treatment encourages perennial ryegrass and other coarse grasses which, although it is certainly strong growing and wear-resistant, has no useful role as a fairway grass. Most golf courses (particularly parkland courses) unfortunately have some ryegrass in their fairways which, although it is the most desirable species for rugby or soccer pitches, does not produce good golfing surfaces. Ryegrass swards are lush and require very frequent cutting, using time and labour better expended in other vital tasks. The ball tends to sink into such a sward instead of being set-up in the way which is mandatory for a good fairway surface. Encouraging ryegrass by fertiliser and lime is therefore definitely not the right way to minimise the divot problem as this approach creates a situation which is worse than the problem it purports to solve.

No, the best fairway surfaces are predominantly made up of finer grasses, particularly bentgrasses, which if well maintained provide enough growth to allow good natural recovery of divot-scarred areas. Such swards can be maintained under moderately acidic soil conditions and where a controlled degree of soil poverty prevails. The ability of such swards to recover from the effects of play can be increased by reducing excessive fibre or thatch accumulation (by spring harrowing or rotary scarification work) and by maintaining good surface drainage and root development (by aeration work, mainly in spring and autumn). Of course, there are situations where soil poverty becomes extreme and even the desirable finer grasses start to suffer, with thin growth, bare soil patches and moss invasion. Here, judicious and circumspect fertiliser treatment (usually with nitrogen and certainly not with large quantities of phosphate) may be useful on chosen localised areas.

In situations where large numbers of divots are lying scattered on a fairway area, a cleaner playing surface may be obtained simply by running over with the gang mower to chop up and dispense the debris. Ideally, of course, all players should replace divots on all occasions but it sadly seems impossible to persuade all members of the average club to act thoughtfully in this respect. Even where members do conscientiously replace the majority of divots, surfaces can remain scarred particularly in dry weather or in the winter when replaced divots are slow to heal. Bird activity can be a nuisance too, with seagulls, crows or starlings picking up and scattering carefully replaced divots. Here, the problem can sometimes be minimised by eliminating insects like leatherjackets, or by controlling earthworms as birds are often looking for food.

On most heavily played courses some reseeding work proves necessary at times even where the necessity has been minimised by attention to the points covered above.

Repair Work

Divot repair is best carried out in the growing season, when labour can be spared, using a good screened topsoil into which a suitable non-ryegrass seeds mixture has been mixed. The seeding rate should be about 17–35 g/m^2, although it is obviously difficult to achieve any great exactitude in such circumstances. The seeds mix used should match the prevailing composition of the existing fairway sward as far as possible with the limitation that the egregious perennial ryegrass should not be included. Repair work should theoretically be carried out when there is good growth and no danger of drought but in practice it tends to be one of those jobs carried out simply when time can be spared from other greenkeeping operations.

WATER FEATURES

Introduction

Ponds and water features, including open ditches, on the golf course are rich habitats for wildlife. They can be very attractive and can represent considerable hazards to play. Natural wetlands throughout Britain have disappeared at an alarming rate. The key to retaining what is left and, indeed, the creation of new sites lies in the recognition of their value. The interests of golf and ecology in this respect are not incompatible. Ponds sensibly managed for golf will, or can, help preserve the wetland habitat and provide a haven for many diverse forms of associated wildlife.

Siting

Siting should take into account the preservation of existing habitats of ecological value and archeological interest.

Existing pipework, ditches, drainage, etc. may also affect the positioning. Natural rainfall, ground water or spring water (surface run-off) should provide the main input source. Siting therefore should be within a low lying catchment area such that it does not destroy the natural topography of the site. The soil type will have a major influence on the siting. Impermeable soils are very difficult to transport to site, therefore it is far better to thoroughly investigate where impermeable soils are located to ensure a successful design.

Siting with regard to adjacent roads, car parks, etc. may need to be considered as oils, petrol and salt may result in run-off and pollution within the pond. Similarly, fertilizer run-off must be considered. It may be necessary to satisfy these requirements in order to investigate the quality of existing nearby watercourses.

If the water features are to satisfy course irrigation, which demands very large volumes of water, then calculations must be considered for both evapotranspiration and actual predicted usage values. These will obviously result in large fluctuations in levels. In this case, 'off-stream' or impounding lakes must be considered. Under the Reservoirs Act 1975, correct construction with overflow facilities must be provided.

Methods of Construction

Total Excavation

Total excavation involves the removal of soil and subsoil to depth, followed by lining and replacement with water.

This method is not very economic – for every cubic metre excavated, only 1 m^3 of water is stored. There is also the additional problem of soil disposal in some cases.

Cut and Fill

This method is more economic. Spoil is used to build the retaining embankments. For every cubic metre excavated, up to 3–4 m^3 of water may be stored. The ideal is to balance the amount of spoil needed for the embankment with that excavated.

The best soils for the embankments are those with a 30% clay fraction (or greater), together with coarse sand/soil loams, giving both impermeability and stability. Silts and fine sands are very unstable.

Size

The excavation should be larger than 5 x 5 metres with a minimum depth of 1.5 metres. Ponds shallower and smaller than this are prone to drying out in the summer months. Algal blooms are a major problem which arise through large temperature and nutrient fluctuations.

Shape

The flatter the slopes, the more stable the embankments. Achieve a gradual fall of 1 : 10 to 1 : 20, at least in key areas for ball retrieval.

Shelves of varying depth should be created for maximum benefits to wildlife.

Materials

Bentonite Clay

Bentonite is a fine powdered clay manufactured to line reservoirs and other large areas. Marketed at Volclay, it is mixed with the soil lining and, upon contact with water, swells to around 15 times its volume to form an impermeable lining – similar to puddled clay, but with the advantage that it is not liable to cracking when it dries out.

Bentonite is very expensive – in small ponds the extensive swelling may severely reduce the depth or volume of the pond.

It is difficult to achieve a satisfactory seal.

Clay

Traditionally, raw clay is puddled around the sides and bottom of the excavations to form an impermeable seal. If the clay dries out for anything more than a few days, puddled clay may crack. Repair involves extensive repuddling which can present major problems.

Cost is variable depending largely on transportation and whether a local source can be found. Because of the sheer bulk of the material needed, the cost of transportation may be very high. Labour costs too may also be quite high. Achieving the correct clay plasticity for puddling may also be quite exacting.

This method is good if existing soils are suitable, i.e. clay content above 30% and relatively free of stone and other contaminants.

Concrete

A great deal of skill is required to construct a waterproof concrete water body lining with respect to bonding new and previously laid concrete slabs. Joints may be necessary to allow expansion and contraction. Specialist advice on pond construction using concrete should be obtained by contacting the Cement and Concrete Association.

Butyl

Butyl rubber is a very effective and modern method of lining a pond or water body and is relatively cheap in comparison to those described above. Costs range from around £3.00 to £4.50 per m² for a gauge of 0.75 mm. The main requirements for laying are that the base and sides need to be firm and all sharp stones removed. Banks should be no greater than 1 in 3 as the soil covering needed to protect the sheeting from sunlight will not stay in place on steeper slopes. It is important that the ground is level before any excavation takes place.

Further details of pond construction and development can be obtained from the Sports Turf Research Institute.

Other Aspects for Consideration

Tree Planting

Caution is necessary with regard to tree planting. Trees should be well back from the pond edge, planted on the northern side to provide shelter from prevailing winds. Planted too close, they can penetrate embankments or linings, causing channels through which the water can pass.

Grant Aid and Costs

Costs of excavating a 0.1 hectare (^{1}/$_4$ acre) pond by a Contractor is likely to be £360.00 (two days at £15.00 to £18.00 per hour, lining material – butyl = £3.00 to £4.00 per m^2).

Additional items would include level adjustment and landscaping works, soils, dams, overflows, etc., which also add to the cost.

Grant aid may be available from the Countryside Commission (up to 50% if of landscape value), English Nature (if objectives are for conservation), and the Ministry of Agriculture, Fisheries and Food.

Vegetation Management

Ponds and other wetlands are not permanent habitats, they undergo a process called succession whereby they gradually fill up with silt, leaves and dead vegetation. Terrestrial plants start to invade, resulting in the eventual scrub/woodland colonisation. To avoid this, ponds need to be regularly cleaned, normally every seven to ten years. Care should be taken to leave blocks of vegetation strategically positioned around the pond to aid re-establishment. Certain species are more invasive than others and may need more regular management. Tree and shrub management is important around the pond – particularly with regard to reducing shading and leaf drop. Floating vegetation can be raked off the surface of smaller ponds, while marginal vegetation can be cut by hand. Chain scythes can be used for cutting submerged vegetation on larger water bodies, but are unlikely to be available for smaller ponds. Cut vegetation should be removed from the water as its decay will cause de-oxygenation with resulting stress to fish and other aquatic life. Removed vegetation is best left on the bankside for at least two days to allow wildlife to recolonise the water body before removal. Algal blooms are a result of increased nutrient level – possibly as a result of organic decomposition, the water source and possible nutrient run-off from adjacent land. While thick algal blankets can be raked off the surface, the long term answer is to simply wait until nutrient levels return to normal. If the pond is being enriched by any source of nutrient contamination, then this must be identified and controlled.

Clearance work should be undertaken on a rotational basis such that the pond is divided into five or more portions depending upon the size. Clearance work should be undertaken on only one portion per annum. This will allow recovery and recolonisation within the pond. Clearance operations should be undertaken during October to November and all vegetation or silt should be left on the bankside for two days before removal to allow excess water and wildlife to re-enter the pond. Free floating material is best dragged or raked from the surface of the pond, and hoeing, dragging or chain scythes may be employed for submerged aquatics. Caution must, however, be given to the type of lining material.

Aquatic herbicides can be used when labour is limited. These can be extremely useful, however their long term effects on the water life are little understood and only a few of the approved chemicals are specific enough to take out only the pest species. Before using herbicides it is essential to read the guidelines for their use in watercourses, available from local Ministry of Agriculture, Fisheries and Food offices. Dalapon is still approved for reed control, it is effective and reasonably specific. Glyphosate is useful for broad-leaved emergence and some floating aquatic plants. The only herbicide which has much effect on algae is terbutryne. However, this also kills non-target aquatic plants and so must be used within the guidelines as directed on the label and according to individual site conditions. Herbicide treatment normally occurs in early spring when the plant biomass is low or late summer when the majority of wildlife have finished breeding, etc.

LARGE-SCALE MECHANICAL AERATION

Aeration machines can be usefully employed on golf fairways. This article deals with the above as distinct from relatively small areas of intensively managed turf such as golf greens. On the latter area relatively small mechanised aerators are most often used, occasionally supplemented by hand forking on localised problem areas. The use of such small aerators on larger fairways is limited because of the time factor, though they can be useful for alleviating the effects of concentrated wear, puddling, etc. in major trouble spots when ground conditions do not permit tractor work.

Reasons for Aeration

In fertile soils with open structure permitting free passage of water and air, surface drainage can be satisfactory and whilst root development is not unduly impeded, the growth of a vigorous, healthy turf is possible. Under playing conditions, however, particularly in winter when the soil is soft and wet, the topsoil surface becomes smeared and destructured, often with a compacted layer in the top 50 or 75 mm causing impeded surface drainage. Play under these conditions rapidly makes matters worse, compaction increases, the affected places become even more smeared and puddled, and with the muddy areas increasing in size. There is deterioration in the grass cover and playing surface, and ill effects can also persist into the summer, affecting root growth, vigour and recovery.

On many courses with sound comprehensive underground drainage, surface drainage can still be affected due to the above factors. The compacted, destructured soil layer prevents quick water movement away from the top into more open soil underneath. The rate at which soil becomes destructured depends on the soil itself, the amount and timing of play, and the weight of machinery such as mowers used in maintenance.

Regular thorough use of machines capable of piercing through the compacted surface layer helps alleviate these problems. Frequent use helps preserve a vigorous turf with good root development, maintains some soil structure to produce the quick draining surface so vital for sports turf.

On very fibrous turf such as exists on some fairways, regular aeration helps water to penetrate the fibrous layer, improves aeration which, in turn, helps breakdown the fibre to some degree. Drought resistance can also be encouraged through improvements in root growth.

Aeration units are also of value for other special purposes. On new grounds with very infertile soil or on sandy, drought-prone fairways, additional organic matter such as dried sewage or Fenpeat can be helped to integrate with the soil through loosening or opening up the surface with aeration prior to application. Similar effects can be achieved following sand applications on heavier soils. Aerators are also useful for loosening the surface soil prior to renovation. Hard pans existing below the immediate surface may also be broken up to some extent by deeper piercing or sub-aeration units.

Machinery Available

The following main types of aerator are available:–

(a) tractor-mounted units and trailed versions hauled by tractors
(b) tractor-mounted Verti-Drain machine
(c) tractor-mounted units that cut continuous slits or relieve compaction with a shallow vibrating mole attachment.

In most cases, tines of different design are available to meet various requirements, e.g. diamond-shaped slitting, chisel or solid for routine aeration and deep piercing, hollow or spoon tines for use where severe compaction exists or to help the incorporation of amendments into soil. The tines are mounted and, in some cases, spring-loaded so as to minimise turf tearing in use. Penetration from 100–150 mm is the normal range, though some heavy duty units achieve 230 mm. A Verti-Drain machine is available penetrating up to 450 mm which also combines tine movement in the soil to obtain positive compaction relief.

When to Aerate

Fairways need regular aeration, and treatment at least once a month, or preferably every two weeks, during the autumn and winter should be the aim. After a dry summer these areas often require more intensive spiking once showery weather develops in autumn to open up the turf, allowing better penetration of moisture to aid recovery growth and to encourage deep rooting in the turfgrasses. On severely compacted traffic routes and walk-offs from greens and tees, it may be necessary to Verti-Drain the area in the autumn to relieve the compaction.

After Aeration

Depending on ground conditions, slight turf tearing or lifting may arise where the tines penetrate. Whilst growth is still occurring, normal gang mowing will often suffice to correct this. Heavy rolling nullifies any benefit from aeration.

TREES ON GOLF COURSES

Many golf clubs carry out extensive tree planting programmes with the object of improving appearance and providing shelter. Carefully sited trees are also used to affect golfing characteristics. The choice of species should receive the same attention as the choice of site. Using unsuitable species will give disappointing results. In many cases the defects may not be noticeable for many years. Large forest trees such as oak, chestnut, elm, beech and sycamore do not reach any substantial size for 50 years or more and often live for several hundred years. The correct choice of species in the correct site can provide pleasure to generations of golfers yet unborn. The incorrect choice can prove a waste of time, effort and money and be a source of irritation until eventually removed. Where medium to large scale tree planting schemes are involved it is essential to seek professional advice.

There are perhaps in the region of 1,700 tree species with innumerable varieties which could be grown somewhere in the British Isles. There are many different points to bear in mind in deciding what type of trees to plant. One of the first considerations must be the size. It is completely pointless planting large forest trees a few yards away from a green or in any other spot where space is restricted. In such situations as soon as the tree has become reasonably well established it will be necessary to either cut it down or, worse still, prune it back severely, destroying its appearance. Where space is available, however, it is well worthwhile planting forest trees. The trees listed below will all reach at least 15 metres, with good specimens perhaps reaching up to 30 metres or more.

Acacia – *Robinia pseudoacacia*
A reasonably hardy tree though it prefers open, sunny situations. It is tolerant of industrial pollution. Deciduous, the tree is of a graceful, open habit with feathery foliage and produces slightly fragrant, pea-like flowers in July. Light soils are preferable – either neutral or slightly acid in reaction. It tends to be rather shallow rooting and grows quite quickly in the early stages.

Ash – *Fraxinus excelsior*
A very hardy tree which will withstand industrial situations and exposed positions. Again, a graceful tree of open habit with pinnate foliage. It will grow in most soils producing an extensive root system. It has a tendency to shed branches and so should not be planted in the vicinity of car parking areas.

Beech – *Fagus sylvatica*
A hardy tree and one of our most beautiful native large forest trees with smooth grey stems, graceful habit, delicate foliage in the spring and good autumn colour. The beech requires a well drained soil and though it grows naturally on chalk or over limestone, it will also tolerate acid soils. Young trees grow well in shaded situations. Several different forms are available including ones with purple foliage which are particularly attractive. Beech hedges are also very popular.

Cedar of Lebanon – *Cedrus libani*
An evergreen which grows best in the warmer parts of the country and prefers a sunny situation. It is unsuitable for areas with air pollution problems but where it can be grown it makes a magnificent specimen tree, flat topped with tiered branches and dark bluish green needles. Though it will grow on a wide range of soils it is best in deep neutral loam. The related blue cedar (*C. atlantica glauca*) is also a good specimen tree and will grow in similar situations.

Hornbeam – *Carpinus betulus*
A hardy deciduous tree suitable for both shaded and windy sites. Sometimes mistaken for beech though the leaves are much more toothed. Tolerant of site but usually grows on clay or chalky soil.

Horse Chestnut – *Aesculus hippocastanum*
A hardy tree with large leaves. The latter can be a nuisance in the autumn, the leaves collecting on fairways and, of course, in gutters and drains of buildings. The common horse chestnut produces the 'conkers' which attract children though there are sterile forms such as 'Baumanii' and hybrids such as *carnea plantierensis* which do not produce chestnuts. The pink flowers of the *carnea* hybrids are particularly attractive. It generally prefers a deep loam and not too exposed site.

Limes – *Tilia* sp.
Large, attractive, hardy, deciduous trees. Common species include *T. cordata*, *T. X europaea*, *T. petiolaris* and *T. platyphyllos*. There are some problems with these trees. Species such as *petiolaris* are narcotic to bees and *X europaea* or the common lime sometimes causes problems as it attracts aphids which then cause the leaves to exude sap and so it is generally best not planted around car parking areas. The trees are quite tolerant as to soil type but prefer a deep loam.

Acers
Norway Maple – *Acer platanoides*
This is a hardy deciduous tree which is reasonably tolerant to air pollution. It tends to be similar in appearance to the sycamore but the leaves are more noticeably toothed. Happy on most soils but best on light, well drained loam.

Silver Maple – *A. saccharinum*
Again, a hardy tree which is reasonably tolerant of wind and pollution and also has good autumn colour. It has similar cultural requirements. Both these species along with sycamore can produce problems in the autumn because of the accumulation of large leaves.

Common Oak – *Quercus robur*
Very hardy, a broad-headed and rugged tree which is one of the longest lived of our native species. Does well on heavy soils and is best transplanted when small but often requires protection from rabbits at this stage.

Durmast Oak – *Q. petraea*
Resembles the common oak but replaces it in wetter areas, particularly in the west of the country. It also tends to withstand exposure rather better.

Holm Oak – *Q. ilex*
One of our finest evergreen trees though it is best suited for milder areas of the country. It is suitable for coastal areas though sea winds may stunt its growth. It can also be grown as a hedge. Tolerant of acidity it will grow in a wide range of soils but does not transplant easily so container grown stock is best. Other species of note include *Q. rubra* (red oak), *Q. coccinea* (scarlet oak) and *Q. cerris* (Turkey oak).

Plane – *Platanus X hispanica (acerifolia)* also *P. orientalis*
Both are very attractive trees, the former being known as the London plane. They are particularly noted for the attractive bark which peels off in patches giving a mottled appearance

to the trunk. This is particularly conspicuous in areas subject to industrial pollution as the patches show up against the remaining blackened bark. They may be grown in all types of reasonably fertile soil but will not grow to full size in chalky soils and may become chlorotic in very shallow chalk soils.

Tree of Heaven – *Ailanthus altissima*
A fast growing tree, once established, the *Ailanthus* is particularly tolerant of atmospheric pollution. It produces very large ash-like leaves. It will grow on a wide range of soils.

Tulip Tree – *Liriodendron tulipifera*
This is a large deciduous tree but does prefer a sunny position and can be damaged by frost. It provides good autumn colour when the leaves turn yellow and is remarkable for the tulip-shaped, greenish yellow flowers produced in July. These flowers are only seen on the mature specimens. The tulip tree prefers a deep rich loam.

Walnut – *Juglans regia*
A hardy tree but one which should not be sited in areas particularly subject to late frosts. It is fairly slow growing but does produce a handsome tree with pinnate leaves. It can only be reasonably relied on to fruit in the milder parts of the country. It is, however, not particular as to soil type.

No list of trees can ever be complete and many good large trees have been omitted from the above. The examples given, however, can be considered for planting on golf courses, bearing in mind the points made. Large forest trees take many years to develop to maturity and so planting them is a long term project, and in tree terms this means perhaps 100 years or more. It was the foresight of our ancestors which produced the woodlands of today. The present day golf club is in a unique position to contribute to the landscape of tomorrow.

TREE PLANTING AND YOUNG TREE GROWTH

Trees not only add character and interest to our landscape, they also provide a habitat for thousands of species of plants, birds, animals and insects. Keeping this in mind, and the likelihood that, if left unhindered, the trees will be present for several decades at the very least, the initial choice of species and location when planting is of considerable importance. All too often unsuitable species are planted in unsuitable locations, usually with the best of intentions but with, at best, disappointing results, both from an aesthetic and ecological point of view. The species planted should, ideally, reflect those present or expected to be present in a native landscape. Native species have evolved with groups of birds, insects and plants which can live in close association and therefore have more ecological value compared with non-native species (known as exotics) which have been introduced to Britain and have far fewer associated species.

Location is also of extreme importance. Foresight is required to envisage what impact the mature tree will have upon the landscape and it must also be placed realistically to fit in with the requirement of the sports area in question. For example, it is pointless planting large forest trees close to a golf green where space is restricted and problems of leaf fall, shading and competition between tree and grass roots for water may develop. So, forward planning is all important, both in terms of species choice, related of course to size, and location.

The STRI can now offer advice on an advisory level for site appraisals, woodland management and tree planting with emphasis on the suitability of species for the golf course.

Size of Young Trees
Trees are available in various sizes for commercial planting, ranging from transplants of approximately 150–600 mm high, whips of approximately 450–900 mm to several categories of standards of 0.3–5.0 metres high. Although the larger standards appear stronger and more capable of withstanding damage and vandalism etc., they are far more costly, need to be staked and they do tend to be more prone to losses during the transplanting process. Transplants and whips on the other hand may be less advanced, but are cheaper, quicker to plant with no need for staking and tend to grow more vigorously in the first few years following planting. Small trees, however, could easily be swamped by high vegetation such as grass, bracken, etc. unless regular weeding is undertaken.

Bare Root or Container Grown?
Trees can be acquired as bare root stock or container grown. Container grown trees are generally more expensive and, once planted, the roots do have a tendency to remain within the original root ball rather than extending into the surrounding soil, which could affect overall stability. Bare root stock on the other hand is usually cheaper and more likely to form a satisfactory rooting system, but may be more vulnerable to damage during transport.

Pre-Planting Care
Care of trees in the transplanting stage is of utmost importance. Tree roots are very prone to drying out and/or frost damage during transport between the nursery and the final planting site, particularly so with bare root stock. The roots must be kept moist by covering them, for example, in black polythene filled with damp peat or newspaper. Straw can also help to protect against frost. All too often trees are planted with their roots already damaged or even dead through lack of care.

When to Plant
The autumn and winter months are most suitable for planting deciduous trees. Deciduous broad-leaved species should be dormant during the transplanting operation, i.e. between

autumn leaf fall and spring when new leaves appear. Generally, mid October to early December tends to be most suitable when the soil is moist but still relatively warm following the summer. During this period the roots are provided with the opportunity to develop whilst relatively little shoot growth is taking place. In spring, there is less time available for such root development before new leaves emerge, placing demands upon the root system for water and nutrient uptake.

Evergreens should also be planted over the autumn and winter, avoiding the colder, frosty weather in December, January and February. Generally speaking, October and March tend to be most suitable. For both evergreens and deciduous species, avoid planting in frosty or waterlogged soils.

The planting period of container grown plants is less defined and planting could, if necessary, be carried out at any time of year, although the above times are to be preferred.

How to Plant

Prior to planting, set aside time to design a planting pattern which indicates desired positions and provides adequate spacings between trees, etc. This will save valuable time and help prevent mistakes once the trees are on site.

There are a variety of planting techniques which can be adopted, depending upon size and number of young trees. Notch planting may be adequate for smaller trees such as transplants and whips which have a relatively small root system. The operation involves opening up the ground in an L, T or H pattern, providing just enough room for the roots to be slipped in before the surrounding ground is heeled down firmly.

For larger trees, container grown plants or difficult situations, pit planting is necessary. A hole should be dug of sufficient width to accommodate the roots fully extended with several centimetres to spare each side. The soil on the bottom and sides should be loosened and, at this stage, some leaf mould or well rotted manure, etc. could be introduced, particularly in low fertility, sandy soils. Correct depth of planting is vital. The tree should be planted to the same depth that they were grown in the nursery. Replace the soil carefully around the root ball, taking care to fill all air pockets and firm at several layers. In light, dry soils, aim to leave the backfilled material slightly lower than surrounding ground to encourage water collection. The opposite should be applied on heavy, wet soils.

Generally, trees which are higher than 1.2 metres will require staking. A suitable stake should be driven at least 300–600 mm into the bottom of the hole prior to planting with the stake remaining above-ground reaching approximately one third of the way up the tree, just below the first branch. Place the stake slightly off-centre and facing prevailing winds. The tree should then be tied a few centimetres below the top and a similar distance from the bottom of the stake using one of the variety of proprietary ties available for this purpose.

Immediately after planting, plenty of water should be applied to provide moisture and aid soil settling. If the soil is known to be infertile, then an application of fertiliser could be given to the surface or worked into the backfill. Guards may be required for protection against rabbits, etc. and to promote faster growth in the first year. Planting tubs can also give protection from the elements.

Aftercare

Following the tree planting operation, a certain level of aftercare is essential to maintain a healthy and vigorously growing tree. Young trees are susceptible to a variety of problems, including moisture stress, nutrient stress, physical damage and competition from surrounding vegetation. Newly introduced stock, particularly those planted in the spring months, or container grown trees planted over summer, should be watered regularly throughout the first year, especially during dry weather. Competition from surrounding vegetation for moisture, nutrients, light, etc. must also be reduced as much as possible. During planting, the surface vegetation immediately surrounding the stem should be removed and kept at bay for the first couple of years. An inverted turf, chopped bark or proprietary mulch mats will help to reduce weed redeveloping and hand weeding may be adequate to remove those which do appear. However, where a larger number of trees are involved, occasional treatments with a total herbicide will probably be more practical to keep the area weed-free. Trees do vary in their susceptibility to herbicide damage and so care must be taken to use only suitable materials. Use a herbicide approved by the Nature Conservancy Council which has been proven to be suitable in environmentally sensitive areas.

Longer Term Maintenance

The planting pattern chosen will determine to some extent the level of longer term maintenance. Whips planted at, say, 1.5 metre spacings will require thinning quite soon, perhaps five to ten years after planting and at regular intervals thereafter.

Standards should be planted at sufficient spacing to allow full development, although judicious pruning may be required to remove dead and diseased wood, as well as for shaping purposes.

The point to emphasise is that thinning and pruning should not be over-looked. All too frequently, management is simply forgotten, resulting in over-crowding and stunted growth. These operations must form an important part of long term maintenance.

Sources of Help

(1) Arboricultural Association, Ampfield House, Ampfield, Nr Romsey, Hampshire, SO5 9PA, Tel: Braishfield (0794) 68717 (Contractors and Consultants throughout the country are members of the AA).

(2) Forestry Commission Research Station, Advisory and Information Service, Alice Holt Lodge, Wrecclesham, Farnham, Surrey, GU10 4LH.

(3) Any Local Authority, Parks Department or Landscape Section.

(4) The Sports Turf Research Institute, Bingley, West Yorkshire, BD16 1AU, Tel: Bradford (0274) 565131.

SHELTERS FOR YOUNG TREES

Careful tree planting has always been an important aspect of maintenance of sporting areas such as golf courses to help provide shelter and to improve a site's general appearance. It is therefore essential that the growth of new trees is given every encouragement during the establishment phase following planting out. With this aim in mind, a fairly recent innovation in arboriculture has been the development of tree shelters. These not only provide protection from the elements as well as damage caused by animals, but they also encourage rapid early growth of the young trees.

Types of Shelter Used
The types of material used for tree shelters can vary but they normally comprise plastic translucent or transparent tubes of an appropriate diameter. These are anchored to the ground either by a small stake or steel rod which can be placed inside or outside the shelter. The normal height for a shelter is between 0.6 and 0.75 metres, although where protection against sheep is required then a shelter at least 1.2 metres high with a stronger supporting stake would be more suitable.

Benefits
A common problem when establishing young trees is the damage caused by various wandering animals such as rabbits, hares and sheep which can strip off large sections of bark. Tree shelters therefore provide a barrier which will discourage such damage and increase the chances of the trees' survival. These shelters can also reduce the water stress on the young trees during dry periods, thus minimising the risk of death following transplanting.

A further benefit is that most broad-leaved trees which are protected by shelters show more vigorous early growth when compared with non-sheltered trees. It has been reported that oak transplants will emerge from a 1.2 metre high shelter in two or three years compared with the five or six years taken to reach a similar height with conventional methods. On emergence from the shelter the rate of growth declines, the crown and branches develop rapidly and the tree shows little difference from others of a similar size except that it will be several years younger. Shelters also indicate the location of newly planted trees, thus enabling chemical weed control measures to be carried out around them without fear of damage.

Construction of Shelters
Sturdy nursery transplants some 200–500 mm tall with a single leading shoot can be protected using shelters. Any large side branches are best removed and the tree should be planted in the normal manner, leaving a loose, level surface so that the base of the shelter can be pushed into the ground. Any remaining weed vegetation should be removed from the prepared surface to prevent it from developing within the shelter and smothering the tree.

It is particularly important to erect tree shelters at the time of or immediately after planting, particularly where damage from local animals is likely to occur. If a stake has been used, then the shelter should be sufficiently large to accommodate this as well as durable enough to last for at least six years. The stake should be firmly hammered into the ground close to the young tree and the shelter then placed over the tree and firmly secured to the stake by a suitable tie. The base of the shelter should be pushed well into the ground.

Weed Control
The presence of a shelter will reduce the overall need for weed control measures around the trees, although spraying may be required for one or two years. If a tree is sheltered then additional protection need not be given when spraying, although the usual precautions against

drifting of the herbicide should still apply. If weeds are found to be growing inside the shelter and are restricting the growth of the tree, then the shelter should be raised and the exposed bases of the weed plants can then be pulled to the outside so that they can be subsequently included in any general control measures.

Removal of Shelter

It is normally recommended that the shelter should remain around the tree for five or six years. This will allow for the initial growth boost and protection needed by the young tree, as well as providing sufficient time for it to develop a healthy crown and strong stem capable of standing on its own. Most shelter materials last for about this period of time and in effect they can be left to disintegrate in situ although any encircling wire ties should be severed.

GOLF COURSES, WOODLANDS AND WILDLIFE

Introduction

Broad-leaved trees and woods are a major feature of our landscape, indeed almost the whole of the British Isles following the last Ice Age some 10,000 years ago was covered with trees. Birch, a main primary coloniser, spread from the South and from the North. This tree, with its fairly rapid growth rate and relatively short life span, was largely responsible for creating and producing the underlying soil conditions which later allowed longer-lived, slower-growing species to dominate. With Britain a predominantly forested country, the wildlife that initially colonised was mainly that preferring a woodland habit. Man's growing intensification of woodland clearing, together with his rapidly expanding technology with regard to the cutting tools used, has meant that our wildlife has had to display a great deal of resilience in order to survive these rapid changes brought about within the landscape. Species lacking such an intrinsic capacity to bounce back have become extinct or, at least, very rare. Britain's wildlife is subject to pressures from many sides.

The Role of the Golf Course

The golf course is well suited to providing a relatively safe refuge from the pressures of farming and other land use industries. Concern, however, has recently been expressed from various quarters, including the Royal & Ancient, who have stated that golf must not be seen as a selfish user of the land. Golf is, however, in a very enviable position with respect to nature conservation and could therefore be seen as a very caring game given appropriate sympathetic guidance. Indeed, many of the golf courses now visited by the STRI have adopted this type of ecologically based approach and are helping to maintain a balance of habitats on and around the course without disrupting the sport or its enjoyment.

There are, however, limitations as to how far one can go with conservation and ecological management on the golf course, as the needs and priorities of the game must be considered. One is aware that several private consultancy services are operating on golf purely on ecological grounds with little expertise in golf course management. If conservation or ecological management and golf are to coexist, it is essential that Ecologists develop an appreciation of the game and of the strategic requirements, traffic flow limitations and suitability of tree species with respect to their position on the course.

Important benefits, both ecological and aesthetic, can result as a consequence of planting trees and shrubs, though long lasting benefit would require a greater emphasis on management than is presently given on most golf courses.

An initial assessment of the course is the key to determining the present qualities and future possibilities. By way of a very detailed and comprehensive report, an Ecologist would be able to advise upon the most appropriate development programme for each individual course.

Many courses visited have had copses at intervals around the course of even aged trees, normally either birch or pine, both of which are pioneer trees or should represent the first colonisers to arrive in more naturalistic settings. Their rapid growth and turnover provide the basic physical conditions which encourage the establishment of the longer lived broad-leaved trees. These plantings often provide the sole source of screening or feature and will inevitably be very short lived. The fungus *Piptoporus betulinus* is a very aggressive parasite causing a heart rot within the wood of the birch trees. This fungus is relatively opportunistic, in that it enters the trees at any age, normally via wounds, ie. where branches have been lost. The result is a gradual deterioration of the copse until all the trees eventually die. This may, for birch, be between 30 and 80 years, depending upon the position, aspect and planting density.

The above is stressed, to demonstrate just how important it is to commence a forward thinking approach for the golf course and to consider a programme of increasing the habitat diversity of these areas.

Thinning and underplanting (enrichment) are vital tools in any woodland management. Gaps created artificially or naturally can be restocked with selected species. The gaps created after thinning should be of a diameter of at least the height of the surrounding trees. Groups of forestry transplants should be utilised, planted in the centre of the gaps. Weeding and protection are always important considerations following planting.

Creating the Woodland Edge

Many golf course woodlands come to a very sharp or abrupt end as high trees end and the semi-rough or fairway takes over. In such cases, but not in all, it may be possible to overlap a wood edge of broken shrub or understorey tree groupings. Not only does the wood edge provide a more gentle transition between grassland and woodland, but it has immense value ecologically; it screens the more untidy woodland floor from view, it helps reduce leaf litter and woody debris encroaching from the woodland out on to playing surfaces, and it also encourages understorey regeneration within the woodland centre. Obviously, individual site assessments are required in order to determine the merits for that site and the extent or quality of edge that can be facilitated.

TREE SELECTION FOR THE GOLF COURSE

A major consideration when selecting trees for the golf course must be that through their choice and placement the trees will be enjoyed. This enjoyment may be derived from their contribution to the immediate surroundings as a feature of the landscape, conveying a pleasing and reassuring sense of naturalness and also offering to the golfer an individually challenging strategic feature which by its, or their, position encourages thought for the well struck shot. On the golf course, the trees must fulfil several other secondary purposes, such as shelter, screening, hole individuality and safety. The individual physical site conditions may be very constraining and this may restrict the number of species and the choice of species available. On the other hand, however, there will often be a large number of potentially plantable species, thus confusing the selection process.

Indications from the Local Landscape

Throughout the country there are marked regional differences in the distribution of trees and it is important that anyone undertaking tree planting schemes observes and broadly conforms with the local regional character. This approach will ensure a measure of continuity for familiar aspects within the local landscape.

Those courses with a very exposed aspect may be almost totally without tree cover. Any attempt to plant trees without expensive natural or artificial screenings will meet with little success.

Maritime courses may be particularly problematic when it comes to enriching the course with appropriate screening or feature vegetation. Gorse (*Ulex europaeus*) has considerable potential in such situations. It has a very wide geographical distribution throughout the British Isles on acidic sandy heaths, often in very exposed positions. Its very thick leaves help to reduce the rate at which water is lost. Gorse is a major component of the roughs on many golf courses, often providing screens of up to 3 metres high. It does, however, require a fairly frequent programme of management.

A second shrub often overlooked is tamarisk (*Tamarix gallica*). This shrub is especially suited to coastal sites and is very tolerant of exposure from strong sea winds and high salt concentrations. The leaves of the tamarisk are reduced to small green scales, again a mechanism employed to minimise water loss and desiccation. It has very attractive ornamental properties and is cultivated for its feathery foliage and haze of pink flowers. In milder areas it can be found flowering from July to December. Its ornamental appeal, together with its hardiness and capacity to grow over a wide range of soil types, makes its especially suitable for golf courses on the South, South East and East Coasts.

Planting Native Trees

On inland parkland courses, a preferred way of selecting trees for a particular planting scheme is to identify the species growing well on comparable local sites. Planting native trees and subsequently managing them to assist their ongoing natural regeneration is to be greatly encouraged for several reasons. By their occurrence in the landscape, the common native trees can enhance our most characteristic scenery. Planting native deciduous trees may help to counter the continuing loss of deciduous woodland cover. Native species have a generally high value for wildlife, their use on the golf course will indirectly help to sustain habitats for insects, birds and small mammals, as well as associated plants which are much under threat in our changing countryside.

Unsuitable Introductions

Introduced trees and shrubs are those trees native to other parts of the world or to other parts of this country, e.g. beech is native to the milder Southern half of Britain. It has been introduced into Scotland, but in the remote or more exposed areas its growth is severely restricted. Rhododendron, a native of the Himalayan mountains, when planted in Britain, and particularly when further sheltered by tree cover, is able to totally dominate the understorey. Because of its alien character, acidifying properties, very dense and very tough leaves, few species of indigenous wildlife can tolerate it. Once in a woodland, an intense management programme may often be required to eradicate and control its growth.

Sycamore is another introduction. However, on the golf course, once established it can completely take over and alter a woodland's character. Again, this tree supports very little wildlife. When positioned adjacent to playing surfaces, the sycamore presents problems due to its large leaf, its rapid seeding and germination properties, and from the copious quantities of honeydew produced throughout the spring and summer from the very high populations of the aphid *Drepanosiphum platanoidis*. As dust collects in the sap, a blackening of the turf may occur. Cutting equipment may also be affected, especially when it comes to cleaning after use.

Certain trees, due to their general morphology, ie. poplars and willows with their water-seeking root systems and suckering ability, should be excluded from sensitive areas. The poplar during its life span is peculiar in that it matures from the inside to the outside, thus older trees become very brittle and can represent considerable danger from falling branches.

The horse chestnut on some courses may prove problematic due to its large leaf size which, if persisting on a grass sward, will result in weakening of the sward. This tree in the autumn is particularly prone to vandalism and attracts children onto the course.

There are several other factors which should be borne in mind before undertaking planting schemes. These include the size and spread of the tree, their position in respect of play, the physical characters of the climate and soil, and the hardiness and physiology of the tree.

Exercise Discretion

A degree of discretion is needed when selecting species of tree to plant on the golf course and the following guidelines may be helpful. Choose in general from the species which have been widely planted already, observe and aim to broadly conform with the surrounding regional character of the landscape. Ornamental species are better confined to suitable areas perhaps around the Clubhouse. Guidance may be derived from the knowledge of what grows well on comparable sites locally. It is important to visualise the effect of the final mature planting as a whole rather than as individual trees and at all seasons. Invasive introductions should not be planted near to any sites of value for nature conservation. Similarly, those with undesirable growth forms should be kept well away from fine turf areas.

It is important to consider whether the planting scheme would be most adequately served with a single specimen tree, perhaps an extra heavy rootballed standard tree or a grouping of a given woodland association. Both have their place depending upon the function intended.

Because of the amount of work involved, it may be worth considering professional contractual expertise. Any planting work to be undertaken should ideally be governed by a strict Specification of Works, which the Institute can provide upon request, so as to minimise disturbance on the course and protect adjacent existing habitats during the construction work.

HEATHER ON THE GOLF COURSE

One very pleasant aspect of playing golf or walking a golf course in August and September is the presence of heather in the rough or in the carry on our heath and moor-land golf courses. One of the best examples of a heathland course covered in heather would be Hankley Common Golf Club, near Farnham in Surrey. It is a great pity that nowadays heathers (*Calluna* and *Erica*) are disappearing on many of our heath and moorland courses.

There are certain factors which the vigorous growth of heather cannot withstand, they are as follows:

- Wear – trampling by golfers.
- Any alkaline material, such as lime.
- Competition from other plants, such as grass and bracken.
- Permitting heather to grow into a too 'leggy' type of growth.
- Being parasitised by the parasitic plant Dodder.

Traffic routes through heather areas should be restricted, particularly in the carry area. Under no circumstances should lime be used in areas where heather is growing or even nearby where lime dust can blow on to heather.

The growth of bracken can be controlled by the use of the chemical Asulox (Asulam) but care should be taken to prevent this chemical from contacting the heather plants. The chemical should be applied in the early frond (leaf) stage. In the past the control of grass in heather was not easy and the use of dalapon was recommended, but this chemical is no longer available. Nowadays, there are other herbicides which are very effective grasskillers, i.e. Clout (alloxydim-sodium). This chemical, if applied at the manufacturer's recommended rate, will kill the competing grass and leave the heather untouched.

The growth of volunteer trees and scrub can also compete very strongly with heather, e.g. volunteer Birch, Hawthorn and Pine seedlings. If such encroachment of trees and scrub takes place into heather areas, then they should be cut back and the regrowth from the stumps sprayed with a brushwood type herbicide.

To prevent heather becoming too 'leggy', the plant should be topped fairly frequently. There are two schools of thought regarding the best time to cut heather. One school of thought prefers early March so that the seeds of heather have truly set and will shed into the soil on cutting and generate new plants, and secondly the thinking which the Institute follows, that heather should be topped when the flowers have died back, i.e. in late autumn. If large areas of heather are present then these can be burnt periodically, but professional advice should be sought before burning is carried out. If heather is checked by Dodder, very little can be done to control this plant parasite.

Many golf course managers successfully transplant heather from areas outside the course on to carries, bunker banks and banks behind greens. Sunningdale Golf Club has used this technique successfully for a number of years. The technique is simply to cut thick turves (25–50 mm deep) of heather with a turf cutter and transplant them during February/March on to the new site.

To preserve the true heathland and moorland characteristics of golf courses the growth of heather should be encouraged by all golf clubs on such sites throughout the country.

CONSERVATION ON THE GOLF COURSE

As more and more land is developed for industry, intensive agriculture or residential estates, there is a growing threat to the habitats which support our native wildlife. Those who are concerned with our environment seek to overcome this threat in two main ways.

Firstly, they conserve such habitats by limiting man's activity to varying degrees in strategic areas. This is achieved by designating certain areas as Sites of Special Scientific Interest (SSSI), Areas of Outstanding Natural Beauty, Nature Reserves and National Parks, etc. This approach can, of course, also be practised on any natural or semi-natural site even if it is not given a special title – this has been the case on many of our motorway verges.

The second approach is to turn areas previously unattractive to wildlife into more appealing areas by creating suitable habitats. This may involve such operations as constructing marshy areas, increasing the floral diversity in grasslands and the use of native species in tree planting schemes.

Golf's Responsibility

Golf courses are very important elements in the conservation picture for a number of reasons. Unlike most other sports, the game actually requires a degree of semi-natural vegetation to provide the rough and other opportunities for conservation exist in the areas between holes. Figures from 1973 suggest that the total amount of golfing rough in the UK amounts to nearly 500 km^2 which is something like half the total area of National Nature Reserves.

Golf courses are spread fairly evenly over the whole country compared to the National Parks which are concentrated in the less populated, upland areas. Many types of landscape are represented on golf courses from coastlands and moorlands to heathlands and parklands, not to mention marshlands (some of which may occur in undesirable places!). Unlike Nature Reserves, golf courses do not tend to attract egg snatchers to the nests of rare birds or flower pickers to endangered patches of orchids. Finally, golf courses also have the advantage of being fairly permanent barriers to development while they themselves are part of the development process, providing recreational facilities for a society which seems to generate more and more leisure time. So, golf courses have an important role to play in conservation and are likely to be encouraged to face up to this responsibility even more in the future.

Getting Started

Some Clubs have already had to start thinking about these issues, having been designated SSSI's. At the last count, there were 84 golf courses so. Others may wish to initiate the process themselves and their first move should be to contact the Nature Conservancy Council or the local County Naturalist Trust. With the help of these groups the potential of each course can be examined and a management document drawn up to outline which species should be encouraged and how this can be brought about. Their support and advice will be vital as some aspects of the conservation work may be regarded as controversial by some club members who may for instance have a favourite cherry tree or conifer thicket on the course. Local Naturalist Trusts can also prove to be a very helpful source of voluntary labour for clearing and planting jobs.

Conflicts and Benefits

In drawing up the management document most clubs will find that it is only the management of the rough areas which are involved. However, in some cases operations such as weedkilling or worm control may be restricted or completely ruled out on the fairways. In such instances conflicts begin to arise between the objectives of producing a good golf course and conserving wildlife. Such conflicts should be few and far between however and can generally be resolved by negotiation between the club and the conservation body. In fact, there are likely to be more mutual benefits than conflicts – the conservation body gains valuable land while the Golf Club will normally receive the results of surveys showing the local flora and fauna. This can be of great value when undertaking any course alterations or tree planting schemes. Knowing which tree species are native to the area can mean a lot of money being saved by avoiding the use of species which will not survive on the course. The Club will also end up with a conservation policy which will encourage wildlife and add to the course's attractions.

The Need for Positive Management
In nature grasslands tend to become invaded with low scrub vegetation and in time, without interference from grazing animals, they become heathlands. These can then be invaded with pioneer tree species such as birch, hawthorn, ash or sycamore and eventually become woodlands. If a Club wishes to halt the development of this process at any one stage, it will be necessary to carry out some maintenance to eradicate the invading species. Habitats such as chalk grasslands are now becoming increasingly rare partly because rabbit populations suffered so much through myxomatosis – in the past their close grazing prevented any hawthorn bushes or other shrubs invading the grassland. Operations such as occasional mowing (after any desirable species have flowered and set seed) may be necessary nowadays, or chemical control of the invasive scrub may also be needed.

To maintain heathland vegetation any invading tree species must be kept out and this is commonly done by rotational burning which encourages the production of fresh heather growth while killing off the trees. However, this is not always practical on golf courses and pulling up seedling trees or chemical control (using the correct rate of a chemical such as glyphosate) is to be recommended. Regular mowing is another possibility though this will encourage regrowth from the cut tree stumps.

In conclusion, it is difficult to generalise on any particular management policies as these should all be tailored to meet each individual site's requirements following negotiations between the Club and conservation body. No Club should fall into the trap of copying the policies of the course 'down the road' as the potential of each site will be different.

Useful Addresses
The Nature Conservancy Council can be contacted at Northminster House, Peterborough, PE1 1UA or 12 Hope Terrace, Edinburgh, EH9 2AS.

The Society for the Promotion of Nature Conservation (the governing body for all County Naturalist Trusts), The Green, Nettleham, Lincoln.

CONSERVATION AND ECOLOGICAL MANAGEMENT ON THE GOLF COURSE

To the Ecologist or Conservationist the golf course represents more than a series of closely mown fairways, tees and greens. It is a wildlife preserve offering a variety of ecological habitats that have been spared the ravages of modern development and agriculture. A significant proportion of British courses do already boast the status "Site of Special Scientific Interest" (SSSI) and are instrumental in the conservation of rare and endangered species or habitats. Many others without such status still offer environments vitally important to the future survival of our native British wildlife.

The earliest golf courses were designed to form an integral part of the natural surroundings and were non-detractory or artificial. Unfortunately, many courses of today are losing the 'natural' appeal and are becoming lost in an unprecedented rash of manicuring and over-management at the expense of the natural beauty which the course previously enjoyed. Some golf course managers are, however, becoming more appreciative of the ecological potential and are looking at ways of managing the course sympathetically with wildlife and conservation in mind, and without detracting from or ignoring the game's needs and priorities.

Heathland Management

The light sandy soils of the heathland course are prone to nutrient leaching and, as a consequence, support a range of plants with specialist nutrient requirements. Managing the heathland course involves maintaining the low fertility by preventing organic accumulations and maintaining a relatively acidic soil pH. Heather, like gorse, is instrumental in reducing the pH of its surroundings. Its initial establishment requires a pH of below 5.0.

Heather and gorse can, without suitable management, become leggy in appearance. Suitable management procedures differ from natural heath and moorland systems, which includes grazing and burning to reduce the organic build up and to stimulate new growth. Management on the golf course must involve frequent physical cutting with the concomitant removal of litter. The cutting should, however, to staggered in a rotational sequence so that habitats remain in all stages of development. It is advisable to leave gaps free of any grass growth to allow the natural invasion and spread of heather. Heather is sensitive to trampling and to competition from neighbouring plants, like bracken and grasses. Traffic routes therefore should be controlled and restricted, particularly on the carry areas. Bracken and grass invasion is best controlled by the use of selective herbicides like Asulox (bracken) and Clout which will kill competing grasses without severely affecting the heather.

Invading scrub on heathland courses is primarily a consequence of increasing fertility, but wherever scrub invasion is a problem physical removal, by hand or by the use of a flail type mower, is the most ecologically sensible method. In more acute situations the chemical herbicide, glyphosate, may be considered.

Parkland Management
Tree Planting
On parkland courses tree planting programmes should concentrate on suitable species which lend themselves to the course environment. They should be native and of local provenance. Such plantings at optimum spacings and density will have better survival characteristics than the introduced alien and exotic species. In woodland plantings, native associations of canopy trees and under-storey shrubs will allow for the natural invasion by native woodland herbs which should eventually exploit the woodland conditions.

With new developments, native species provide the greatest ecological potential and therefore attract a rich diversity of wildlife. Young trees however, if they are to maintain continued growth and vigour, will require an ongoing maintenance and after-care programme. The trunk base should be kept free of weeds for at least until the canopy closes otherwise the competitive effects of nearby weeds will result in a retardation of growth.

Old woodland, often in a state of neglect, would benefit from enrichment and thinning programmes. This would include the planting up or filling of gaps to improve the density and woodland structure. Weak and dying trees may be selectively thinned, though it is worth bearing in mind that dead trees offer probably the greatest ecological value in a woodland. The dead or dying trees therefore should be left in the wood to rot down and perpetuate the natural woodland cycle of death and regrowth.

Wild Flowers
Wild flowers too have their place on the golf course. Many areas out of bounds to the game continue to be mown to the height of the fairway or semi-rough. Such areas could be sensibly managed in the style of traditional hay meadows. The management programme adopted would depend upon the type of meadow required and the flowering height; cutting would vary from only two cuts to six or eight cuts per year. A large range of native wild flowers are now available from nurseries, ranging from tall annual cornfield mixtures to the very low growing (prostrate) herbs which would suit certain applications immediately adjacent to green areas.

Water Features
Water features too add to the beauty of the course and can present a considerable challenge to the game. They represent valuable habitats and refuges for the vast majority of our native wildlife. The major problems associated with water features are silting and increasing acidification, nutrient enrichment and pollution due to fertilisers and herbicides, and the ongoing process of succession or terrestrialisation. Siltation is principally a result of sediment and litter accumulation causing the water to become shallow, this greatly increases the rate of succession. Alongside this, the accumulation of litter will increase the water's acidity and encourage anaerobiosis (oxygen starvation). De-silting operations involve infrequent dredging. The frequency varies due to site conditions and whether silt traps or other methods are employed to reduce the silting process.

With the continued deposition of organic material, water features may become highly acidic and, consequently, lose much of the wildlife interest. This can be overcome by the use of champagne chalk which, when applied, settles in the silt, encourages microbial activity and organic breakdown, and increases the water pH.

Terrestrialisation is the tendency of any water feature to undergo a successional change from the aquatic phase through to fen, scrub and finally woodland. Suitable ecological management to prevent this involves stopping the succession at a desired level and maintaining this in terms of the desired management objectives, which, on the golf course, include preserving an attractive and challenging feature whilst still providing the ecological and wildlife requirements. Water features should maintain a balance of open and sheltered water. The control of emergent plants is usually concentrated around the shallows and outer margins, and is therefore usually possible from the banking. Unfortunately, this zone is the most ecologically interesting and so care should be taken to minimise disturbance.

Methods of controlling the rate of growth and spread of emergent vegetation include the use of containers or the creation of artificial shallows in deep water, either of which will restrict root development.

In established ponds, the frequency of management should be anticipated as every six to ten years in the lowlands or ten to fifteen years in upland regions. Both physical and chemical methods can be employed for the control of vegetation. Physical methods involve cutting, digging and raking or the use of chain scythes. It is important that all debris be collected and laid on the banking for at least two days to allow the wildlife time to migrate back into the water. Chemical herbicides can, if correctly applied, be a valuable aid to water management. Problems arise when the herbicide which is deemed suitable for a particular target weed also has the capacity to affect the growth of non-target or desirable species. Correct timing of application is important, and any plants killed should be removed from the water.

It is clear that as more 'natural' habitats are lost to developments of one form or another, the golf course will assume an increasing role in the conservation of Britain's natural heritage. Many courses are now adopting a more ecologically sensible management approach and it is hoped that many more will follow suit.

BRACKEN: FRIEND OR FOE ON THE GOLF COURSE?

Introduction
Pteridium aquilinum, or bracken as it is more commonly known, is often thought of as a total undesirable on the golf course. This, in the majority of cases, is true.

Before passing sentence on this species however, it may be worthwhile considering its ecology from the point of view of both the prosecution and the defense.

Ecology
Bracken is an opportunist able to associate with quite diverse communities. It usually achieves dominance in gaps and clearings within open woodlands. It is normally suppressed as the tree canopy develops. Once dominant, its large leaves or fronds cast a dense shade which, together with the large quantity of litter, tend to totally suppress the growth of higher plant species.

Occasionally bracken-dominated stands may be ecologically quite important, forming communities which are relatively species-rich. Here, because the bracken effectively suppresses aggressive summer flowering species of both grass and flowers, and because the fronds are late in unfolding, vernal or spring flowering communities may be preserved. In the cleared copse areas or open wood/screen edges, bluebell, wood sorrel and possibly even rarer species may be found. The preservation of this flora may also have very positive benefits for the associated invertebrate fauna and so on.

Bracken-dominated stands do offer cover for the nests of several birds, though actual numbers recorded in bracken are much less than would be found in most other habitat types. On the heathland golf course the change in habitat type from predominantly relatively open heath grassland to bracken may result in a total loss of reptiles and snakes as the open basking areas are reduced.

The very invasive nature of bracken in Britain is normally thought to cause an alarming reduction in habitat quality, often resulting in the further fragmentation of already very small roughs, etc.

Management
Physical cutting and chemical spraying are the two most successful methods of bracken control. Both are expensive in resources or labour and have various problems associated with them. There is a need for continued or periodic retreatment to prevent its regrowth. Because bracken increases the nutrient status of its surroundings, there is often a tendency towards its replacement with fast growing, weedy species rather than the slower growing, desirable flora.

Before any management work is undertaken in areas of bracken invasion, an ecological appraisal would be useful to fully evaluate the ecological potential of the communities present overall.

A five-year programme of eradication involving both physical and chemical control may be most successful, with chemical control methods being adopted in the first and fifth years. The careful use of asulam has proven to be very effective in bracken control. Spray drift will, however, kill underlying vegetation. This is particularly important in heather dominated communities. The dicamba-based herbicides are also effective and are less aggressive to the understorey. Dalapon and dichlobenil, also approved, will kill underlying perennial grass species. Spraying should be carried out during calm, still periods in June once the fronds have fully opened.

Physical control should concentrate upon cutting or physically lifting and should be carried out through June/July when the nutrient reserves in the rhizomes are low.

Summary
Whether judge or jury, prosecutor or defence, a site evaluation to determine all the relevant facts should be a prerequisite before embarking upon an expensive programme of bracken eradication.

SECTION 5

BUNKERS

SAND BUNKER CONSTRUCTION AND MAINTENANCE

Sand bunkers have given rise to much discussion, often heated, from the earliest days of golf and long may they continue to provoke argument. However, no-one disputes that well placed, properly built and regularly maintained bunkers, be they on fairways or at greenside, can make an otherwise uninteresting hole a challenge to be conquered.

There are no set limits for the size and shape of bunkers. Their dimensions result from the architect's requirements and perception as to how a particular hole should be played. Their primary function is to exact a penalty for a badly hit shot and design, construction and maintenance must keep this in mind.

Bunker design must relate not only to the architect's concept of its strategic and visual impact at a hole, but also to soil type, degree of exposure, natural land contours and have due regard to future maintenance and costs.

Links
On a seaside course drainage will usually be good and there are no real worries about excavating to shape a bunker and creating a pond instead. Indeed, within reason, depth can help from a maintenance viewpoint since we need to minimise wind effects blowing out the fine dune sand that is most commonly used as fill. By the same token, such bunkers need to be narrower, though they should always allow a full back swing of a club.

Depth helps too in limiting the height of build up at greenside bunkers, which have often to be constructed in the traditional and expensive way, with turf. This involves establishing the rear line of the bunker, excavating a flat, level foundation and then building up a wall of old, preferably fibrous turf cut 600 mm x 300 mm x 50 mm thick. The turves are then built up like a brick wall with bonded joints, each layer of turf set back slightly from the edge – in other words 'revetted'. Sand should be well packed behind the turves in order to produce a solid, stable face to the bunker which lies at a slight angle, though more nearly vertical than is practicable with other forms of construction. Vary the outline of the bunker top but always aim for a gentle slope, easily maintained to the very edges with modern, wider cut surround mowers.

Always allow for a definite 'surround' to a putting green – the contrast between green surround and fairway heights of cut is pleasing, sets the green off to perfection and the slightly longer grass of the surround area is much less susceptible to drought effects which arise as sand splash from the bunkers builds up with time.

Bunkers such as the above are expensive to build, especially with regard to the amount of turf required for the wall and time spent in construction. However, on links this is the only satisfactory method of construction, especially for bunkers that face south-east around to the south-west aspect, i.e. those more exposed both to wind and hot sun. With a more northerly aspect, it is sometimes possible to use turf rolled over the bunker face and brought part way down the bank, though always on a sufficient depth of good sandy loam topsoil.

Inland

Here different problems are encountered, from intractable, impermeable subsoils which nature never intended to be free draining, to gravels and chalky soils where stones or subsoil continually work up into the sand. These place constraints on the form of construction but bring advantages too. On poorly drained subsoils, bunkers must be built up rather than excavated deeply into the ground. Using selected fill to build up the rear mounds, the problems with stones working into the sand can be minimised, as can problems with drainage, since the floor of the bunker may only be a matter of 230 mm or so below general ground level and in normally freer draining upper soil layers. However, pipe drainage is required too. The face and the sand thereon are much more visible to golfers, and architects can indulge the fashion for larger, flat expanses of sand and, in turn, the greenkeeper can resort to mechanical rakes for maintenance, since the shallower sand areas are much better suited to entry and exit at varying points, minimising damage to the turf edges.

Drainage

During construction of any bunker consideration must be given to external as well as internal drainage. Sloping fairways and surround areas will inevitably shed heavy rain as surface run-off, particularly as routes that are used by golfers on approach areas and out to the next tee become hard-packed, reducing natural infiltration of water. Areas around bunkers, particularly to the front and higher side, need careful shaping during construction since the bunker is required to gather the badly struck shot while preventing an influx of water every time it rains, washing out sand, eroding the soil face and edges and adding to drainage difficulties. In most cases a shallow grass swale (grass hollow) around the front and sides, which are most affected by run-off, serves the purpose well, shedding surface run-off to the lower side of the green and, if possible, away from the route that the golfers will use to reach the next tee. In some situations bunkers that are behind or to one side of a green on steeper sloping sites can be protected with a catchwater drain on the higher side – gravel filled to within 50 mm of the ground surface and then topped up with coarse sand.

Internal drainage must be positive. First, shape the bunker floor and, for longer wrap-around bunkers, grade evenly to a central low area the length of the bunker. Those of smaller dimensions may simply be graded to one low point near the front edge. Introduce plastic perforated pipe drain, minimum size 80 mm, laid centrally in a shallow trench through the lowest point and lead the drain away at a minimum fall of 1 in 200 to a positive outlet, such as a suitable fairway drain, ditch or stream. Soakaways should be regarded very much as a last resort and always sited in the rough, preferably on a down slope.

The drain pipe laid in the trench will be surrounded with 8–10 mm gauge clean, hard gravel aggregate, this being brought up to bunker floor level. The gravel must then be covered with a suitable material to prevent ingress of fine sand which would otherwise rapidly work down into the gravel and eventually silt up the pipes. Years ago, it was common practice to cover gravel in trenches with a fibrous, thinly cut, upturned turf or perhaps strips of hessian sacking. Today's approach is to use geotextile fabrics that combine strength, permeability, durability and which are relatively cheap. These too will eventually clog with sand – there is no perfect solution – but, if the correct weight of fabric is chosen initially and properly installed, they will last for years. The fabric may be laid as a strip overlapping the trench by 150 mm either side and well tucked into a slit in the clay base. Where subsoil or stones work up into the sand to cause problems, the geotextile fabric can be laid over the whole base of the bunker, ensuring that free edges are well tucked under surrounding turf and that the slopes at the back and front edges are adjusted to an easy gradient that will retain sand on the smoother, more slippery surface of these fabrics. Sand depth is critical and must be checked and topped up regularly, maintaining at least 100 mm over the bunker floor.

155

Maintenance

Raking – Daily raking by the greenkeeping staff is the ideal to aim for, maintaining a loose sand top over a firmer base with the sand well raked up the face and rear edges. This is especially important in narrower links bunkers and the pot bunkers that are almost exclusive to that windy environment. The sand must form a shallow central depression which will gather the badly placed shot, yet will still allow sufficient room for back swing and at least the prospect of recovery. On an inland course with flatter, more open bunkers the main dangers lie in determining whether the ball is actually in the hazard or not, particularly now that mechanical rakes are in vogue. It is all too easy to destroy the bunker lip on the approach side entering and exiting with a mechanical rake and none too easy to draw sand up the face or into the lip with such an implement. This often results in an overhung lip and too little sand on the face. Indeed, power rakes are only really effective over larger, flat areas and the operator should hand rake up the faces and into the edges separately.

Weed Control – Raking will help control most weeds if carried out regularly enough. Occasionally there are problems with creeping weeds and grasses, such as clover, sedges and couch grass, even creeping bentgrass, and chemical control is an option to consider. There is certainly no place for persistent total weedkillers used on the sand – splash out and sand contaminated with the chemical can easily be carried out on golf shoes to scorch and damage surrounding turf.

Use non-persistent total herbicides with either contact action, such as paraquat or diquat, or translocated action, such as glyphosate, which will do the job and which are rapidly inactivated in the sand. The practice of using such chemicals to check grass growth around the edges of the bunkers is very unsightly and to be deplored. For this purpose, use a power edger or strimmer to trim back longer grass several times through the growing season and an edging iron annually to re-define the sharp edges.

Conclusion

Bunkers should be well constructed so that they drain freely, be kept well supplied with sand which is clean, of the correct size range and preferred colour. A sufficient depth of sand should be maintained and regularly raked throughout the year, whilst edges are kept neatly trimmed in the growing season.

BUNKER CONSTRUCTION

Bunker design must relate to the architect's concept of their strategic and visual impact at a hole, and also to soil type, degree of exposure, natural contours of the surrounding land, as well as future maintenance and costs.

Inland Sites

On inland sites, especially where impermeable clay subsoil exists, drainage must have priority. Ensure that external ground contours are shaped so as to shed surface water run-off around the bunker. This will vary according to site from a gentle rise to the bunker lip of some 25 mm, to a carefully shaped shallow grass swale around the front and sides most affected by run-off.

On poorly drained subsoils, build up, rather than excavate deeply into the ground. The base need be no more than 150 mm below general ground level to minimise difficulties achieving a suitable drain outlet. Shape the bunker floor to provide a uniform fall to a drain running the length of a larger bunker, or to one low sump point from which an outlet drain can be provided.

Pipe drains – clayware or perforated PVC – should be laid centrally in a drain trench some 230 mm below the bunker floor, and with a uniform fall of not less than 1:200 to connect with a convenient outlet drain. Backfill the trench with clean, hard stone aggregate, 8-12 mm gauge to subsoil formation level, and make evenly firm.

It is essential to stop finer particles from the bunker sand filtering through to rapidly block up the pipe drains. In the past, upturned fibrous sods or old sacking were used to cover the gravel. Nowadays the trend is to use a geotextile membrane, taking care to choose one of a suitable grade (consult suppliers of e.g. Terram, Typar, Lotrak). The fabric should be cut to overlap each side of the trench by 150 mm and then be firmly fixed into the subsoil, pushing the free edges into a 75 mm deep slit and firming in.

At sites where the bunker floor is gravelly, or is the type of subsoil which works into and quickly contaminates the sand, it is worth using the geotextile membrane over the whole base of the bunker.

Provide 150 mm firm depth of topsoil over surrounds and bunker banks to ensure satisfactory grass growth. Allow for a definite 'surround' to a putting green. The contrasting heights of cut set off the close mown putting surface to advantage, and the intermediate height of surround turf is much less susceptible to drought effects (inevitable as sand splash builds up).

Ensure that slopes to banks and surrounds near bunkers are graded and finished with smooth, easy contours that allow maintenance with modern triple-cut mowers.

Links

On seaside or naturally sandy soils, drainage will usually be satisfactory and, within reason, depth can help minimise wind blow of the finer dune sand commonly used for filling. However, check the winter water table level of the chosen site, and keep well above this if possible. Such bunkers need to be narrow to check wind erosion, though they should always allow a full back swing, and this requirement must be taken into account when raking and maintaining such bunkers.

Depth helps limit the height of greenside bunker mounds, the faces of which are still often stabilised in the traditional, expensive, though very satisfactory way by building a turf wall.

The leading edge of the bunker is established and a flat, firm and level foundation is prepared. Build up a wall of old, preferably fibrous turf (weed and weedgrass-free, links-type grass) cut 600 mm x 300 mm x 50 mm thick, laid (grass side up) in courses with bonded joints. Each course of turf should be set back slightly from the edge of the previous course to form a stable, 'revetted' face, 2:1 or steeper to suit the design. As the building proceeds, pack sand firmly and solidly behind the 'wall', finishing at the surface with a minimum 150 mm firmed depth of sandy soil for establishing surround turf.

The above is a very satisfactory method of construction for bunkers facing south east around to the south west; exposed to both sun and wind. Bunkers with a more northerly aspect may be more satisfactory, with the face covered with 150 mm of sandy loam topsoil and turf 'rolled over' the top and brought part way down the face.

BUNKER SANDS

The selection of a good bunker sand is one of the more difficult tasks facing a Head Greenkeeper and one which requires a good deal of thought and attention. First of all, we must decide on the criteria which are required of this sand. From a golfer's view, the sand is required to be of a light colour such as white, light grey or tan to provide a sharp contrast with the surrounding turf and should be visible from a distance. If the bunker is to provide a fair hazard, it is important that when a ball lands in the sand, the surface is neither so hard that the ball bounces out of the hazard, nor too soft that the ball plugs to an excessive depth. The sand should be stable underfoot and, ideally, stacked to a high angle on the bunker face.

Specifications to meet the above requirements for golf bunkers have been developed in the United States. The recommendations state that sands are required to fall within a particle size of 0.25–1.0 mm diameter, with ideally 75% of these particles falling between 0.25–0.5 mm diameter. These sands are said to provide the best all round conditions in terms of ball lie, firmness of footing, minimum surface crusting, internal water drainage and ease of bunker maintenance. However, this does not say that any sand which falls within this range will be an excellent bunker sand. What it does suggest is that a sand falling within this range will have a better chance of being a good bunker sand, rather than one which falls outside this range. Particles greater than 1.0 mm in diameter should be avoided as the particles tend to lie on the green surface which could lead to slow play due to golfers removing visible grains from the putting line. Large sand grains also have the potential to blunt mowers and damage bottom blades. Particles smaller than 0.25 mm are prone to wind blow; can cause a reduction in drainage of water and where sand has a significant proportion of silt and clay, the sand is likely to set hard and form a surface crust.

On links courses, where bunkers are generally deeper and smaller than on inland courses, dune sand materials with particles in the range 0.125–0.5 mm are often used since they are generally cost-free and maintain the characteristics of this type of course.

Ideally, bunker sand should have slightly angular particles which provide a good lie and a firm surface. Round particle sands, especially of a single size, provide a soft, fluffy surface in which balls can become buried and on which it is difficult to achieve a firm stance for the recovery shot. Recent studies at Bingley have confirmed that very uniform materials, particularly those with spherical grains, should be avoided because of their instability and susceptibility to ball plugging. Stability will be improved if sands with greater than 60% of grains in the rounded or well rounded shape categories or highly spherical grains are avoided, though the main specification should be based on particle size distribution.

On any golf course it is essential to retain consistent playing characteristics between the bunkers, which can only be achieved by using the same sand both in each bunker and for topping up purposes. Avoid at all costs placing a good bunker sand over a poor bunker sand – it is always best to empty the sand from the bunker and replace it completely with clean material. Where different sand is used to top up, this leads to variable characteristics between individual bunkers on a course and consistency is lost. Fresh sand should be introduced whenever the sand depth has decreased below a minimum of 4–6 in. on the bunker floor or 2 in. on the face. Redistributing the sand from low areas to high areas will often suffice and actual topping up will be required only every three to five years.

For as long as there are bunkers on a golf course there will always be controversy over the size and shape, placement, need, type of sand used and depth. Low handicap golfers prefer one type of sand; higher handicappers another and, depending on local supply, the quality of bunker sand may not be good from the start. This article has aimed to qualify the criteria which are set out for bunker sands to provide the standards expected.

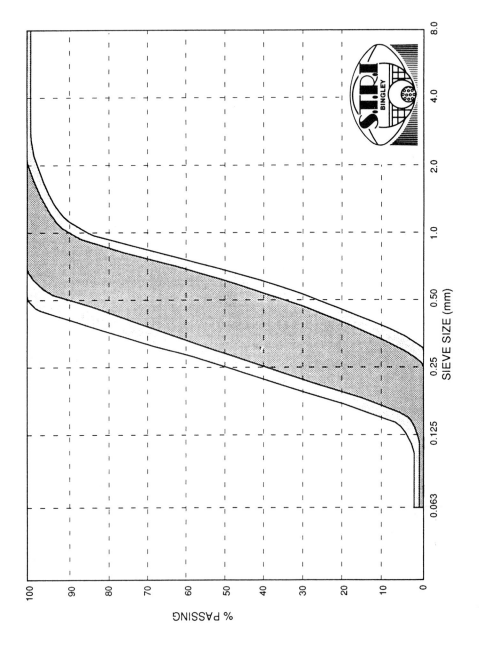

FIGURE 12: Grading curve defining recommended and acceptable limits of sand size for golf bunkers on inland courses.

SANDS FOR GOLF BUNKERS

Greenside and fairway bunkers form a fundamental part of golf course design. On inland courses bunkers should be constructed to give good drainage and certainly the ground contours should be shaped to avoid channelling surface run-off into the bunkers. Except in very free-draining sub-soils, pipe drainage should be installed below the bunker floor. The drain trench is usually filled with gravel and covered with a suitable geotextile membrane, which on difficult gravelly or unstable soils may also be used to cover the whole floor of the bunker to prevent contamination of the sand. The sand itself will usually have a firmed depth of about 100 mm minimum.

In selecting sand for an inland course there are a number of considerations:

[a] The sand must be free-draining and not clog, causing water to pond at the surface. The size of the grains is also an important factor in the case of wind blow and very fine materials should be avoided.
[b] The sand may be chipped onto the green and therefore it should be compatible with top dressing material, i.e. free from coarse particles and of low lime content.
[c] The sand should be a fair hazard to the golfer and neither set as a crust (a characteristic of sands with a high fines content) nor allow the ball to plug excessively after a direct ball impact from a high iron shot. This can happen with coarse rounded sands, and these can also be troublesome because of a lack of stable footing for the golfer.
[d] It is helpful if the sand is angular rather than rounded as this affects the stacking angle at the bunker face.
[e] For golf bunkers aesthetic considerations are important and generally tan, light grey or white materials are preferred.

On links courses, drainage is generally satisfactory unless there are water table problems. Because fine dune sands are generally used in bunkers on seaside courses it is wind erosion which is often the greatest problem. To minimise the effects of wind erosion, bunkers on links courses are relatively deep and narrow. Traditionally, the bunker face will have been stabilised by a wall of old fibrous turf sods laid to form a 'revetted' face of 2:1 or steeper.

161

SECTION 6

CONSTRUCTION AND DRAINAGE

GOLF COURSE ARCHITECTURE: SOME THOUGHTS

"A thing of beauty is a joy for ever", a line from John Keats' poem, Endymion (Book 1).

If you can say that of the Architect's work, then truly he has read the site and drawn from it all that it has to offer. He has handed down a legacy for which the next generation will be eternally grateful.

Sadly, the above is far from being the norm. Golf development in recent years has amounted to a rape of the British and Irish landscape. The reason for this might crudely be laid at the door of sheer ignorance. Two features of life as it is led today also have a bearing, and these are lack of concentration and living in the fast lane. Bring these two major ingredients (as part of your philosophy) to bear on the development of a site for golf and you have the recipe for another monument of horridness.

WHAT IS A GOOD GOLF COURSE?
The formation of 9, 18 or 36 holes born out of hours of walking a site, pondering, **concentrating**, working on and finally producing a layout which uses all the inherent characteristics of the site to the fullest advantage. Do not destroy what nature already offers. If it is offering an opportunity to create a unique golf hole, accept it thankfully.

Adjustment to existing levels may be necessary, let us say, to help with a sight line or perhaps to open up a majestic panoramic view beyond, but such adjustment should be kept to the absolute minimum.

Always keep in mind that the site is far more important than anyone involved in its development. It has been in existence for thousands of years and if you treat it with respect, it will respond in kind – the final outcome of the Works is likely to be successful. This is so because the natural features which you have found on the site are now at the very heart of the strategic and aesthetic qualities offered by the golf course and it is these which challenge and excite the golfer. The golfer never becomes tired of such a course, frustrated perhaps but he appreciates its fairness as well as challenge. While he/she continues to be surprised or deceived into taking the wrong club, they will return time after time in an effort to conquer.

WHERE IS THE STARTING POINT FOR THIS ADVENTURE?
Time on site is invaluable in order to become as conversant as possible with its strategic and aesthetic qualities.

Having established the best position for the Clubhouse, it is useful in these days of heavy play to have two fairly long starting holes of relative ease simply to get golfers away on their rounds. Thereafter, the holes should be formed and again fall into place as suggested by the site's natural features. The imagery of two par 3 holes, two par 5 holes and five par 4 holes on each loop of nine with a balanced yardage, etc. can lead to a very dull golf course. The desire of certain authorities in this respect is, to say the least, devoid of imagination. Imposing your will upon a **whole** site takes you down a very dangerous road indeed. You have now entered into the realm of tampering with nature and, as is widely recognised, nature always has the last laugh. The outcome could be a golf course exuding symmetry (a characteristic not to be found in nature) and therefore one with a very contrived appearance. As such, it is unlikely to stand the test of time.

While symmetry is not to be found in nature, harmony is. It is harmony which is the key to unlocking the secrets which the site offers. If the site is saying, yes, two par 3's or two par 5's in a row, then accept this concept. At the end of the day it will look natural and 'feel right' because the finished product will blend into the existing landscape in an imperceptible manner. This is fundamental to offering a course which "..... is a joy for ever".

The aim of the golf course architect amidst all of this is to offer a series of golf holes which provide a challenge to every class of golfer. Equally, as the golfer makes his/her way around the course, they should feel that each hole played is quite memorable in its own inimitable way. Do remember that length has very little to do with merit. Length is a detrimental aspect of many golf courses built today. Likewise, reliance on artificial hazards, i.e. sand bunkers around greens, has destroyed the real artistry of approach play.

THE PART PLAYED BY INDIVIDUAL HOLE DESIGN
The green is the focal point of the hole and should at most holes dictate play. Green orientation, greenside bunkering (if any), putting area (and falls), surround contouring and width of entrance all have a major bearing on the difficulty of individual holes.

Visibility of the putting surface is desirable, particularly at par 3 and short par 4 holes.

Natural hazards, e.g. ponds, streams, ditches and woodland or fairway bunkers can all influence the optimum route of play to the green. The shaping of the fairways also contributes to strategy and therefore playing interest. Informal edges between fairway and semi-rough leads to a blending in of through the green to the surrounding landscape. There are no straight lines on a golf course.

Tees need not be formed at an elevation higher than the architecture of the hole dictates.

Ultimately, easy maintenance is of prime importance, therefore when considering green and tee positions, shapes of fairways and width of landing areas, etc., traffic routes, walk-offs, proximity of trees, featuring of surround mounds, batters to fill or cut banks, areas and shapes of putting surfaces, width of green entrances, depth and shape of bunkers are among the many factors to be seriously considered by the Architect during the final preparations of his layout and individual green and tee drawings.

STRATEGIC AND AESTHETIC CONSIDERATIONS
Successful golf architecture depends on a complementary blend of these two essential elements.

Strategic design provides different options for playing a hole in accordance with the proficiency (and ambition) of the golfer with the objective of providing an equitable and enjoyable test of golf for all.

Inextricably linked with the strategic element, there is the aesthetic appeal of the golf course. The latter is greatly enhanced by using the natural features of the site, e.g. woodland, local topography (mounds, slopes, grassy hollows), gorse/heather banks, streams and ponds, etc. Existing flora, fauna and linking habitats remain untouched and indeed the ecology of the site may even be greatly enhanced by sensible planting schemes, etc.

CONCLUSION

Artificiality which often arises from unnecessary earth movement and level adjustment results in the delivering up of golf holes which are devoid of interest and genuine excitement. They may never come to maturity and more often than not remain an ongoing maintenance problem for the greenkeeping staff. This is not good golf architecture, it is design, and how sad it is to see so much of it throughout the land and beyond these shores.

As the sincere Architect walks the site for the umpteenth time utilising all his creative processes, listening to what the site is saying to him and using what the site offers, the end product is a golf hole or series of holes of which it can be said – "Its loveliness increases; it will never pass into nothingness".

CONSTRUCTION OF A SAND AMELIORATED GOLF GREEN

Attention to detail is essential in order to obtain a green with a make-up on which a good putting surface can be perfected.

Early Planning
On opening up a site, particularly one in situ, work must proceed steadily whenever soil conditions and/or time is available, with no delays occasioned by lack of materials. Early measuring up of areas involved, estimating for quantities of materials, receipt of representative samples of aggregate and sands with quotations, placing of orders and delivery of approved materials to site should be completed, therefore, preferably before the commencement of work.

Where the work is being carried out by direct labour no detailed specification (as would be essential for a contract) is required but it is useful to write out an outline of the various stages of the work. A drawing is of importance, showing existing levels which are used to establish the proposed finished levels related to surrounding ground levels, and for determining falls on pipe drains.

Timing
If the new green is to be formed on an area of the golf course not in play, the necessary work should be completed under dry conditions through the summer to permit sowing in August or turfing in early autumn. Where a green is to be constructed in situ, timing is more critical. The onset, particularly of inclement weather, demands that the work is started as early as possible in September to allow returfing by the beginning of November.

Method of Construction
The green is formed with a gravel/stone drainage layer blinded with coarse sand and tapped by an emptying pipe drainage system. Over the drainage layer is spread a special mixture, prepared off site, of topsoil and suitable sand, on which the sward is established by seeding or turfing. Because of the presence of the gravel/stone layer with emptying drains, the inherent drainage properties of the subsoil forming the green foundation and surrounding the green are of no consequence. The green can therefore be used to the maximum possible intensity throughout the year. This is a useful method to adopt on heavy clay sites.

Design
It is desirable that the green should be constructed to provide a minimum 500 m^2 of actual putting area so featured that at least 70 per cent of the surface can be used for pin space. The putting surface should have a general fall of between 1 in 50 to 1 in 100 in an appropriate direction and while featuring is provided within the general fall, formation of local low, moisture-collecting hollows should be avoided. Any mounds to be formed within the green surrounds should be landscaped to give them a pleasing appearance with slopes not exceeding 1 in 4, and their surfaces should marry in imperceptibly with the surface of the putting area and ground around the green. Mounds should be designed so they can be cut with sit-on triple mowers and little Flymo-ing or strimming is required.

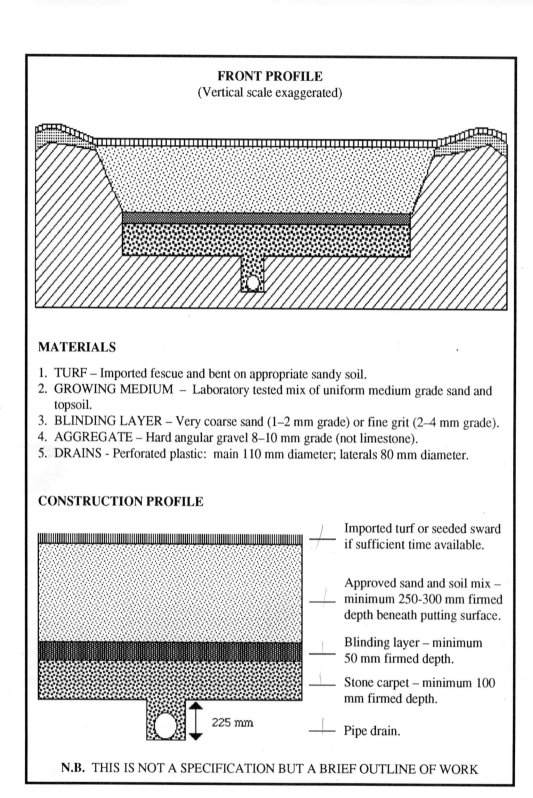

FRONT PROFILE
(Vertical scale exaggerated)

MATERIALS

1. TURF – Imported fescue and bent on appropriate sandy soil.
2. GROWING MEDIUM – Laboratory tested mix of uniform medium grade sand and topsoil.
3. BLINDING LAYER – Very coarse sand (1–2 mm grade) or fine grit (2–4 mm grade).
4. AGGREGATE – Hard angular gravel 8–10 mm grade (not limestone).
5. DRAINS - Perforated plastic: main 110 mm diameter; laterals 80 mm diameter.

CONSTRUCTION PROFILE

Imported turf or seeded sward if sufficient time available.

Approved sand and soil mix – minimum 250-300 mm firmed depth beneath putting surface.

Blinding layer – minimum 50 mm firmed depth.

Stone carpet – minimum 100 mm firmed depth.

225 mm

Pipe drain.

N.B. THIS IS NOT A SPECIFICATION BUT A BRIEF OUTLINE OF WORK

FIGURE 13: Golf Green Construction, Drainage Carpet Method

Procedure of Work

Turf removal

Where the green is being constructed in situ the turf is removed. While there is latitude regarding the width and length to which the turves are cut, it is important that it is cut thinly, i.e. at 12–18 mm thickness, thus removing a turf with as little fibre in its base as possible. The cut turf is laid out in a nearby convenient situation, preferably on polythene sheets to prevent it rooting into the soil or sward below. In many cases if in situ, turf will be dominated by *Poa annua*, therefore bought in fescue/bent turf will be necessary.

Grading

The topsoil is now carefully removed, avoiding subsoil, and, if it is suitable, stacked in a nearby convenient situation for re-use. The exposed subsoil is graded to provide falls and featuring as discussed above. In conjunction with this, the formation surfaces for proposed bunkers, the all important approach and surrounds are formed. If there is a deficit of subsoil, this might be obtained from a borrow pit in adjoining rough. Specialist equipment is required for the topsoil stripping and subsoil grading, and this would normally be hired with operator.

Drainage

An emptying pipe drainage system, suitably designed and consisting of agricultural clayware pipes to BS 1196:1971 or perforated plastic pipe to BS 4962:1989, introduced to a depth of, say, 225 mm into the subsoil formation of the green and immediate surround, with adequate outlet drain to a positive outlet. Within the area of the proposed putting surface the drains are backfilled with 8–10 mm gauge hard aggregate, e.g. gravel or stone, up to subsoil formation level.

A drainage layer consisting of 100–150 mm firmed depth hard aggregate and used to backfill drain trenches, and blinded with 50 mm firmed depth of suitable coarse sand, is then spread over the entire putting surface of the green and immediate surround.

Other pipe drainage

If pipe drainage is to be introduced into the bunkers, this is likely to be done at this stage, suitably backfilling up to bunker floor level, and covering backfilling with upturned turf or constructional membrane. The bunker drainage is connected to the green drainage system or led off to its own positive outlet. Where ground of higher elevation exists beyond the green, provide for introduction of a suitable catchwater drain(s) led off to a positive outlet(s) and suitably backfilled up to the surface.

Special soil mix

This is prepared by mixing a prescribed quantity of approved sand with a quantity of topsoil stripped off the green, or with a given quantity of imported topsoil if the original is inadequate. A tractor and bucket can be used to produce a rough off-site mix in the correct proportions, turning the heap several times, with final mixing being achieved by passing the initial mix through a screen, soil shredder or possibly mixing in a concrete mixer. To protect materials in periods of inclement weather, allow for adequate covering with polythene sheeting. The prepared mix is spread over the putting surface of the green and surround to provide an even and minimum firmed depth of 250 mm. In some cases, a proprietary brand of rootzone mix will have to be imported.

While approaches are in general treated similarly to the surrounds, serious consideration ought to be given to placing an even and minimum firmed depth of 150 mm prepared mix as spread over the green.

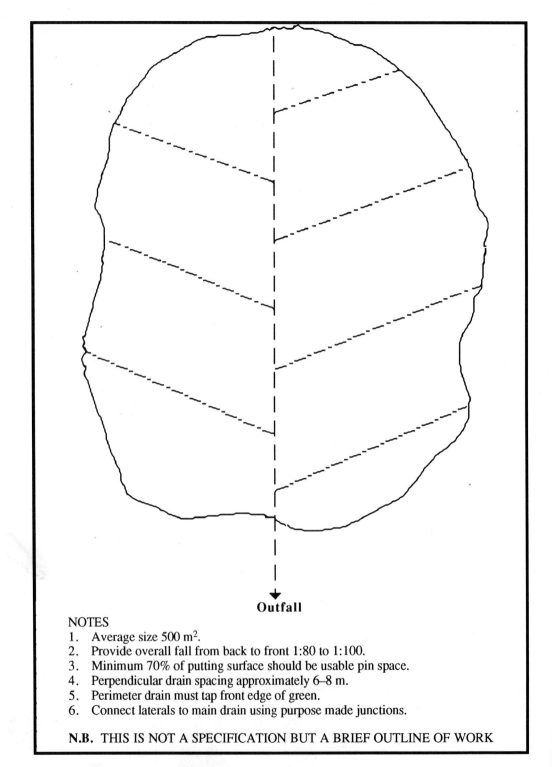

Outfall

NOTES
1. Average size 500 m^2.
2. Provide overall fall from back to front 1:80 to 1:100.
3. Minimum 70% of putting surface should be usable pin space.
4. Perpendicular drain spacing approximately 6–8 m.
5. Perimeter drain must tap front edge of green.
6. Connect laterals to main drain using purpose made junctions.

N.B. THIS IS NOT A SPECIFICATION BUT A BRIEF OUTLINE OF WORK

FIGURE 14: Schematic Plan of Golf Green.

Water supply
Allow for amending any existing water supply or introducing a new one, the work being done to the requirements of the local water authority and at an appropriate stage.

Establishment
Following spreading of the soil/sand mix, an adequate turf bed is prepared by alternate hand raking and heeling, a suitable fertiliser is evenly applied and the turf neatly relaid. On completion of turfing, roll once only with a 250 kg hand roller and top dress with approved sand at the rate of 3 kg/m², brushing the sand into any cracks, etc.

Examination of Materials and Soil Tests
For appropriate fees the Institute will examine materials for drainage prior to bulk purchase being made, and carry out the necessary mechanical analyses and hydraulic conductivity tests required to ascertain the proportion of approved topsoil and sand to be mixed together to give the required design drainage rates.

After Care
Whatever the method of construction, it is imperative to see the need for and to implement good initial maintenance. The main item in the programme is top dressing to perfect the levels, particularly on the putting surface and approach. Adequate quantities of compost which match the mix of soil and sand on the putting surface and approach should be prepared, stored under dry conditions and used as required to obtain the good putting surface which the golfer quite rightly expects.

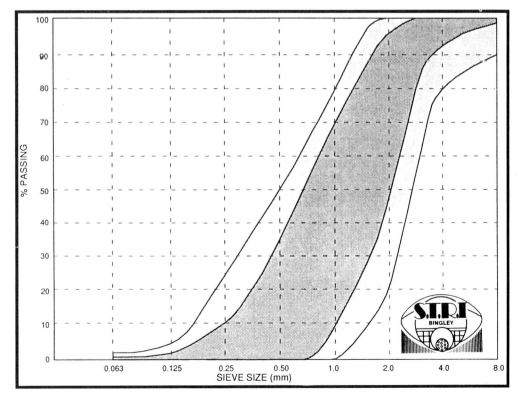

FIGURE 15: Grading curve defining recommended and acceptable limits of sand size for blinding a 5–10 mm drainage aggregate.

SANDS FOR GOLF GREEN CONSTRUCTION

A wide variety of sands are required for different aspects of golf green construction, drainage and maintenance. Particle size, uniformity of the size distribution, the resistance of the individual grains to breakdown by crushing and the chemical composition of the sand are usually the most important criteria in sand selection, although factors such as grain shape also exert some influence on the subsequent performance.

This article considers some of the principal purposes for which sand is required on golf greens and suggest particle size ranges that may be appropriate for these applications, whether lime is acceptable or not and the reasons for the specifications.

Soil Amelioration for Fine Turf Areas
Particle size range: 0.2–0.7 mm diameter. (See Fig. 8.)
Lime content: lime-free.

In the construction of golf greens by ameliorating soil with sand, the principal objective is to achieve a free draining rootzone mix which has satisfactory properties in terms of aeration and water retention. Addition of the right quantity of sand is vital and should be determined by laboratory analysis, but the selection of which sand is used is equally important. Uniformity in the size of the sand particles is essential: if the sand consists of material that falls into a large number of size categories all that will happen is that the finer grains will be forced into the gaps between larger particles, reducing the number of large pores. This will decrease the drainage and aeration potential of the rootzone mix.

The optimum size for the grains is a compromise between the high rates of aeration and drainage that a relatively coarse sand will give and the better water retention properties of a fine sand. Consequently, a sand with the majority of its particles in the range 0.2–0.7 mm diameter is advised. For most fine turf constructions a lime-free sand will be specified: this can however be relaxed for construction on links golf courses.

Blinding Layers
Particle size range: 0.25–2.0 mm diameter. (See Fig, 15.)
Lime content: high quantities should be avoided on fine turf areas.

Blinding layers are required in constructions where fine textured rootzone material is placed over a gravel carpet and for capping over the backfill of pipe drains. In both cases the objective is to prevent fine material filtering into the gravel. Downwards migration will occur, according to theory, if the finer overlying material is less than one-sixth the diameter of the gravel in the drainage carpet or the trench backfilling. Typically gravel will fall into the 5–10 mm diameter category and thus a general specification of sand for a blinding layer should be of 0.25–2.0 mm diameter material.

SANDS FOR CONSTRUCTION OF GOLF GREENS

It is generally agreed that the game of golf originated in Scotland, typically on the areas of medium-fine dune sand which are found along the east coast. Later, inland courses were developed using the native soils at the site and although many were of high quality, an increase in the popularity of golf and the amount of leisure time (giving more rounds per course each year), gradually exposed those courses where the native soil did not have adequate drainage. Thus for areas receiving high wear, particularly golf greens and to a lesser extent tees, the use of sand in construction has increased rapidly in the last twenty years.

In particular, research work financed by the United States Golf Association (USGA) throughout the 1950's and early 1960's was paramount in establishing the use of sand as a building material for golf greens. In 1960 this work lead to a USGA Green Section Staff publication outlining specifications for green construction and this was subsequently revised in 1973 to give the following main requirements:

[a]   A three layered construction (Fig. 13) involving a rootzone mix of at least 300 mm overlying a coarse sand blinding layer and a gravel carpet.

[b]   The rootzone mix should be compounded from locally available sand, soil and organic amendment to meet closely specified performance criteria for which laboratory testing is essential. The infiltration and transmission rate of compacted laboratory samples should be between 50-250 mm/h and ideally in the range 100-150 mm/h. The total porosity of the compacted mix should be between 40-55% and the volume of non-capillary pores, drained at a tension of 40 cm of water should not be less than 15%. The bulk density of the mix should be between 1.20-1.60 g/cm^3 and ideally 1.25-1.45 g/cm^3. The available water capacity should be between 12-25% by weight.

[c]   The topsoil mixture should ideally contain no particle larger than 2 mm in diameter. However, 3% particles >2 mm is permissible if most of these are smaller than 3 mm. The total soil mixture should not contain more than 10% particles >1 mm and no more than 25% particles <0.25 mm. In addition, the mixture should contain <5% silt and <3% clay.

As an alternative to a sand-soil mix over a gravel base, pure sand constructions have also been used, for example, the University of California have advocated sand constructions with 300 mm of sand over the native soil. The sand is chosen to have 85-95% of its particles between 0.1–1.0 mm diameter with over 60% between 0.25–0.5 mm diameter. No gravel drainage layer is used but pipe drains are usually added at approximately 3 m centres. However, where the parent soil takes water at over 6-12 mm/h, a pipe system may not be necessary if heavy rain and excessive irrigation are not a problem.

Pure sand golf greens have been built using other construction methods, e.g. with a gravel drainage carpet or as an enclosed system with an impermeable membrane. However, in Britain sand-soil rootzone mixes have generally been favoured to pure sand constructions because they give a less hard surface with lower management requirements in terms of nutrition and irrigation than sand greens. Sand-soil mixes must be to a high technical specification and there may be problems at sites where a good topsoil is not available.

171

TEE CONSTRUCTION AND ENLARGEMENT

Think Long and Hard

Tee building should not be embarked upon without careful consideration of a number of factors. In the first place tees were never simply constructed at a set distance from a green, they form an essential part of the architect's design and strategy for play at a particular hole relating strongly to line, good landing area and hazards on fairway and approach. With the incessant search for greater length on golf courses these days, it is never simply a question of building a new tee x metres behind the existing ones. Some courses are littered with sites of tees built with considerable effort and at no little cost by the greenkeeping staff only to be abandoned within a year or two when the Green Chairman whose project they were retires. It is also a sad but true fact that increased traffic on the course leads to extra wear on areas unable to support it. Therefore, tee changes which tend to disperse traffic are preferable to those which concentrate it.

Site

New tees should be reasonably close to the preceding green, certainly no more than 50 metres away. Drainage must be at least adequate, not so much from the tee point of view, which are normally slightly elevated and should not suffer ill drainage, but in order to maintain satisfactory access for players. Alternative routes to a tee are also valuable in helping spread wear and aiding sward recovery.

Sloping sites present their own special problems and a cut and fill formation will generally be more economical and also more stable than one built up by filling. Guard against surface water run-off from higher slopes on to such tees and especially take care that the surface does not slope towards the rear cut bank which provides no escape route for heavy rain.

Tees in the Wood

This is a favourite ploy of Committees with little appreciation of the maintenance problems created by such sites. Fearful of criticism from conservationist members, they are too timid in removing enough of the trees surrounding the site. Thus the tee may look attractive for a spell in summer over a year or two but it will be pretty awful in autumn and winter. The best grasses for tees have their natural environment on windy, open moor or links not the moist, airless and dark woodland clearing. Little wonder that in such situations the best turf fails to thrive, deteriorating into a soft morass of spongy annual meadow-grass and moss during winter or a dry, thread-bare and imperfect surface in summer. Grass species are versatile and several have adapted to the woodland environment but avoid using so-called 'woodland' seed mixtures. These grasses cannot withstand normal fairway cutting height, let alone that adopted on tees. If there is no alternative to a tee in a woodland setting, be bold in its construction. Remove enough trees and branches to allow good light on to the tee surface and an adequate flow of air. Avoid long, narrow formation and ensure that the clearing fans away at the front to avoid play concentrating on the tee centre.

Building

Construction work must be carried out when soil conditions are reasonably dry if severe drainage problems are not to be created through soil compaction or loss of structure. Enlargement of existing tees should commence in early October and where new sites are developed away from general play it makes sense to get on with earth work during the drier summer months, i.e. importation of fill if this is needed. Remove and dispose of rank grass growth, scrub and especially tree roots, all of which eventually rot and decompose in time to cause settlement if merely pushed in as fill or buried. Strip all recoverable topsoil off the site and its surrounds and stack it close at hand.

172

Tees will normally be slightly elevated to give an adequate view of the target area and possible hazards from the back as well as the front, which must be borne in mind on longer tees. If not levelling by cut and fill, utilise clean subsoil fill from a convenient borrow area in the rough. The fill should be free of large stones, bricks, etc., which hinder good drainage and the completion of essential secondary drainage aids like subsoil cultivation. Build up the material in consecutive layers 230 mm deep, ensuring each layer is evenly firmed to avoid settlement. This point is most important – many a grand tee has subsequently become a liability through settlement destroying the surface levels and the blame must lie with poor or hasty preparation. This applies even more so to tee enlargement where simply filling to extend the area is often the easiest approach. Loads of subsoil tipped along the edge of a tee and pushed down will inevitably settle unevenly. The correct procedure is to tip small loads, level out and build up in evenly firmed layers. When all is done, replace the preserved topsoil to provide a minimum cover of 150 mm firmed depth on the tee surface, rather less on banks, say, 75 mm firmed.

Plan and Gradient
Since the end of the 19th century the rectangular tee with sides parallel to the line of play has been the norm, with much to commend it. Banks must not be too steep, a slope of 1 in 4 with edges well rounded off allows scope for maintenance with modern wide cut triple units or even at need the use of gang units.

It is desirable that the upper surface of a tee should have a slight gradient but no more than 1 in 80. This is scarcely visible to the player but still enough to allow surface water run-off. As a general guide, tees at uphill holes should slope upwards from back to front and those at downhill slopes, downwards.

Size
For ease of upkeep, reducing bank maintenance to a minimum and providing scope for modern, faster and wider aeration, top dressing and cutting equipment, it is better to have one large teeing area. However, site considerations and Par for the hole will determine the best approach and it may be necessary to have championship and medal tees separate. Also, separate teeing areas for ladies, men and medals allow for different lines of attack at any hole which helps variety. It is advisable to allow for 300–350 m^2 at Par 4 and 5's and 400–450 m^2 at Par 3's. Where separate tees are provided, ladies will only require a forward tee of about 50 m^2, the general tee should be at least 200 m^2 and the medal tee 100 m^2.

Drainage
Most tees on normal soils will not require special pipe drainage systems. They are slightly elevated which keeps them further removed from any water table problem in winter and also helps surface run-off. If they can be given a slight gradient, so much the better. It is, however, vital that compaction in fill material and topsoil is properly relieved so that any panned layers do not impede drainage away from the surface. After returning topsoil, use a tractor-mounted subsoiler, making at least two passes along the length and then across the width of the tee, pulling out at the sides and ends. The implement should be set to work at a depth of 460 mm and at 600 mm centres.

Pipe drainage will only normally be required as a catchwater drain or limited system around the foot of the bank at the rear and possibly the side of a cut and fill tee in order to trap run-off before it can affect the surface.

Preparation
Restore the tee surface following subsoiling using a tractor-mounted bar grader if necessary. Then complete rigid tine cultivation or use a power harrow to produce a workable, fairly fine

soil tilth. If any sand amelioration is required it should be thoroughly worked in at this stage. Carry out hand raking and heeling at least twice to produce a fine and evenly firmed soil surface, removing stones 12 mm and over in the process. Corner and intermediate pegs should be set at the required level and with a tight line stretched across, these allow a check on surface levels as the work proceeds. Adequate firming of the topsoil by heeling without over-compaction is essential to locate and remove softer pockets of soil at this stage. If left, these will invariably settle to create unevenness. A roller will not do the same job since it tends to bridge softer spots.

Establishment

Apply and rake in any lime needed, usually only where the soil is very acid, and a light application of fine bone meal. Turfing is the best method of getting the new tee into play and fits well with the normal autumn construction period on established courses. Bought in turf may be the easier option but ensure it contains the desirable bent and fescue grasses with no coarse ryegrass or no weedgrass – annual meadow-grass – and allow time for it to establish properly before use. The commonest and often least satisfactory method is to lift turf off the practice ground or fairway which may be full of weeds, certainly fibrous, and then chop it down to tee height. Not surprisingly, such turf establishes poorly and is hacked up the first summer. If using turf from the course, plan in advance and give the chosen area initial preparation including a light feed, spiking, summer scarification and weed control if needed, taking the height of cut down a little. Fibrous turf must be cut thinly for it to establish quickly and it should be laid working off boards placed on the turf surface not the carefully prepared and levelled soil bed. Give a fairly heavy top dressing of suitable sand or compost afterwards and lute this into the joints.

Seeded areas take longer to establish before they are fit for play – from an August sowing, perhaps 18 months; seeding in April, often two years and that with good management. Prepare as described for the turf bed, raking in a little pre-seeding granular fertiliser then sow with a bent/fescue seed mix, possibly including a proportion of a finer leaved, hard wearing cultivar of smooth-stalked meadow-grass.

Winter Tees

Where grass tees are small and subject to heavy play, there is no other practical alternative except to close early and renovate by seeding. During the winter period artificial teeing surfaces, which must include an appropriate hard wearing stance area as well, can be used or alternatively, as many clubs do, a selected piece of fairway. It is important to site such winter tees with care so that traffic during this period from green to tee and tee to fairway is diverted away from routes that are heavily used all summer. The latter areas can then be rested; it may provide an opportunity for renovating them, and skilful siting of winter tees can bring alternative fairway landing zones into use, again saving wear and tear on areas affected by summer play.

GOLF COURSE DRAINAGE

Good drainage forms the foundation of the golf course and it is no coincidence that inherently free draining sandy links and chalk downland usually provides the premier terrain for golf course development. The adverse effects of inadequate drainage are inextricably linked with the poor condition of many of our golf courses. The common symptoms of this deficiency include *Poa annua* dominated turf, excessive thatch build up and lack of playing surface uniformity on a year-round basis. Course closures, due to waterlogged playing surfaces, also represent loss of vital revenue for the Club and often engender the antipathy of the golfers due to the frustration of not being able to play.

Wet turf surfaces are predisposed to disease attack, notably fusarium patch disease, and algae or moss colonisation is encouraged. In these situations, direct treatment of the symptoms, through chemical control measures, will only be a short term palliative and the underlying cause must be tackled, i.e. the inferior drainage properties of the soil.

Drainage problems have certainly become more acute in recent years due to escalating levels of play. Soil compaction – leading to impeded water movement – is the most insidious by-product of the greater pressure imposed by golf traffic. Unfortunately, the problem tends to feed upon itself, therefore measures must be implemented to break the cycle and restore satisfactory rates of soil drainage. Routine aeration may suffice to achieve this objective, but this does not necessarily preclude the need for supplementary drainage. Certainly, machines such as the Verti-Drain have revolutionised golf course aeration. However, this should not be seen as a universal panacea and its potential will only be realised if it can make a direct connection with more permeable soil layers below.

Pipe drainage may already exist as a legacy of previous farming activity, but this rarely meets the requirements for golf course drainage in terms of intensity and the techniques or materials employed. Very often the drainage trenches have simply been backfilled with the indigenous soil, therefore the benefits of the pipe drains are largely negated by the very slow downward movement of water. Alternatively, slag may have been employed for backfilling purposes (which is prone to cementation) or limestone which may be subject to breakdown in acid soil water. Furthermore, damage or displacement in these pipe systems are not uncommon and these can be difficult to trace and subsequently rectify. This problem is further exacerbated by the general lack of recorded plans of the drainage systems!

The intensity of pipe drainage installed within fairway areas will largely be dictated by the nature of the land. On heavy clay-based soils excessively close spacing of the pipe drains is unlikely to have the desired effect and the introduction of slit drains would effectively by-pass the heavy topsoil and ensure that water can pass rapidly from the surface to the pipe drains beneath. On flat land it may prove difficult to observe the **absolute** minimum fall of 1 in 300 on pipe drains. Remember that their depth must also be sufficient to avoid damage by heavy tackle, i.e. minimum 450 mm.

The greens are invariably the focal point of the golf course and therefore drainage must be of the highest order if the playing surfaces are to receive universal approbation throughout the year. On many of the older courses greens were specifically designed to hold water before the advent of efficient irrigation systems. Concerns about compaction, soil aeration and adequate moisture infiltration were either secondary considerations or not thought to be important with the very light playing levels at the time. Subsequently, the misguided policy of applying liberal quantities of water with automatic irrigation systems to create holding greens during the summer months has undoubtedly aggravated the inherent drainage deficiencies of these greens.

A proven constructional method has now been developed which effectively isolates the drainage of the green from the native soil. This basically consists of a drainage layer of hard aggregate which acts as a reservoir for the drainage water which percolates through the rooting medium above and the underlying pipes only act as an emptying system. An intermediate layer is introduced of coarse sand or fine grit which is compatible with the drainage layer below and rootzone mixture above. In some cases a geotextile membrane is substituted for this intermediate layer, but with the passage of time the pores in this fabric can become blocked with finer particles migrating down from above. Therefore, this is not recommended. The concept of using large quantities of sand to improve the drainage qualities of the soil is now well accepted by golf course constructors. However, it is imperative that the components are thoroughly blended in the correct proportions by off-site mixing, otherwise the downward percolation of water can be severely impeded. The phenomenon known as Black Layer is only one manifestation of this problem.

Introducing a blanket system of pipe drains through a golf green is not a viable solution to drainage problems as it creates a pattern of well drained sections of turf (in close proximity to the pipe drains) separated by poorly drained areas.

Elevation of tees above surrounding ground level and formation of a slight but constant gradient usually precludes the need for the installation of an intensive drainage system. However, allowance must be made for the introduction of a sufficient depth of sandy soil beneath the turf surface. Furthermore, catchwater type drains strategically placed at the toe of cut banks will intercept surface water (and sub-surface seepage) before it can affect the playing surface.

During the wetter periods of the year the small, semi-permanent ponds, which in a moment of enthusiasm are described as bunkers, are the result of excavation into heavy, clay-based subsoil without adequate regard for drainage. Drainage of bunkers must be of paramount importance and in this context the bunker floor should be shaped to provide a uniform fall to a drain running the length of a large bunker or to one low sump point from which an outlet drain can be provided. It is essential to stop finer particles from the bunker sand filtering through to rapidly block up the pipe drains. In the past, up-turned fibrous sods or old sacking were used to cover the gravel. Nowadays, the trend is to use a geotextile membrane, taking care to choose one of a suitable grade. On poorly drained subsoils it is preferable to build up rather than excavating deeply into the ground to help minimise water collection within the low point of the bunker.

Any drainage system is only as effective as its outlet and if these do not provide a clear flow, the system cannot be expected to function effectively. Therefore, any accumulation of debris must be removed from culverts and manholes checked for excessive build up of silt or other rubbish. Where mains discharge into an open waterway, brick, concrete or fibre-glass reinforced headwalls should be introduced and a splash plate and guard against vermin provided.

Ditches are the main arteries of the drainage system, therefore their integrity must be maintained by annual maintenance. The build up of silt and organic debris can dramatically hinder the rate of water flow, as well as reducing the carrying capacity of the ditches. Consequently, it is essential to remove this deleterious material and weed growth must also be controlled along the water channel. However, take care to avoid exposing bare soil on the banks as the roots of grass and herbs make an important contribution to the stability of the ditch sides and their complete removal will tend to accelerate erosion and collapse.

Soakaways are generally a poor substitute for a more positive outfall and their introduction should be restricted to those situations where the drainage water can egress into indigenous, permeable strata. They will be of little value if this condition cannot be satisfied.

Catchwater type drains (i.e. those with trenches backfilled with aggregate and then blinded with a finer material up to surface level) are invaluable for protecting playing surfaces from the flow of water running off from higher ground above. Since their function is primarily to intercept surface run-off, this will obviously be greatly impaired if the surface of the catchwater becomes capped with soil. In these circumstances, remedial measures will involve removal of the soil to expose clean aggregate in conjunction with topping up to surface level to make good any deficiency.

Tree roots have a remarkable propensity for seeking out drain lines leading to silting up and total blockage over a relatively short period of time. Moisture-loving poplars and willows are particularly notorious in this respect, therefore the introduction of access and inspection chambers would be a sensible precaution within any potential danger areas where drains run close to trees. Indeed, where there is a recurring problem, the sections of drain at risk could be lifted prior to replacing with sealed, unperforated pipe.

DRAINAGE PROBLEMS ON THE GOLF COURSE

Introduction

Water, wet feet and unnecessary wear result from poor drainage on the golf course and they also create a hindrance to play and complicate maintenance works. Satisfactory drainage is, therefore, the first essential requirement on a golf course if the most pleasing and best possible conditions for play are to be provided for the maximum period throughout the year. In golf course design and construction measures are usually taken to ensure adequate and efficient drainage and it is often the clubs with old established courses on inland sites which suffer most from drainage faults. In many of these cases the greens were not drained intensively enough to provide the conditions needed for the intensity of golf played today. Often drainage which does exist is of an old agricultural type which becomes silted up or lacks the intensity and requirements for the drainage of a golf course. One often finds time and money being spent on trying to modernise such systems and in the majority of cases it is very questionable as to whether the improvements obtained justify the effort and expense. Where a real drainage problem occurs it is generally wise to ignore what exists and study the situation anew, bearing in mind the requirements of golf course drainage and modern techniques.

Fairway Drainage

Introduction of pipe drainage into the whole of the fairway area on a golf course is rarely necessary and more often than not problems are confined to local regions. These may be parts which are relatively flat and where surface water run-off provides little aid to drainage, they may be low lying regions of generally undulating land or parts where changes in levels on an area with generally sloping ground checks subsoil water flow and/or surface water run-off. The drainage requirements of such parts should be given individual study as the pattern of pipe drains needed and their intensity will be dependent on the contours of each region and their soil type.

Generally on fairway areas a grid system of drains is most commonly used, for example, on an area where the maximum fall is diagonally across the line of play the lateral drains would run more or less straight across the fairway to feed a main drain running parallel to its lower side (see Fig. 16). On the other hand, where the contours form, for example, a shallow, fairly

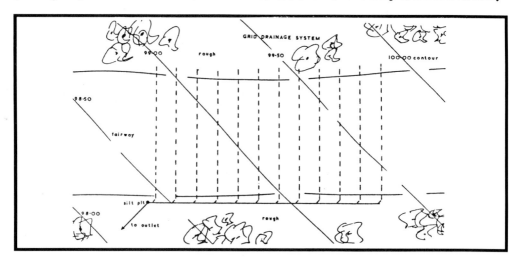

FIGURE 16: On fairways a grid system of drains can be used where the fall is diagonally across the line of play.

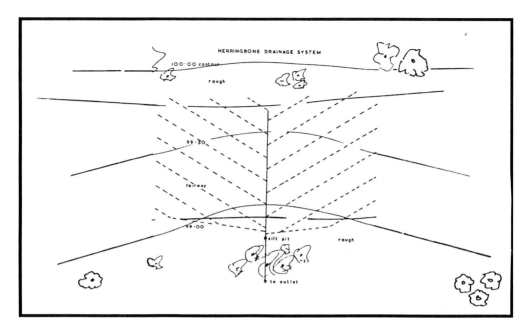

FIGURE 17: **On fairways where the contours form a fairly wide valley running across the fairway, a herringbone system of drainage can be used.**

wide valley running across the fairway a herringbone system might be considered (see Fig. 17). In this case the main drain would run across the fairway through the lowest levels of the valley and lateral drains would feed this at an angle of 45–60° from both sides. No hard and fast rules can be made on the intensity of the lateral drains but they could be as wide as 10 metres on lighter, naturally free draining land but as close as 4–5 metres on heavier clay soil with slow natural drainage.

As an alternative to pipe drainage of wet areas, consideration could be given to mole draining as this can be beneficial, though the operation would have to be repeated on occasions. The work could not be effectively done in very stony subsoils and it is most efficient where the clay content is 35% or more. Mole drains prove most beneficial when their spacing is no more than $4^1/2$ times their depth which is usually between 460 and 610 mm. Pipe main drains laid a little below the depth of the mole drains should be provided, their trenches being backfilled with small gravel or hard broken stone except at points where they join open outlets, e.g. ditches.

On fairway area where slow surface water drainage causes problems due to the heavy nature of the topsoil or the fact that it is a catchment area and in spite of satisfactory under-drainage, a suitable pattern of slit drains supplementing the pipe drainage would give much improved conditions. Slit drains 50 mm wide cut at intervals of 610 mm to 1.2 metres according to site conditions and to a depth which would allow their backfilling to directly link up with the backfilling over the pipe drains would allow surface water to quickly bypass the slow draining soils. The narrow trenches would be excavated with a small trenching machine and they are usually cut across the fall on the land. Backfilling is done with suitable small gravel or hard broken stone topped off with suitable lime-free sand or completely with lime-free sand alone right up to ground level. This relatively new drainage technique can be done by contract or by the green staff using suitable plant hire equipment.

179

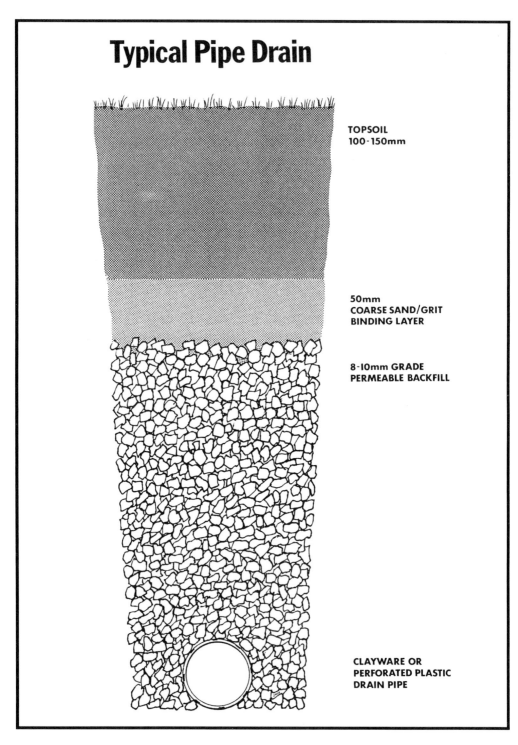

Typical Pipe Drain

TOPSOIL
100-150mm

50mm
COARSE SAND/GRIT
BINDING LAYER

8-10mm GRADE
PERMEABLE BACKFILL

CLAYWARE OR
PERFORATED PLASTIC
DRAIN PIPE

FIGURE 18: Cross-section of pipe drain suitable for drainage of fairways, etc.

Drain Laying

Pipe drainage systems should be formed with clayware field drain pipes (BS 1196:1971) or perforated plastic drain pipes (BS 4962:1989) of appropriate sizes and all connections should be formed with purpose made junction pipes. Sealed pipes should be used in the vicinity of trees. The drains should be laid at a minimum depth of 610 mm to invert below ground level and at even falls of no less than 1 in 200, though 1 in 300 could be accepted as an absolute minimum where circumstances demand. Lateral drains should run at an angle across the maximum fall on the land and wherever possible systems should be designed to utilise existing falls on the land so that the drains can be laid at a constant depth. Where this can be done, introduction of the drainage system is simplified, excavation is kept to the minimum as is the cost of backfilling materials, but the essential requirements, with regard to depths and falls, must be satisfied. Where this cannot be done, the requirements must be obtained by laying the drains to increasing depth to obtain the falls advised.

Drain trenches should be some 50 mm wider than the diameter of the pipes (unnecessary width involves increased excavation and backfilling) and after the laying of the pipes, backfilling should immediately follow. Trenches of all drains which are expected to collect and carry water should be filled with suitable small gravel (8–10 mm diameter) or hard broken stone.

All drainage systems should have positive outlets otherwise they will not function correctly. Outlets can be ditches, streams and rivers or existing surface water drains might be used if they have adequate capacity. The water levels at the outlets, particularly in the winter, in relation to the depths of the drains is of consequence as an unimpeded water flow is important. Soakaways are of limited value unless they can be situated in an area where the subsoil has very good naturally free draining qualities.

CONSTRUCTION OF CATCHWATER/CUT-OFF DRAIN

The purpose of a catchwater drain is to intercept any flow of water that might enter an area over the surface or along water bearing strata. Such a drain is often useful for intercepting water around the perimeter of a golf green or tee. Catchwater drains are usually located at the toe of banks or slopes, i.e.

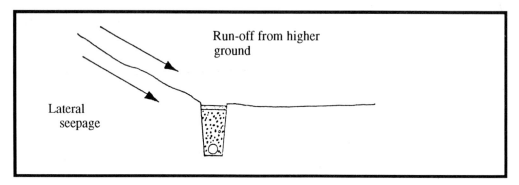

FIGURE 19:   Catchwater drain.

For full effect, catchwater drain trenches should be filled with permeable material usually up to within 25 mm of ground level. The requirements of the site, however, may dictate that a turf cover is maintained above the drain so that play is not interfered with, e.g. around golf greens. In general, catchwater drains which are not covered with turf are more effective.

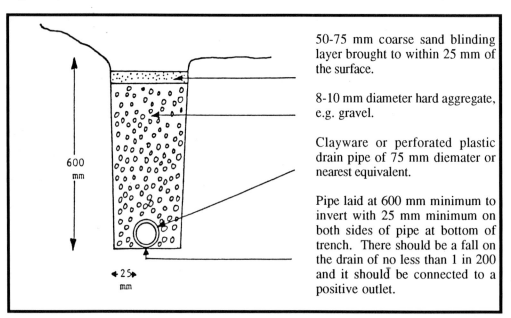

50-75 mm coarse sand blinding layer brought to within 25 mm of the surface.

8-10 mm diameter hard aggregate, e.g. gravel.

Clayware or perforated plastic drain pipe of 75 mm diemater or nearest equivalent.

Pipe laid at 600 mm minimum to invert with 25 mm minimum on both sides of pipe at bottom of trench. There should be a fall on the drain of no less than 1 in 200 and it should be connected to a positive outlet.

FIGURE 20:   Detail of catchwater drain

N.B.   If a turf cover is required over the drain line, then the turves should be laid slightly dished to hold water. In most cases the covering of such drains with turf is not recommended.

ESTABLISHMENT OF NEW AREAS FROM SEED

Seeding is a relatively cheap way of establishing new turf areas. However, the ultimate success of the turf as a playing surface will depend on important decisions taken with regard to major level adjustment, pipe drainage and if necessary improvement to the drainage qualities of the topsoil. All the above operations are fairly expensive nowadays and the way in which they are carried out and their timing can affect establishment and ultimately the quality of the surface produced. Naturally, these decisions will be based on available finance and the standard of playing surface required.

The big advantage of seeding is that no heavy soils are being introduced (as could happen with turfing), especially on sandy golf green constructions.

Timing
August or September is the optimum time for sowing seed in this country, particularly for the finer turf areas. At this period the soil is still warm and the early autumn usually provides adequate natural rainfall so that the young seedlings do not suffer from drought with reasonable growing weather after germination for them to establish before hard frost occurs. In the autumn there is also markedly less competition from developing weed seedlings.

Equally, if not more important, sowing at this time of year allows those preliminary operations requiring heavy equipment and traffic over the site such as earth moving, pipe drainage and soil amelioration to be carried out during the drier months of May and June which helps to keep damage to soil structure that occurs with these operations to a minimum.

Soil Type
For golf a sandy, free draining soil is required which is often produced by adding a quantity of suitable sand to the existing soil in amounts determined by laboratory tests. Off site preparation of the soil mix is the preferred method and must be completed thoroughly so as to produce a very uniform mixture of the constituents. After spreading the soil mix on the green, ensure there are no hard, panned layers by adequate cultivation through the full depth of soil, though make sure any underlying drainage carpet materials are not disturbed.

Sterilisation/Fallowing
Fallowing can be useful in reducing competition from weeds and even weedgrasses like annual meadow-grass. However, time is necessary to allow the weeds to develop when they can be killed off by cultivations in dry weather or alternatively spraying with appropriate non-persistent weedkiller based on paraquat or glyphosate. Even a short fallowing period is better than none at all but if the aim is to achieve a seed bed free of annual meadow-grass, soil sterilising would be a better option.

Soil sterilising using methyl bromide is fairly quick and can be very effective, although it is costly and requires professional operators. Dazomet, another soil sterilising agent, may also be tried, although an adequate period (often weeks) must be allowed for the gas to escape before seeding.

Surface Levels
During seed bed preparation heeling and raking will be required a number of times to produce a fine soil tilth that is adequately and evenly firmed over the whole area though without being too compacted. During the work, surface stones should be removed.

Where surface levels are crucial, accurate level pegs should be set out on a grid pattern and the seed bed raked and firmed to correspond with the top of the pegs. Levels are less critical for tees, and on golf greens some gentle undulation is desirable to produce an interesting putting surface. Care in producing a good tilth and satisfactory levels at this stage will be more than repaid later on by the ease and speed with which levels are perfected for play through top dressing.

Lime and Fertiliser Treatment
To aid germination and rapid early development of a complete grass cover, over acid soil conditions should be corrected by liming where necessary to achieve a pH of about 5.0. There must be adequate amounts of the main plant nutrients phosphate and potash available in the upper layers of soil. Where no serious deficiencies of these nutrients exist an application of a mini-granular or powder fertiliser that contains 6:9:6 or with similar analysis can be used at 50 g/m^2 and raked in.

Seed Mixtures
The traditional approach has been to sow 80% Chewings fescue and 20% browntop bent and this is still very satisfactory today. The fescue germinates and grows quickly to nurse along the much slower bent: with a suitable soil and correct management a good proportion of the fescue may survive though quite frequently once established the strongly competitive bent will take over. There are a number of excellent new cultivars of both these grasses available and a choice should be made from the lists in our publication "Turfgrass 1992" bearing in mind the qualities required for the particular turf area. Seed rate should be 35 g/m^2, sowing as evenly as possible, the seed then being carefully raked into the immediate surface soil – it must not be put too deep and surface levels should not be disturbed.

Disease
Occasionally damping off disease will affect young seedlings, especially under wet, cold seed bed conditions. The seedlings keel over and develop a typical reddish/bronze colour and, if noticed, affected areas can be treated with a wide spectrum fungicide such as chlorothalonil.

Early Care
When the young grass is about 25 mm long and the ground is dry, remove any remaining small stones 12 mm) and over. Follow up by a light flat rolling. When the grass reaches 40 mm in length carry out the first cut but removing no more than 12 mm of foliage. Timing of this first cut is important since early mowing will check any annual weeds that may develop and it also encourages the grass to tiller and thicken out. To avoid damage to surface levels the ground must be firm and in very wet periods, to prevent the grass growing away it may be necessary to top lightly with a Flymo type mower initially. Subsequent cuts should be with a cylinder mower, boxing off the cuttings and gradually reducing the height of cut to about 12 mm. The latter height of cut should be maintained until surface levels have been improved sufficiently by top dressing to permit closer cutting.

Top Dressing
Several applications of an appropriate type of bulky top dressing (e.g. sandy compost for greens) will be necessary in the growing season at a minimum rate of 2.0 kg/m^2. This should provide sufficient material to work in using a lute to eliminate minor surface irregularities which always occur. The treatment should be repeated a number of times until the playing surface is satisfactory.

TURF NURSERIES

Turf is often needed for patching and repair work on golf courses and good turf is not always easy to obtain from outside sources, especially at short notice. Every golf club should therefore ideally have its own private supply of turf in the form of a turf nursery. This should be sited in a convenient situation, e.g. near maintenance sheds, where it is not likely to be neglected, on a well drained site. If possible, watering facilities should be provided.

Method of Establishment
A minimum depth of 150 mm of topsoil should be laid down – a sandy topsoil being preferred in the case of golf greens. The soil should be freed of weeds and weedgrasses (particularly annual meadow-grass) by repeated cultivations or by chemical sterilisation. The grass seed, to be sown on a well prepared and adequately fertilized seed bed, should be chosen to suit the area for which the turf is destined. In the case of golf greens and golf tees the turf should consist of bents and fescues only. Good cultivars should be used – see the STRI leaflet "Turfgrass Seed 1992" (updated annually).

Management
The turf nursery should be maintained in a similar fashion to the green in which it is to be used, so that it will be as similar as possible to existing turf. It is never wise, however, to lay nursery turf directly into central parts of a playing area like a golf green since it is not likely to match up exactly. It is better to move completely matching turf from the edge of a green to the centre and then patch the edges with turf from the nursery.

Turf is not usually strong enough to be lifted and used for patching until it is two years old in the case of the average nursery, although younger turf is successfully used in commercial practice. As turf is removed from the nursery, the gaps left should be topped up with suitable soil before resowing with the appropriate seeds mixture.

Management of a turf nursery should involve fertiliser treatment, a single spring dressing each year being usually adequate to maintain good growth except on very sandy soils where supplementary summer dressings might be required. Such fertiliser should consist mainly of nitrogen, the use of excessive quantities of phosphate being avoided as this tends to encourage undesirable annual meadow-grass. Scarification work will also be needed regularly during the growing season to reduce horizontal growth and prevent thatch accumulation. Control measures against disease, weeds and earthworms should be carried out as appropriate.

Cutting should never be neglected, the turf nursery being maintained at the same height as the area the material will be used on. There is often a tendency to neglect mowing of turf nurseries which are not used for play, and this cannot be too strongly condemned. In the growing season nurseries should preferably be cut two or three times per week.

Working Down a Nursery from Existing Turf
This can sometimes be feasible if the soil type and grass are suitable, e.g. on the practice ground or to the side of a fairway. If such areas are reasonably level or they can be top dressed with suitable material to improve levels and permit close, frequent mowing (removing clippings), and operations such as verticutting, weedkilling and feeding are carried out as appropriate, a nursery of good quality may be produced in six to twelve months. Here again, it must be stressed that the nursery site should not be too remote – out of sight, out of mind – unfortunately, nurseries always have a tendency to be neglected.

PATHS: THEIR APPLICATION AND INSTALLATION

Traffic routes within golf courses such as approaches to greens, the walk on surround to the next tee, and from tee to fairway are often narrow, controlled by artificial features such as bunkers and mounds, and it is in these areas that the turf cover is readily destroyed by constant traffic. Often, the natural contours of the site have been utilised in a very clever way by the architect who designed the course to provide interest and a real test of players' abilities. It is perhaps unfortunate that in the days when the majority of our older courses were designed and built, no architect, however brilliant, could have foreseen the tremendous upsurge in the popularity of the game that has taken place over the past 20 years and the enormous pressure this has placed on these areas of our courses, where, of necessity, traffic is channelled.

Heaven forbid, however, that British architects should venture down the road being followed by so many American architects who have taken on the role of God and literally move mountains of earth to create forced, artificial features to greens, "spectator mounds", and provide for the ubiquitous tarmac roadways for golf buggies. All this, with no regard whatsoever for the damage to soil structure and drainage, the maintenance of which is paramount in our climate and soils if a satisfactory quality of turf and year-round playability are to be provided.

The traditional British golf course Architect's approach was and is to make the very best of the site contours and to fit the design and layout into whatever nature has provided. It has served well, in many cases brilliantly, for a century or more, and you will find many a Scottish green design slavishly copied in the totally alien environment of America or Japan where it looks completely out of place.

As an example, Royal Troon golf course has been designed to accommodate minimum wear patterns. Here, the 2nd to the 5th holes out exemplify what should become an integral part of modern golf course design, and indeed should be applied wherever the strategy will fit in on older courses. This course design deals with not only golfing aspects either, although the stratagem does offer a great variety of choice in the way these holes are played. At each of them there are two separate sets of tees – the regular summer tees set to the right nearer the sea, whilst on the opposite side of the green and thus well away from the summer wear patterns there is an alternative set of tees. Most of these are used mainly in the winter period but they can, in emergency, be pressed into summer use. Indeed, this concept is so useful, especially on a busy course such as Royal Troon, that successive Green Committees with the ready forbearance and, indeed, support of members have extended the provision of alternative tees and access routes at as many holes as practicable. The idea is simple, provides much needed extra teeing space, alters traffic patterns both near greens and on carries which are pretty fragile on links courses, quite often varies the landing zone on fairways, and, where there is space in siting these alternative tees, may not even shorten the course. Where there is space, this approach is recommended.

One will have gathered by now that paths on the golf course should be resorted to when all else has failed and, to some extent, one should regard their introduction as a failure.

Maintaining Grass
Before even considering the provision of paths which, no matter how well built or disguised, always look out of place on the golf course proper and far too often intrude into areas which come into play, we must reassess maintenance practices.

If turf is to be tough and hard wearing it must be mature, well established in free draining soil and contain the right grass species. On the majority of our golf courses the finer browntop bents and, in the right situations, fescue grasses fill the bill. To survive however, even these hardy grasses need good soil aeration to encourage a vigorous root system and an occasional rest from the battering of traffic to allow recuperation and for any necessary repairs to establish. We are, after all, dealing with living plant material.

Let us be quite clear that it is constant foot and trolley traffic over the same narrow routes used by golfers that compacts and seals the top, reduces air content in the soil, affects drainage and physically wears away the leaves and mat of plant tissue. The advent of golf trolleys has made the situation far worse since their use inevitably dictates certain routes, usually the shortest and easiest between two points. It is the constant hammering the same tracks receive summer and winter which results in deterioration – wide or narrow wheels make little difference, although the heavier battery-powered units with a skidding drive wheel on wet ground add to the problems.

The first and essential operation must be to ensure adequate aeration is carried out and as early as possible in September since we want better root action, and getting moisture to penetrate hard paths is just as important as letting in air and relieving soil compaction. Suit the tool to the circumstances, be it hollow tine coring, deep or shallow slits, or in compacted conditions, which so very often apply, the favourite is the Verti-Drain or a tool for air injection and possibly in the future the newer concept of water injection.

Having achieved a basis of more open soil, keep up regular but more shallow slit tine aeration as ground and weather conditions permit through the autumn and winter. Move traffic off the worn places and carry out such repairs as are necessary by turfing wherever this is practical. For preference, use a tough, mature turf off the course rather than softer, immature, bought-in material – seeding is rarely satisfactory.

Where aeration has been tackled properly in autumn, a little mild feeding may help in the spring or late summer. Above all, limit maintenance traffic in these places. Effective winter aeration is quickly nullified by thumping around surrounds with heavy tractors or gang mowers twice a week. Equally, there is no excuse either for thoughtless greenkeeping staff regularly tracking these routes with a Cushman or Hydromain when carrying out routine tasks such as hole changing, tee repair, etc.

Traffic Direction
One thing absolutely clear is that golfers carrying clubs and especially when hauling trolleys will have to be given far stronger direction as to the routes that they can use, particularly between October and April. In the non-growing period constant traffic over the same ground can lead to bare soil or, at best, a broken, disturbed surface, and that whether the winter is hard or open since the briefest interlude of improved weather nowadays means a positive deluge of golfers on the course.

The best approach is undoubtedly that adopted by some tough-minded Committees who impose a complete ban on trolleys for a set period of the worst weather and ground conditions each winter.

Actual direction of traffic can take many forms, from simple metal hoops to deter the right-of-way developing around the collar of greens or the damage within inches of the run into greenside bunkers. White lines along with appropriate notices are also used to good effect, occasionally both summer and winter. Where golfers are used to and prepared to accept them, white lining is particularly versatile, as one set of lines fades the next can be marked out a little further away to avoid tracks developing right at the edge of the lines. At some clubs there is nothing else for it but to resort to posts and ropes to provide physical barriers.

When All Else Fails
In situations where the above measures are clearly failing to provide satisfactory conditions, one is forced to resort to pathways. These will commonly be require alongside tees, preferably sited to provide as wide access at either end as possible – try to limit the tendency of paths to become extended at entry and exit points.

Paths should be at least 1.2 metres wide to take two pedestrians side by side or a pedestrian pulling a golf cart. Where there is choice, the route should be as direct as possible to avoid golfers taking shortcuts; where deliberately longer to get round an obstacle and prevent damage close into greens, then clear signposting is essential.

Construction
Sound basic construction will provide not only a well drained, firmer and longer lasting path, but will allow one to get the best out of the more expensive surfacing materials.

Cut out the basic shape, removing turf and topsoil, to the required depth usually 150 mm. To provide a neat, firm mowing edge and to help contain the construction materials, it is better to use edging boards nailed to supporting pegs, the wood treated with appropriate preservative. Finish the top of the edging flush with the adjacent soil level. The two edges of the path should be an equal distance apart and having set in and established the first edge, use a simple wooden measuring gauge to ensure the second one is parallel. The path should have a slight crossfall.

Fill in with hardcore or crusher-run material to a minimum firmed depth of 100 mm, rolling to consolidate. Drainage into surrounding topsoil may well be adequate where soil conditions are pretty open, but on heavy clay soils make provision where necessary to tap into existing drains or provide new ones, especially through lower lying sections of the path.

For pathways down slopes some care is needed to minimise erosion problems. A trap drain along the higher side of the path may be necessary, and wooden cross battens angled across the slope of the path with, say, 12 mm upstands to check the downward flow of water. The alternative would be to use proprietary products such as Fin drains.

Surfacing
Over the years many different types of surfacing material have been tried with varying success. On links or on courses where it is freely available, crushed shell can be very effective, but does need to be well bedded down to provide a tight, well bound surface; if near putting greens, the material used should not be too noisy when walked upon.

Coarse stone, particularly if it has no finer particles mixed with it, is totally unsatisfactory, being unstable, uncomfortable to walk upon and often too easily spread by feet or trolleys on to mown areas, damaging cutters. Any stone content which is used must have sufficient fines in order to help bind it and form a stable surface. Quite often the 5 mm down quarry waste materials that have been used for surfacing hard porous pitches are very satisfactory, obtained in grey, tan or ochre colours – red shales or white limestones either look out of place or glare off the surface in summer can affect the eyes.

In recent years tree bark has been much used, often to quite good effect. However, choice of product needs care, the finer and softer grades of bark rapidly break down in this situation into a wet organic mush, often after only a couple of years or so. Coarser and harder grades of bark last rather better but are still expensive and, of late, there has been a move to use wood chips or wood fibre. These products may cost slightly more but last far longer, are clean and comfortable to walk on and do not damage golf balls or other equipment.

These latter points sum up the requirements for the surfacing material itself and if the design is right, pathways should merge naturally and as unobtrusively as possible into the golf course site.

DEVELOPING NEW GOLF COURSES (1991 PRICES)

Over the past 12 months the Institute has received a steady stream of enquiries from farmers and landowners investigating the possibilities of developing new golf courses. This renewed interest has been brought about by reforms in the EEC Common Agricultural Policy which, in order to reduce surpluses, is encouraging farmers to diversify and look towards finding alternative uses for their land. These changes are coming at a time when a survey conducted by the English Golf Union (EGU) has shown that following the upsurge in the popularity of golf the demand for new courses has never been greater.

In England, more than one third of golfers do not have access to membership of a Club which has led to a call from the EGU for another 500 courses to be built before the end of the century. The R&A estimate the need for about 700 new golf courses by the year 2000. However, potential golf course developers do not always appreciate the high constructional costs involved compared with agricultural investments. Also, it may take several years to produce a realistic return from the development once established.

An 18-hole golf course will require between 50 to 60 hectares (120 to 148 acres) of land which should accommodate all the necessary safety margins which are needed both internally between greens, fairways and tees and externally in relation to roads, paths and housing. Golf courses built on areas of less than 40 hectares (98 acres) will inevitably have holes of restricted length and a number of bottleneck areas. Courses built on such small areas are often a danger to players.

A new golf course will need to be located near a large catchment area, otherwise throughput and potential income will be severely limited.

The overall costs of actually constructing the course are dependent on numerous factors, the most important being the suitability of the land for development. Obviously, costs will increase if extensive tree and shrub clearance is required beforehand or conversely widespread tree planting may be deemed necessary on more exposed sites. The need for earth-moving in shaping the course will also influence the overall development costs. If the area of land has naturally gentle undulations, then the requirement for level adjustment should be minimal. Less suitable sites are those which dictate the need for extensive cut and fill techniques in order to produce manageable as well as playable holes.

The most crucial requirement for a golf course is that is should be well drained, particularly in view of the modern day demand for all-year-round golf. At no time can a golf course afford to be closed due to waterlogging of greens, tees or fairways. If the native soil has good natural drainage properties or overlies a porous sub-base, such as gravel, sandy soil or fractured rock, then the drainage works could be restricted to greens only. However, in most situations at least some drainage will be required on fairways, the intensity of which will be much greater than that employed for agricultural purposes. Wherever pipe drains have been installed, a positive outfall is needed into which water can discharge. Ideally, the outfall should take the form of an existing open ditch, stream or other water course.

With regard to construction of greens, their needs are normally catered for by using a gravel or broken stone drainage carpet tapped by a series of pipe drains. For the rootzone mixes, the native topsoil is usually ameliorated with pre-determined quantities of an approved sand to provide a freely draining mixture on completion. If, however, the topsoil is of a totally unsuitable nature and alternative soils are not available in the vicinity, then the use of bought-in sand/soil mixes could be considered.

The cost of developing an 18-hole golf course can range from between £750,000 and £2 million depending on the suitability of the site and the standard of construction. These figures are based on a specialist contractor carrying out the work. It would be inadvisable for a land-owner or farmer to tackle the works themselves without specialist knowledge using his own or hired equipment, unless there is a minimum requirement for drainage and/or earth-moving works.

In general, a public (pay and play) course would cost less to develop than a proprietary club competing in a higher standard of market. At the top end of the scale, large hotel chains have invested sums of up to £20 million on new golf course complexes, these incorporating hotel buildings, conference and other leisure facilities.

A more detailed breakdown of the development costs indicates that the cost of each green could range between £18,000 and £22,000 when provided with a full drainage carpet and rootzone layer. Tees can cost between £3,500 and £5,000 depending on their size and extent of earthworks required. The largest cost variation will be on through the green areas, this depending on the need for level adjustment as well as drainage. Development costs for each through the green could range between £5,000 to £20,000 or more with pipe drainage works costing around £8,000 per hectare. Tree planting could cost as much as £40,000.

Another major cost item is the provision of an automatic irrigation system utilising water drawn from the mains or a bore hole. Alternatively, a new lake may have to be created by damming an existing stream which would naturally add to the overall cost of this item. A modern day comprehensive irrigation system would comprise pop-up sprinklers for both greens and teeing areas, costing in the region of £80,000 to £100,000 to install. Fairway irrigation is not usually considered necessary, although allowance could be made for installing a series of hose connection points down the sides of the fairways if required.

When budgeting for a new golf course development, an important factor which should be considered is the period of time required for establishment of the various turf areas. Once construction works have been completed, then a minimum period of two years should be allowed before the course can be considered sufficiently well established to support play.

Additional expenditure will be required on maintenance equipment for the course, this including mowers, tractors, trailers, aerators and a general turf management system for greens and tees. If a full range of new maintenance equipment is required, then this could easily use up a further £120,000.

Taking the above factors into account, it is clear that although there is a potential demand for new golf courses, if a scheme is going to be feasible then a number of crucial considerations must be taken before proceeding. Firstly, its potential will depend on the local market, the size and composition of which must be assessed. Development costs are high compared with agricultural ventures and a preliminary professional assessment of the potential site is usually recommended as there is a thin borderline between success and failure. Even if a course is ideally situated and has been well designed and constructed, its profitability, even if managed to a high standard, cannot be necessarily assured.

SEEDING VIS-A-VIS TURFING

Choice

Renovation of thin areas on a golf course invariably involves seeding as opposed to turfing. The choice between the two comes when a bare section develops or a new surface is being prepared. Here, a number of factors are involved in selection as highlighted in the table below:

Seeding	Turfing
1. Delay in bringing the surface into play.	A significant reduction in the time before the surface is brought into play. For example, one would expect to bring a newly turfed green (autumn) into play after approximately seven months, yet for an equivalent autumn sowing the wait would be at least 20 months.
2. Restricted sowing period within the main growing season.	A much wider time span allowed for turfing, i.e. at almost any time of the year.
3. Reduced cost.	More expensive in relation to seeding, particularly for larger areas.
4. Precise selection of grass species and cultivars desired.	Restriction on manufacturer's choice of grass species and cultivars.
5a. Sowing into a uniform chosen growing medium.	Apart from a small percentage of seedling grown turf or washed turf available, the majority is grown in a different soil medium to the soil profile the construction and this can lead to problems with management and drainage (see 5b and c below).
5b. Good surface drainage rates.	A significant reduction in the infiltration rate permeability due to the turf growing medium. This is particularly pertinent to golf greens.
5c. An increased management requirement for developing a mature sward cover.	Less initial management, although with the soil layer there would be a necessity for soil exchange, i.e. hollow tining. On a new green following an autumn turfing, a spring hollow tining would be recommended (if feasible) before the green is brought into play. Hollow tining would also be repeated in the autumn and possibly during spring and autumn of the following year.

On a more specific level, prevailing resource availability and the political situation within a Golf Club (timing) also plays a part in determining the preference for turfing, seeding or a combination of the two, yet generalisations can be made.

Greens and Immediate Surrounds

For new green constructions the overwhelming consideration is often the pressure to bring the green into play in the shortest possible time, which necessitates the turfing option. Where sufficient time has been allocated for the project, seed is often the preference for cost, cultivar choice and soil compatibility.

Drought, wear and disease scarring are just a few of the possible causes behind the formation of thin and bare areas on exiting greens and for small and large bare sections plugging and/or turfing is the only feasible choice. The aim here is to establish a grass cover which will survive wear, and whilst seeding will fill in to some extent in a number of situations, the sward cover will not be mature or dense enough to withstand further stress due to weather and wear from foot traffic and the effects of mowing, verticutting and so on.

Within the body of a green, patch from the perimeter to achieve as good a match as possible and then renovate the perimeter area from an alternative good quality source. Any thin areas can be oversown and for the best chance of success, seeding (and turfing) should be scheduled for the early autumn. Any seeded, plugged or turfed sections at the edge of the putting surface should be brought into the collar or apron height of cut by recontouring green mowing. It should be stressed at this stage that whilst we do not want any thin and bare areas on putting surfaces, when they do occur it provides an excellent opportunity to introduce fine grasses, especially as it is invariably annual meadow-grass that has died out. It is still surprising to see how many annual meadow-grass/Yorkshire fog/perennial ryegrass plugs we see during a year!

Green Surrounds and Traffic Routes

Moving into general surrounds, here there is more leeway for seeding with increased spreading of wear and a higher height of cut with less verticutting and so on. An autumn sowing is still the best time to achieve the desired results, although if the weather conditions are slightly out of the main growing season, then the process of germination and establishment of seed sown can be improved through the pegging down of one of a number of proprietary protective grow covers now available on the market.

For heavily worn traffic routes, the renovation programme must involve an aspect of turfing to have any chance of surviving wear again the following main competition season; seeding is a waste of time, money and effort.

Tees/Fairways

The policy of an ongoing progressive divoting programme is essential for maintaining good levels and restoring a uniform, dense, healthy grass cover as soon as tee markers are moved – these are the two main requirements for tee management. If there is the facility to rest the main tees over the winter period, then a general autumn hollow tining/top dressing/over-seeding will prove invaluable in speeding up this aspect of the management programme, although where a time limit is imposed there is always the option of turfing.

The larger the area to be considered the more the cost factor comes into play, so for fairways seeding is invariably the choice unless a section of fairway needs to be returfed for political reasons (timing) or as part of a relevelling scheme for instance. The option for semi-rough/rough is almost exclusively for seeding.

Conclusion

The major considerations for the Greenkeeper in determining the choice of either seeding, turfing or a combination of the two relies on a number of factors, namely cost, urgency for bringing the surface into play, timing of work to be completed, soil compatibility and grass choice. Short and long term presentation, wearability and surface playing quality depend on it.

SECTION 7

PESTS AND DISEASES

SEEDLING DISEASES

The term 'damping-off' is often used to describe seedling diseases. There is relatively little information on seedling diseases – partly because of the variety of species of fungi that may be involved. Among those found on affected seedlings of turfgrasses are species of *Fusarium*, *Drechslera*, *Pythium* and *Cladochytrium*. Concern about seedling diseases has increased because the standard chemicals previously used for treatment (fungicides containing inorganic mercury compounds) are no longer available.

Recognition
Attack by fungi can occur before or after the seedling emerges.

When pre-emergence damping-off occurs, there may be no visible symptoms except the poor emergence of the grass. Of course, such a condition may have other causes, for example if seed of low percentage germination is sown or if environmental conditions do not favour seed germination and seedling establishment. In order to confirm the presence of a pre-emergence seedling disease, ungerminated seed needs to be recovered from the soil and examined microscopically.

Post-emergence damping-off tends to occur in patches. Affected seedlings often turn red, purple or yellow and they usually die. The disease may spread very quickly and cause almost complete destruction of the stand.

These two conditions are actually different even though many of the same fungi are involved. A grass species may be more susceptible to one than to another although environmental conditions also have an effect.

Conditions that Favour Seedling Diseases
As seedling diseases are very difficult to control satisfactorily, emphasis should be placed on prevention and much can be done by sensible cultural practices to reduce the risk. The diseases are usually most common when the soil is too wet, too cold or deficient in plant nutrients. They are also encouraged by over-crowding of the grass seedlings which may result from sowing seed at an excessive rate or sowing unevenly.

Adequate seed bed preparation should include attention to drainage and working the soil only in suitable conditions so that the soil structure is not damaged. An application of fertiliser to the seed bed is necessary in order that the grasses may grow as quickly as possible through the stages at which they are at risk. Fertiliser should be harrowed or raked in before sowing.

Care should be taken when sowing to adhere to the recommended sowing rate and every effort should be made to apply the seed evenly.

The most common cause of failure in establishment of seedlings is sowing in very unsatisfactory growing conditions. All too often there is a temptation to sow the seed too early in the spring when the soil is still too cold. Soil has a much higher heat capacity than air and a few warm days in March will not cause the soil to warm up sufficiently even though they may make us feel that spring has arrived! Autumn sowings should not be delayed much

194

after the beginning of September since it is important that sufficient remains of the growing season for the plants to become well established. In a mild autumn, later sowings may succeed but, if the cold weather comes before the seedlings are properly established, the risk of disease damage may be very high.

Most grasses can be subject to seedling disease but the larger and more vigorous seedlings of perennial ryegrass seem in general to be less likely to be affected than those of small seeded grasses such as bents. The sensitivity to pre-emergence and post-emergence damage may also differ, but little information is available to make generalisations on this subject.

Recommendations for Control

The major problem in deciding on control measures for seedling diseases is that several different species of fungi may be present in a single disease outbreak.

For **pre-emergence** damping-off, control measures need to be undertaken at the time of sowing. The usual method is to dress the seed with a suitable fungicide such as proprietary products containing thiabendazole and metaloxyl. Whether the extra cost of seed treatment is justified very much depends on how much damage will be done and unfortunately this cannot be known beforehand. However, in practice it seems that in most cases the damage suffered is not very great and sufficient seed remains to produce a satisfactory stand.

Fungicides likely to be available in the future will probably not have as wide a spectrum of activity as those used in the past. If the organisms responsible for **post-emergence** damping-off can be identified, particular chemical compounds, e.g. chlorothalonil, suitable for their control can be recommended but this identification process may take some time during which the disease may already have done much damage.

Such treatments may also have some effect on post-emergence damping-off.

FUSARIUM PATCH DISEASE

Fusarium patch disease, caused by the fungus *Microdochium nivale* (formerly *Fusarium nivale*), was first recorded on golf greens in 1931 and described as being the commonest, most disfiguring and damaging disease of turf known at that time. Nearly 60 years later, despite the development of effective fungicides, this statement is still true today. Throughout the year requests for information on fusarium patch disease are received by the STRI. The cultural and environmental conditions that favour the disease and the most effective prevention and control methods available are described below.

Recognition
Great care must be taken in identification as chemical or fertiliser scorch may appear surprisingly similar. Remember, samples of turf may be sent to the STRI for examination. An incorrect diagnosis may lead to wasteful (and expensive!) applications of fungicides.

Fusarium patch usually usually first appears as small (up to 50 mm diameter) orange/brown, water-soaked circular spots which, under favourable conditions, may increase rapidly and coalesce together to form large circular patches. Correct diagnosis of these early signs is important as the best possible control will be achieved if the disease is treated at this early stage. Under prolonged humid conditions, sparse white or pink mycelium may be seen around the edges of each patch which tends to mat the green leaves together. A pale straw colour at this time indicates that the disease has become less active, perhaps due to a drier climate. Eventually scars are formed which, particularly in the winter months, heal up slowly and are consequently prone to invasion by moss, undesirable grass species and weeds. If treatment is delayed until these later stages of disease development, poor control only will be achieved.

Conditions that Favour the Disease
Fusarium patch is favoured by cool, wet weather and is consequently most troublesome during the winter and spring months. The disease is found generally damaging fine turf, e.g. golf greens, especially where the sward contains a large proportion of annual meadow-grass (*Poa annua*), as this grass is highly susceptible to attack. High fertility conditions often created by late-season top dressing or fertiliser application also favour fusarium patch. Fine turf that is shaded from the sun or in a sheltered location, e.g. due to the close proximity of tall trees or buildings, will dry slowly and is therefore susceptible. Fusarium patch is also favoured by the presence of a deep thatch layer, as thatch is often moisture retentive and its constituent dead plant material is a natural substrate for the disease. Also, the disease is most active in alkaline turf, created perhaps by ill-advised applications of lime or top dressing sands with a lime content.

Recommendations for Control
The ready availability of fungicides must not reduce the attention paid to those practices that reduce the risk of disease. Any management practice that helps to keep the turf surface dry, such as switching, spiking or slitting, will reduce the likelihood of fusarium patch occurring. If necessary, reduce the moisture-holding thatch layer, e.g. by scarification, as this will again help to keep the turf surface dry. Surface drainage may also be improved by aeration and top dressing with a sandy compost. It is also a good idea to promote air circulation over and evaporation from the greens by not siting trees, shrubs or tall buildings too close as this will inhibit the removal of surface moisture by the wind and sun.

Effects on Disease
During cool wet weather, fusarium patch disease may cause serious damage to fine turf. The fungal pathogen which causes fusarium patch, *M. nivale* is most active under neutral or

alkaline conditions at the turf surface where the fungus is active. Consequently, sulphate of iron by acidifying plant tissues and thatch to which it comes into contact will help control the disease. Although not as effective as a fungicide spray, regular use of sulphate of iron will help minimise incidence and severity of fusarium patch and thus reduce the need for fungicide application. As well as fusarium patch another disease namely take-all patch is favoured by an alkaline turf surface. Re-acidifying the turf surface with sulphate of iron may limit the spread of take-all patch disease.

Annual meadow-grass is very susceptible to fusarium patch and consequently a sward containing a large percentage of this grass could suffer severe damage. Good turf management, in its aim of promoting a healthy, vigorous sward of fescue/bent, both of which are much more resistant to the disease, will consequently discourage fusarium patch. Great care must be taken when applying fertilisers as excessive nitrogen, especially the organic types such as dried blood, applied during cool, wet weather can lead to severe disease outbreaks. The use of lime on golf greens is only recommended under exceptional circumstances and is best avoided as, as well as encouraging fusarium patch and other diseases, it leads to invasion of annual meadow-grass, weeds and worms.

In situations of prolonged cool and wet weather, despite all cultural control measures being implemented, fusarium patch disease is still likely to attack on many courses. Fortunately, if the need arises, then the disease can be controlled with fungicides, providing they are used wisely and according to the manufacturer's instructions.

BROWN PATCH

For many years brown patch (caused by the fungus *Rhizoctonia solani*) has been considered an important turfgrass disease in the USA but it is only in recent years that the disease has been seen on fine turf in the UK. Brown patch is now recognised as a serious disease of turf that occurs occasionally in the summer months.

Recognition
The symptoms of brown patch vary greatly depending on the prevailing weather conditions. The disease is only damaging during warm, humid weather that gives prolonged periods of leaf wetness which is necessary for plant infection. If these weather conditions prevail, watch out for light brown circles of blighted grass up to 15 cm in diameter which may develop extremely rapidly. All species of turfgrasses may be affected, although there is some evidence to suggest that the bents (*Agrostis* spp.) are more susceptible.

Recommendations for Control
Brown patch can be prevented from occurring by regular scarification, if necessary, to reduce water-holding thatch and also by switching to remove dew each morning to remove the conditions of prolonged leaf wetness that favour the disease. As brown patch is also favoured by high nitrogen fertilization, applications should be light and frequent rather than one large application. Fungicides, in particular chlorothalonil and iprodione, are effective against brown patch but, as the disease can spread rapidly, they must be applied promptly at the first signs of the disease.

ANTHRACNOSE

Anthracnose, caused by the fungus *Colletotrichum graminicola*, was first recorded in the UK on a cricket square in 1953. It has been reported on a wide range of turfgrasses, but annual meadow-grass is particularly susceptible and is often attacked.

Recognition

The disease is seen usually between late summer and late winter. Watch out for the presence of yellowing individual annual meadow-grass plants in the sward with the youngest leaf on each plant turning an orange-red colour. In cases of severe attacks, small patches of infected grass develop which may increase up to 15 cm in diameter. In the cool, wet conditions that prevail in the UK, the disease causes mainly a rotting at the base of the plant. At later stages of disease development at the base of the plant on rotted leaf blades, small black structures may be seen. These are called *acervuli* which are fungal sporing structures embedded in the host tissue. Anthracnose is considered to be a 'biological indicator', i.e. if the disease is present, then certain turf conditions are likely to be far from satisfactory. The disease is favoured by low fertility, prolonged soil wetness and compacted soils.

Recommendations for Control

Try to relieve compaction by reducing traffic over an affected area, e.g. by moving the pin position on a golf green. Regular aerating and spiking is also beneficial. In the summer months, improving fertility with timely and moderate nitrogen applications will also discourage the disease. This approach is not recommended for the winter months as fertiliser application could lead to severe attacks of more damaging fusarium. Good turf management practices that aim to reduce the amount of annual meadow-grass in the sward will also reduce the likelihood of disease outbreak. Fungicides are not normally recommended if adequate disease control can be achieved by improving growing conditions. In cases of severe attacks the fungicide chlorothalonil may be effective.

TAKE-ALL PATCH DISEASE

Take-all patch is caused by the fungus *Gaeumannomyces graminis* which was until recently named *Ophiobolus graminis*, hence the old common name for the disease, Ophiobolus patch. Take-all patch was relatively unknown in turfgrass until the 1950's when it was the practice to correct extremely acidic turf with applications of lime. As liming encourages take-all, many severe outbreaks were recorded. In recent years, take-all patch has been a relatively uncommon disease but when it does occur it can be very disfiguring and damaging. Due to the very destructive nature of take-all patch, its persistence and the absence of an effective chemical control measure, it is regarded as potentially a serious problem in turf management.

Recognition

Symptoms of take-all patch usually appear in late summer or autumn. On fine turf, the disease often appears initially as saucer shaped, slightly depressed bare areas consisting mainly of dying bentgrasses, which are very susceptible to the disease. A photograph of take-all patch may be found in the STRI's booklet "Turfgrass Pests and Diseases". Send a turf sample to STRI if help is needed in diagnosing the disease. (A hole cutter sized plug to a depth of 0.1 metres, taken from the boundary of healthy and affected turf is required). These small patches may then enlarge into a ring, measuring up to 0.3 metres in diameter, of bleached or bronzed **bentgrasses**, the centre of each ring being occupied by plants resistant to the disease such as fescues, annual meadow-grass and broad leaved weeds. Eventually, adjacent rings may coalesce together resulting in large irregular patches on greens and fairways. Dying bentgrasses can be easily removed from the turf, due to their rotted root systems. Affected bentgrass roots and rhizomes are blackened due to extensive colonisation by the take-all fungus.

Conditions Which Favour the Disease

Surveys of UK golf courses have indicated that the fungus which causes take-all patch, *G. graminis* is nearly always present in turf but at very low population levels unable to cause disease. Present in the turf and soil are many other fungi and bacteria which are antagonistic to take-all patch and these suppress the disease to such an extent that its pathogenic activities are almost totally inhibited. If these antagonists are not present e.g. sand constructed greens are naturally low in antagonists, or a reduction in antagonists due to the excessive over use of fungicides or sterilisation has occurred, then the area may be prone to take-all patch. A rapid increase in turf surface pH by the application (often unwittingly) of alkaline materials can lead to severe take-all attacks. Also, as the take-all fungus overwinters in the thatch layer, excessive thatch will favour the spread of the disease. Take-all patch spreads in the water film between soil particles. Consequently, poor drainage will favour the movement of take-all patch to new areas.

Recommendations for Control

It must be explained that once the disease has become established, there is no effective control measure. Until recently, organo-mercury fungicides were used with some success but they are now banned under new pesticide regulations and cannot therefore be used. Consequently, all efforts must be aimed at **preventing** outbreaks of take-all. Firstly, recognise the situation in which take-all patch is likely to occur. Sand construction greens are particularly vulnerable, as are situations where seed bed, construction or top dressing materials have been sterilised. By far the best prevention of take-all patch can be achieved by avoiding the application of alkaline materials. Avoid applying lime unless it is absolutely necessary. Have all sands used for construction or top dressing analysed for their lime content. Irrigation water, if taken from a borehole source could be quite hard i.e. contain lime.

If take-all patch does occur then a long term solution to the disease is offered by a phenomenon known as take-all decline, in which, given the right conditions, the disease will become less severe and eventually disappear. This decline is due to the build up of antagonists in the turf whose activities inhibit the take-all patch; it is extremely rare for take-all patch to re-occur once the decline process has been completed. Consequently, the best strategy for the long term control of take-all is to provide the conditions which favour take-all decline. This can be done as follows:–

(1) Identify the possible source of alkalinity responsible for the disease. Try to eliminate them e.g. by changing to a lime-free sand. Take-all patch rarely causes extensive damage in acidic turf. Have pH readings made of infected greens and if necessary, acidify the turf surface with a fertiliser programme based on acidifying fertilisers such as ammonium sulphate.

(2) Light applications of sulphate of iron (4.2 g per m^2) may also be made at 3-4 week intervals to promote further acidification of the turf surface.

(3) Fungicides recommended for control of take-all patch (chlorothalonil and carbendazim) will at best only partially suppress the disease and could actually make the disease worse by inhibiting soil antagonists responsible for keeping the take-all patch at low levels. Thus, keep the application of fungicides to an absolute minimum. However, do not delay fungicide application if fusarium patch disease occurs.

(4) Maintain good turf vigour by supplying adequate nutrition. Most soils have sufficient phosphate and potassium but if in doubt have a soil analysis done. Appropriate fertilisers can then be applied after discussion with your advisory agronomist.

(5) Ensure the turf surface is free draining by regular slitting, spiking etc. Remember, take-all patch spreads rapidly in wet, water retentive turf.

(6) If necessary, deploy thatch reduction operations such as scarification and hollow tining to reduce the amount of dead plant material available for the take-all patch to live on.

(7) Badly scarred areas can be renovated by oversowing disease scars with fescue which is highly resistant to take-all patch.

FAIRY RINGS

The biology and control of fairy rings has been the subject of a four year research programme at STRI, sponsored by the Royal & Ancient Golf Club of St. Andrews. Fairy rings are very common on amenity turf in the UK and consequently most greenkeepers will have experienced them on the turf under their supervision. For instance, they are particularly common on golf course fairways – few courses do not have one or more rings. However, the damage that these rings cause depends very much on the type of ring, their location and abundance.

Type 1 rings are defined as those that actually kill the grass, e.g. as caused by the fungus *Marasmius oreades*. If a Type 1 ring is examined closely three distinct zones can be detected. The most noticeable feature is a ring of dead grass (usually 10-30 cm in diameter) in which mushrooms may be found during early summer and autumn. This dead zone is surrounded by inner and outer rings of stimulated lush-green grass. These rings are a direct result of the activities of *M. oreades* in the soil. Excavation of Type 1 rings has shown that under the dead zone the fairy ring mycelium is at its highest density. As this mycelium is extremely water-repellent (hydrophobic) and the mycelium can extend to a depth of up to 1 metre in the soil, any water applied by natural rainfall or irrigation will not percolate through the soil to the grass roots but will be shed away from this area. Consequently the grass is water stressed and dies to leave the characteristic ring of bare ground. The zones of lush grass growth adjacent to the dead zone are due to the feeding activities of the fairy ring fungus in the turf. Experiments conducted as early as 1917 revealed that *M. oreades* (along with other fairy ring fungi) is primarily a decomposer, i.e. it can release nitrogen from the organic matter in the thatch and soil below. Consequently, grass over these areas can utilise this nitrogen and lush growth is produced. On turf intensively managed for its appearance, e.g. golf greens, Type 1 rings may be disfiguring and further problems can be caused by the invasion of moss and weeds into the bare part of the ring. On lighter soils, e.g. on links courses, and in dry summers bare areas can become very conspicuous and consequently detract from the visual attractiveness of the area. If Type 1 rings occur on an area of fine turf, such as a golf green, then, due to the areas of dead turf produced, the playing quality of the area can also be significantly reduced.

Type 2 rings are those that produce a stimulated ring of grass only and do not cause any direct damage to the turf. Often, they are caused by the puff-ball fungi such as *Scleroderma* and *Lycoperdon* spp. These fungi do not produce extensive mycelium in the turf but are usually confined mainly to the thatch layer. Lush grass growth is produced in the same way as in Type 1 rings – uptake of nitrogen released by the fairy ring fungus through thatch decomposition. Type 2 rings are important as they have a marked effect on the visual quality of an affected area but, as they do not harm the grass directly, the playing quality of the turf is usually not really diminished.

Type 3 rings are those where a ring of mushrooms or toadstools is formed with no apparent effect on the grass, i.e. no lush or dead zone. To date over 60 species of fungi have been recorded as forming Type 3 rings on turf. In general, Type 3 rings are often ignored but they can present a nuisance value if the production of fruiting bodies is extensive.

Recommendations for Control

A solution to fairy rings has been sought for about 60 years and several traditional control methods have been developed. For example, the continuous drenching of rings or fertilizing with manure has been met with some success, but these methods have not proved reliable. Removing fairy rings by excavating all soil and turf containing mycelium has proved effective, particularly if combined with a soil-sterilant such as formaldehyde. However, this technique is very laborious and, as recent work has indicated that formaldehyde may be harmful to humans, the use of this technique has been discouraged.

From early research in the 1950's where drenches of sulphate of iron and potassium permanganate were tried for fairy ring control, it was realised how difficult it was to apply chemicals effectively due to the water-repellent properties of soil containing fairy ring mycelium. If a fungicide was applied it would be shed to areas not containing the fairy ring mycelium and consequently not be able to exert its toxic effects. These water-repellent properties have been alleviated by using wetting agents applied with the fungicide and also by combining the fungicide with special organic solvents. However, even with these methods, control has often been unsatisfactory.

Initial research at the STRI concentrated on how this water-repellent nature of fairy rings can be alleviated. As the fairy ring can make the thatch water-repellent, removal by scarification will enable fungicides to penetrate the ring. Hollow tining (shown to be preferable to spiking) provides channels down which the fungicide can flow into the fairy ring. Both scarification and hollow tining are thus recommended prior to fungicide drenching. If the fairy ring mycelium has penetrated deeply into the soil, then additional spiking may also be necessary. The water-repellency factor can then be alleviated by pre-soaking the ring with wetting agent. Experiments at STRI are under way to evaluate chemicals such as strong alkalis and organic solvents which will attack the water-repellent mycelium directly and thus promote the effectiveness of fungicides subsequently applied. Mechanical means of placing fungicide solutions in fairy rings are also under test – particularly the effectiveness of applying chemicals after treatment with the Verti-Drain and soil injection equipment such as the Terralift.

There have also been developments in the testing of more effective fungicides. Since the introduction of benodanil, oxycarboxin and triforine for fairy ring control, several new chemicals which may be possible candidates for toxicity against fairy rings have become available. Laboratory screening techniques have revealed that several chemicals, apart from those mentioned above, are highly effective against the mycelium of fairy rings and, as these chemicals may also persist in the soil, they may give more long-lasting control than those currently available. Full-scale field trials at sites in North East England are now under way with this material and preliminary results suggest that these fungicides could give effective and long-lasting control of fairy rings.

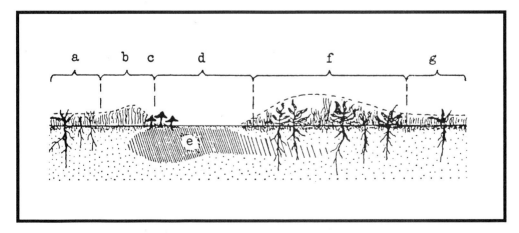

FIGURE 21: Cross-section through a Grade 1 fairy ring caused by *Marasmius oreades*. (a) outside the ring; (b) outer stimulated zone; (c) fruiting bodies of the fungus; (d) bare zone; (e) mycelium (hatched) in the soil (dotted); (f) inner stimulates zone; (g) inside the ring.

SUPERFICIAL FAIRY RINGS

In recent years, superficial fairy rings have caused widespread problems on golf greens.

Recognition
Some superficial fairy ring fungi produce only sparse mycelium in turf and consequently have little apparent effect on the sward. The most common type are not aggressive pathogens, but are able to cause some plant stress resulting in a ring of yellowing turf. Situations in which annual meadow-grass predominates are particularly prone to invasion by this type of superficial fairy ring. If a core of turf is taken from an affected area, fine white or cream-coloured mycelium may be seen in the thatch or around plant bases, and the core will have a faint or sometimes in severe cases, a strong musty smell resembling that produced by dry rot. It is these two diagnostic features, the presence of mycelium and the musty smell, which are highly characteristic of superficial fairy rings.

Other superficial fairy ring fungi may produce areas of stimulated grass growth, either in saucer-shaped patches or distinct rings. This is due to the fungi decomposing the thatch, releasing nitrogen in a form available for uptake by the grass, resulting in dark green lush growth. Thatch decomposition may take place to such an extent that surface depressions are formed which may have a marked effect on the playing qualities of the surface, especially on golf greens.

Occasionally, superficial fairy rings may form small arcs or circles of bleached grass where the grass plant has been attacked and killed. Affected turf has a very strong musty smell.

Conditions which Favour Superficial Fairy Rings
Superficial fairy rings are caused by a large and varied group of fungi known as basidiomycetes of which only a few in turf have been identified. As little is known about the basic biology of these fungi in the turfgrass situation, there is correspondingly little information on the cultural and environmental conditions which favour their development. In most cases, superficial fairy rings are apparent between early-summer and late-autumn when soil temperatures are high enough to enable fungal growth and associated thatch decomposition to occur. However, there are other superficial fairy ring fungi which are active at low temperatures and may cause problems in the winter months. Dry weather also promotes superficial fairy ring activity as air may penetrate deeper into the turf profile, thus allowing aerobic fungi to thrive. This is possibly the reason for the many reported cases of superficial fairy rings during the dry 1989 and 1990 summers. Also, mycelium of superficial fairy ring fungi may sometimes be seen following deep rooting in hollow tine or Verti-Drain holes – further evidence that these fungi require aerobic conditions.

Superficial fairy ring fungi have water-repellent hyphae an effect that is most apparent in the early morning as dew will not settle on affected areas. Consequently in certain cases their activities may lead to the formation of dry patch (see earlier article).

In general, the activities of superficial fairy rings are confined to the litter and thatch layers of the turf and as such are sometimes referred to as 'thatch fungi'. This term is misleading as any fungi in the thatch (and there are many present) both beneficial or detrimental would be included and therefore the term is best avoided. Also, whilst the damage done by superficial fairy rings is often most severe in situations with a thatch problem, they have also been recorded in situations with no appreciable thatch, e.g. newly established all-sand construction golf greens.

It is interesting to note that superficial fairy rings were relatively uncommon 10 years ago, and speculation on the reasons for their increase and spread over the last decade has implicated changes during the same period in the fungicides available for control of turfgrass diseases. It is thought that the use in the past of persistent broad-spectrum organo-mercurial compounds for control of fusarium patch disease were also inadvertently inhibiting superficial fairy rings, which were consequently not noticed. Also, it is suggested that the recent use of systemic fungicides has led to this problem by possibly eliminating antagonistic and competitive fungi in the thatch, leaving superficial fairy rings to thrive. Whilst there is a scientific paper published in the 1970's to support this argument, a recent study has shown no association between systemic fungicides and superficial fairy rings.

Recommendations for control
In situations where there is excessive thatch, the reasons for this should be identified and the most appropriate control methods implemented. Thatch reduction is essentially removing the food supply for the superficial fairy ring fungi and will thus help to limit their activities. It must be emphasised that there is no evidence that the aeration techniques used in turf management are making the problems worse, they just allow the fungus to move deeper into the soil profile.

Any shallow depressions in the turf surface may be levelled by selective top dressing. The appearance of superficial fairy rings may also be marked by light applications of sulphate of iron or a liquid iron formulation. If dry patch is apparent then treatment with a non-ionic wetting agent to improve water infiltration into affected areas will be beneficial.

In cases of severe superficial fairy ring activity where appreciable surface disruption is being caused, treatment with an appropriate fungicide is probably justified. For several years two fungicides, namely oxycarboxin and benodanil have been used and some suppression of superficial fairy ring fungi achieved. Recently, a new fungicide for control of fairy rings, based on the active ingredient triforine, has become available.

RED THREAD

Until recently, red thread (Corticium disease) was believed to be caused by *Corticium fuciforme* but recent studies have revealed two different fungi are involved. This discovery has resulted in a major taxonomic revision of the causal fungi and two separate diseases being recognised. The new names are red thread when *Laestisaria fuciformis* is the causal fungus and pink patch (rarely seen on fine turf) when *Limnomyces roseipellis* is the causal fungus. From the practical viewpoint, however, both diseases cause similar symptoms, may occur together, are generally indistinguishable and can be prevented or controlled in the same way. Although both diseases have been reported in the UK, little is known about their relative distribution and importance.

Red thread is most often seen during the summer and autumn but may persist into winter if conditions remain mild. Any type of turf may be attacked but red fescue and perennial ryegrass are most often affected. The diseases are most likely to occur under conditions of low fertility, particularly insufficient nitrogen, during cool, moist weather.

Recognition
The intensity of red thread attack can vary from withering of a few leaves only, in which case it is often overlooked or ignored, to large scale damage resulting in death of infected plants. Look out for patches of damaged grass initially 20–30 mm in diameter with a pink colouring. The patches may spread to 0.35 metres across and develop an irregular outline when grass growth is slow and favourable conditions for disease development exist.

Unique to red thread is the production of red needles (stroma) from the tips of infected grass leaves which have a survival role in the life cycle of *L. fuciformis*. Under conditions of high humidity infected plants may be bound together by a webbed mycelium and cottony flocs of mycelium may also be found in the sward. Pink patch first becomes evident along the margins of leaf blades as small blotches of pink mycelium. This pink mycelium never becomes as pronounced as the stroma of the red thread fungus.

Recommendations for Control
Pay particular attention to choice of cultivar, therefore consult the STRI booklet "Turfgrass Seed" especially if red fescue is being considered as this can help prevent red thread and pink patch. Generally, slow-growing, low-maintenance cultivars are more susceptible to attack. Adequate fertiliser, particularly nitrogen, during the growing season will also prevent severe attacks. However, care is needed as extreme nitrogen can favour other problems such as fusarium patch disease. All things considered, it may be better to rely on the timely and judicious use of fungicides. When the grass is growing actively, fungicides containing benomyl and carbendazim will give good control of red thread but these fungicides are much less efficient against pink patch disease. As both diseases often become most severe when grass growth is slow, contact fungicides may be the most effective. When applied as a preventative spray, reliable control may be achieved with fungicides containing iprodione, vinclozolin or chlorothalonil.

TURF FUNGICIDES

In turf, pathogenic fungi are often present in the thatch and soil, but disease will only occur under suitable environmental conditions. Therefore, good cultural and management practices can do much to prevent disease by providing conditions unfavourable to disease development. However, the weather is unpredictable and errors of judgement may be made, resulting in a disease outbreak. Then, an application of fungicide may be necessary to limit disease severity and to produce a high quality turf surface. Applying fungicides involves many considerations such as choice of material, application method, application rate and timing to achieve effective disease control. This leaflet is a brief guide to the efficient and judicious use of fungicides.

Disease Identification
When disease appears the first step is correct identification from the symptoms observed. If in doubt reference may be made to the STRI publication "Turfgrass Pests and Diseases" or a turf sample may be sent to STRI for disease diagnosis and our recommendations for control.

Fungicides currently available for use on turf can be divided into two groups. Systemic fungicides, so called as they can be absorbed by the grass leaves and roots and redistributed to protect all plant parts, are most effective when the grass is **growing actively** i.e. between spring and autumn. Also, if applied in late autumn as a preventative treatment they may protect the grass from disease through the winter months. The most common systemics are those belonging to the Benzimidazole group, mainly used for control of fusarium patch and red thread diseases. Contact fungicides, so called as they can only protect plant parts or eradicate disease from areas which the chemical touches, are most effective when grass growth is slow i.e. during the winter. If a disease has become established contact fungicides have the best 'knock down' effect. However, as contact fungicides are not absorbed into plant tissues they may be washed off more easily than systemic fungicides during rainfall or removed when mowing, and consequently give reduced disease control.

Application of Fungicides
Generally, fungicides should be applied at the first signs of the disease rather than routine preventative spraying. Regular inspection of turf areas is essential as disease outbreaks may occur rapidly under favourable conditions. Usually it is best to treat the whole turf area to minimise disease spread, although spot treatment of active disease using a knapsack sprayer may also prove beneficial. To avoid problems of fungicide resistance (strains of the pathogen developing which are resistant to the fungicide) it is best to alternate fungicides from different groups of active ingredients.

Fungicide Groups

Benzimidazoles	*Dicarboximides*	*Others*
benomyl	iprodione	chlorothalonil
carbendazim	vinclozolin	quintozene
thiophanate-methyl		
thiabendazole		

For example, a fungicide spray programme designed to minimise the possibility of resistance occurring in fusarium patch disease would be a Benzimidazole in spring, followed by a Dicarboximide or either chemical under the 'Others' heading during the winter. When using fungicides the Manufacturers instructions found on the product label should be followed carefully – many of them are now legally binding.

Choice of Chemical

In our experience, the best fungicide to use against the more common turf diseases is shown in the table below. All fungicide/disease combinations are approved by MAFF under the Control of Pesticides Regulations 1986.

ACTIVE INGREDIENT (PRODUCT NAME) — TURFGRASS DISEASES

ACTIVE INGREDIENT (PRODUCT NAME)	FORMULATION	GREY SNOW MOULD	PINK SNOW MOULD	FUSARIUM PATCH	FAIRY RINGS	LEAF SPOT/MELTING OUT	RED THREAD	DOLLAR SPOT	BROWN PATCH	ANTHRACNOSE
Benomyl (Benlate)	WP			✓			✓	✓		
Chlorothalonil (Daconil Turf)	SC	✓	✓	✓		✓	✓	✓		✓
Carbendazim (Fisons' Turfclear Mascot Systemic)	SC			✓			✓	✓		
Dichlorophen (Super Mosstox Mascot Moss Killer)	SL						✓			
Thiophanate-methyl (Mildothane)	SC			✓			✓	✓		
Benodanil (Clearing)	WP				✓					
Oxycarboxin (Ringmaster)	LI				✓					
Triforine (Fairy Ring Destroyer)					✓					
Iprodione (Rovral Green)	SC + GR	✓	✓	✓		✓	✓	✓	✓	
Quintozene (Quintozene)	WP			✓			✓	✓		
Thiabendazole (Tecto)	SC	✓	✓	✓			✓	✓	✓	
Vinclozolin (Mascot Contact)	LI			✓			✓	✓		

*WP = wettable powder   LI = liquid   GR = granular   SC = suspension concentrate   SL = soluble concentrate

Pesticides Regulations 1986

All concerned with pesticides should make themselves aware of legislation and obligations under the Pesticides Regulations 1986 by consulting the publications "Amenity Pesticides" and "Pesticides : guide to the new controls".

MANAGING THE EARTHWORM

Earthworms are very abundant in the soil, particularly in areas of natural grassland where densities of 260–500 worms per m^2 are commonly found. High densities are also likely to occur under grass covered golf areas because of similarly favourable conditions of environment and food supply and thus the management, or control, of earthworms becomes an integral part of turf care. Earthworm populations are composed of a number of species – Britain has around 25 types, although obviously not all occur in turf areas – all of which have vastly different behavioural characteristics. Aspects of this behaviour must be understood if management is to be effective.

Distribution – Why should we have Earthworms in Golf Areas?
Earthworm numbers and species are very much influenced by the environmental conditions of soil texture, pH, moisture, temperature, aeration, the presence of inorganic salts and food availability. They tend to be more of a problem on the parkland course, rather than the heath, moor or links.

The highest natural earthworm populations occur within soil textural types that are common beneath golf turf, i.e. light and medium loams. Low populations are associated with gravelly deposits, very sandy conditions and peat soils. Soil texture exerts a general control on species composition.

The acidity of a soil has a major influence on the number of earthworms. Acidity also affects species composition; most species favour a fairly neutral pH and many are not found where the pH is less than 5.0. Certain species are, however, known to be acid tolerant, e.g. *Bismastos eiseni*, *Dendrobaena octaedra* and *D. rubida* are usually associated with a soil pH of between 3.7 and 4.7.

Moisture content affects earthworm distribution and very droughty soils are avoided. Nevertheless, earthworms have considerable ability to survive adverse moisture conditions, either by moving into a more suitable area or becoming dormant until favourable conditions return. Most species of worms can survive prolonged periods of submergence but in general saturated soils are avoided. So, from the point of view of moisture, most golf turf soils, except perhaps some very sandy constructions, provide ideal conditions for earthworm activity. Grass covered surfaces also produce a favourable temperature regime by insulating against extreme conditions. This maintains optimum conditions for activity, metabolism, growth, respiration and reproduction.

Food supply is the other main factor influencing population size, species composition, growth rates and levels of fertility. Earthworms are selective feeders; dung is preferred by some species and various types of plant material are more palatable than others. Litter with a high content of soluble carbohydrates is preferred and that with a high total polyhydric phenol content is avoided. Again, turf areas meet the nutritional requirements of many earthworm species.

Behavioural Patterns and Vertical Distribution
Differences in behavioural characteristics produce a vertical structure to the earthworm population. Species such as *D. octaedra* and *B. eisnei* live in the surface organic horizon. *Allolobophora caliginosa*, *A. rosea*, *Lumbricus castareus* and *L. rubellus* commonly occur within 8 cm of the soil surface as do immature individuals of certain deeper dwelling species. In general the species living near the surface do not have permanent burrow systems and

instead they push their way through crevices and only occasionally excavate burrows. *A. longa* and *A. nocturna*, on the other hand, have fairly permanent burrows, the walls of which are cemented together with ejected soil and mucous secretions. These species usually penetrate to about 45 cm while the burrows of *L. terrestris* frequently reach the 1 metre depth and penetration up to 2.4 metres has been recorded.

Effects of Earthworms on the Soil

Earthworm activity is responsible for both physical and chemical changes in the soil. Physical changes are brought about by burrowing activities and soil aggregating effects. There can be around 100–300 burrows per m^2 in grassland and these tunnels provide important routes for water and air movement through the soil, increasing the effectiveness of soil aeration, drainage and irrigation. Rates of infiltration are often more than doubled. Physical characteristics are further improved by aggregation, since the intimate mixing of ingested soil and partially broken down organic matter in the earthworm's gut creates water stable aggregates.

Organic Matter Breakdown

Soil microflora and microfauna are capable of acting on very soft plant and animal residues but tougher plant leaves, stems and root material does not break down without first being disintegrated by soil animals and acted upon by enzymes in their intestines. In this respect, earthworms are vital in the decomposition of organic matter. The amount of organic matter consumed can be enormous, for example in apple orchards *L. terrestris* has been found to remove more than 90% of the autumn leaf fall during the course of the winter, the dry weight of which was calculated to be 1.2 tonnes/ha. Translated to a golfing venue, this organic breakdown represents an important control of thatch development.

This organic matter breakdown is very important in the nitrogen cycle, increasing amounts of soluble and available N. Worms also raise the base exchange capacity of soil giving more exchangeable Ca, Mg and K and increasing available P.

The Problem of Casting

In the agricultural context earthworms are rarely regarded as a problem, but on golf turf their habit of casting is viewed with disfavour. When casting is heavy the ejected material is unsightly, causes an uneven surface which can interfere with the run of a golf ball, and forms a muddy, moisture retentive playing surface. The strength of the turf, so important for players to maintain a good grip, can be adversely affected and was found to decrease by 17% and 19% in areas of heavy casting during experimental work on two professional sports grounds. Earthworm activity can also have indirect effects through the spread of weeds and possibly disease and also by encouraging moles.

All earthworms are persecuted for this casting activity but it is in fact only a few species that are responsible. Of the 8–10 common field species of earthworms in Britain only three, *A. longa, A. nocturna* and *L. terrestris*, regularly produce casts on the surface of the soil. All three species have permanent burrows. However, in compacted soil, particularly appropriate to golf turf, there is also evidence of casting by *A. caliginosa, A. chlorotica* and *A. rosea*, which usually expel their faeces into cracks and crevices below the soil surface. There is some seasonality in the intensity of casting, this being most severe during mild and moist periods in the spring and autumn, and yearly totals can rise to 50 tonnes/ha where no control is applied. In Europe individual casts seldom exceed 100 g, but pity the poor Burmese groundsman faced with casts of the giant *Notoscolex* earthworms which can be 20–25 cm high and 4 cm diameter. One such cast weighed 1600 g.

Management through Cultural Control

Some control of the earthworm population is required, particularly to reduce heavy casting, but the beneficial effects of earthworms must also be remembered so the total and permanent removal of earthworms cannot usually be encouraged, except on fine turf surfaces such as golf greens. Effective chemical methods that selectively kill the casting species have yet to be developed, but cultural practices can be used to minimise the earthworm problem. The sensitivity of the earthworm population to environmental factors has already been discussed, and in good greensmanship manipulation of pH and food supply can be used to maintain a relatively low earthworm population. This will alleviate the problems of heavy casting.

Two of the main casting species, *A. longa* and *A. nocturna* are acid-intolerant, so a low pH will reduce numbers of these species but may well allow the beneficial effects of other types of worm. A pH of about 5.0 represents their lowest tolerance and this can be used as a cultural control on golf greens. A much lower pH will affect grass growth but a balance with a slightly acid soil which favours fine grass growth and which decreases, but does not entirely eliminate, earthworms is preferred. Care must therefore be taken with corrective liming and sea-sand dressings should be avoided as they encourage alkaline conditions.

An abundant food supply will encourage high earthworm populations so this can be used as a second cultural control. Allowing clippings to fly provides good material, so as a general rule boxing off should be used on fine turf areas. In addition, where organic fertilisers are used regularly there is a tendency to increase the earthworm population.

Management through Chemical Control

Earthworms cannot tolerate acidic turf, so applying an acidic material such as sulphate of iron will keep earthworms away from the turf surface and thus keep casting to a minimum. Thus, the problem of earthworm casts providing seedbeds for weeds, creating muddy conditions and interfering with play may be reduced. In a current trial at STRI applying sulphate of iron at rates between 4 and 8 g/m^2 in the early winter months has inhibited earthworm casting for 2 to 3 weeks. Termination of approvals for the use of chlordane (the most effective earthworm killer) have now been introduced for large areas of turf and from 31 December 1992 the use of chlordane will no longer be permitted on any type of turf. It is possible that sulphate of iron may play an increasing role in earthworm management programmes in the future.

When rates of casting get out of hand a more immediate method of control is required. This can be achieved by chemical methods. Traditional expellent wormkillers (e.g. Derris dust, Mowrah meal, potassium permanganate and copper sulphate) were used to bring worms to the surface without necessarily killing them. The worms were then swept off. These chemicals have been superseded by poisons (e.g. carbaryl) which give effective control for a longer period of time. These worm control measures are usually best taken in autumn and possibly spring, during mild, moist weather when the worms are actively working in the surface layers of the soil and are therefore more likely to be affected by the wormkilling agent. Preliminary spiking will also help the effectiveness of the treatment by increasing penetration.

However, good management involves judicious use of these wormkilling agents. They should only be used when casting intensity reaches levels that are unacceptable for satisfactory playing conditions, e.g. when a golf green is becoming soft and muddy. Further treatment should only be applied if casting levels return to an unacceptable level, since a regime based on at least some earthworm activity should be encouraged. For larger areas, e.g. fairways, only those parts of the fairway with a serious problem should be treated, this has the twin advantages of reducing the cost of the chemicals required and secondly allowing some of the beneficial aspects of earthworm activity to continue.

Finally, some thought may be given to the selection of the wormkiller to be used. In some instances there might be a case for using a less permanent killing agent such as a fungicide based on benzimidazole, e.g. benomyl or carbendazim. This will act as an immediate, but not long lasting, control of earthworms, giving time for management to be improved so that a regime based on low earthworm numbers can be established.

Earthworm Substitutes

The proposed management regime, based on low earthworm numbers, attempts to minimise the casting problem whilst still harnessing the beneficial effects of the earthworm in terms of aeration, aggregation and organic matter breakdown. However, the soil-plant system is in a delicate balance and some compensation for the lower levels of earthworm activity may be required, with the mechanical substitutes of spiking and scarification replacing the earthworm's role in drainage channel formation and thatch control.

OTHER TURF PESTS

Possibly the worst pest of all, especially in fine turf, is the earthworm because of the harm done by the surface casts, but worm control is a subject on its own and merits separate treatment. Second in importance is the leatherjacket – the larval stage of various species of *Tipula* (the crane fly or 'daddy-longlegs') – which feeds on the turf and its roots. The adult crane flies are on the wing in late summer and autumn; they mate immediately after emerging from the pupal cases and lay about 200–300 eggs per female insect. The eggs hatch out into larvae in about 14 days, and these larvae remain in the soil and turf for about 9 months, feeding on the turf and its roots. They are very susceptible to drought in the early stages and this is just one of the reasons why myriads of crane flies observed in August or September do not necessarily imply a plague of leatherjackets the following year. Eventually the larvae go into the pupal stage where they remain for 9–10 days and then when the pupa is ready it works its front end above ground, and it is common to see the brown sheaths of the empty pupal cases sticking up out of the turf after an emergence of a flight of crane fly.

Fibrous Turf Favoured
Leatherjackets cause trouble mostly in turf growing in sandy soils and they particularly like a fibrous turf such as is often found on golf fairways. They have tended not to be so common in the more intensively managed fine turf of golf greens because of the recent widespread use of chlordane for wormkilling – the chlordane kills the leatherjackets too. (Use of this chemical is now prohibited.)

Control in November
By spring leatherjackets have increased considerably in size and if large numbers are present they will be causing considerable damage, eating away at the roots to such an extent that the turf dies right back, especially if the weather is dry. Secondary damage results from birds like starlings and rooks searching for the larvae; in fact quite often the birds act as an early warning system, alerting the attention of the greenkeeper to the presence of the leatherjackets. A tarpaulin or damp sack left overnight on the turf will usually give some idea of the numbers present, and if these exceed 20 per square yard on a golf fairway it is advisable to apply a suitable insecticide. In fine turf like greens there should really be no leatherjackets at all. About November is the best time to apply an insecticide, before the year's generation of grubs has grown sufficiently large to do any appreciable harm, and for large-scale work insecticides based on gamma-HCH are relatively cheap and effective.

Fever Fly Larvae Also Damage Turf
The larvae of the fever fly (*Dilophus febrilis*) and two species of *Bibio* (St Mark's and St John's flies) are sometimes mistaken for leatherjackets, but they are smaller and have a distinct brown head. The eggs are laid in clusters, and therefore the larvae tend to create local damage rather than affecting a wide area like the leatherjackets. There are two broods a year, the flies (rather like house-flies in appearance) emerging in May and September. The grubs cause similar damage to the turf to that produced by leatherjackets, though usually on a smaller scale. Control measures are the same as for leatherjackets.

Some Minor Insect Pests
Chafer larvae (the larvae of the cock-chafer, the garden chafer, the summer chafer and the rose chafer) cause a good deal of damage on golf course turf on the Continent, but in this country the pest is less common. Nevertheless, cases of damage, mainly to golf course fairways, do occur from time to time, and the usual culprit turns out to be the garden chafer. Control is not easy but gamma-HCH, chlorpyrifos or diazinon may be tried, preferably after a thorough

spiking of the turf, and the younger the grubs are the more successful the control is likely to be. Mining bees (about 60 British species but *Andrena fulva* perhaps the most common in turf) sometimes cause the little mounds of soil which appear on turf grown in sandy soils, these solitary bees excavating vertical burrows (which may go down as deep as 600 mm) in which they lay their eggs. The harm done by these rather attractive insects is minimal really and they can hardly be accused of causing appreciable amounts of damage. Nor can ants, frit flies, dung, dor and oil beetles, cutworms and mole crickets which occasionally occur on the British turf scene, though some of them, like the cutworms, are a sore trial to the managers of fine turf on the Continent, especially in the South. In a hot, dry summer the longer grass in the rough of the golf course – particularly the fescue grasses – will assume a red colouration which is rather puzzling to the inexperienced eye, but the phenomenon is due to the action of certain species of leaf-sucking aphid.

Rabbits

Rabbits are once again causing considerable damage, particularly on golf courses, having gained some measure of immunity against myxomatosis. On fairways and tees, especially where the soil is light and sandy, they will enlarge by their scratching and burrowing any areas which have been damaged initially by play – divot holes for instance. In a bunker they can create absolute havoc. Nor are the greens immune, and rabbits will crop the grass right down to ground level, causing uneven putting surfaces and light coloured patches in the turf. Trapping, gassing and shooting at night in the headlights of a Land Rover or similar form of transport are the most effective means of control, but the position is difficult where there is abundant cover available to the animals. Foxes are on the increase too, and though they help to keep the rabbits down they can be responsible, by scratching and urinating, for a certain amount of damage to the turf themselves.

Moles

The harm caused by these creatures on a golf course can be horrific. Trapping or gassing are also effective against moles, whilst worm baits dipped in strychnine and inserted in the runs at strategic points provide a method which is popular with the professionals. Strychnine is, of course, a very dangerous poison; permits are only available from the Ministry of Agriculture, Fisheries and Food and issued only to suitable applicants. An indirect method of keeping moles out of golf turf is to get rid of the worms and thus the attraction for the moles.

Really, thanks largely to our cool climate, turf in Britain escapes relatively lightly with regard to numbers of pests, particularly insect pests, compared with turf in tropical or semi-tropical countries, and if we consult the appropriate American literature for example we find we have much to be grateful for in this respect.

SECTION 8

WEEDS

GUIDE TO WEED CONTROL

The aim of the greenkeeper is to produce the highest possible quality of turf with the resources available. In general, this means that the presence of broad-leaved weeds in any number is unacceptable not merely from an aesthetic point of view but also because weeds can actually influence play.

If weeds are beginning to become a problem, there may well be an underlying reason. The most common causes are over-acidity of the surface soil, poor drainage, or poor nutrition. Weeds can act as indicators of an underlying problem and without tackling the underlying cause then weeds will always be present. It is a wise policy to try to discover why weeds are present, particularly if they are a recurring problem, and to adjust turf management in conjunction with chemical control measures accordingly. For example, sheep's sorrel (*Rumex acetosella*) is associated with an over-acid surface soil, creeping buttercup (*Ranunculus repens*) is often found in damp, boggy corners and white clover (*Trifolium repens*) is often seen in areas that have not been fertilized for several seasons.

The greenkeeper must be familiar with the common broad-leaved weeds and if there is any doubt about identification, then advice should be sought.

Established Fine Turf
(a) *Hand Weeding*
Before reaching for the sprayer it is always worth considering hand weeding, particularly in small areas. Much effort and money can be saved by always carrying a knife to remove weeds during the course of the day. Even some grass weeds can be significantly discouraged by regular slashing, for example the spread of Yorkshire fog (*Holcus lanatus*) can be limited in this way.

(b) *Spot Treatment*
In general, spot treating individual weeds needs to be done carefuly as so often weedkiller is over-applied with the result that as well as the weed, surrounding turf is killed out. A single nozzle, lance-type sprayer is not recommended for spot treating weeds in turf for this reason. However, provided great care is taken, correct doses can be applied to small areas using, for example, aerosol spot weeders.

As is the case when hand weeding, spot treating weeds is really only practical over fairly small areas.

(c) *Spraying – Choosing a Herbicide*
Once it has been decided there is a weed problem and the weeds have been identified, the next step is to choose the appropriate herbicide for selective control.

Commonly available selective herbicides are based on the active ingredients MCPA, 2,4-D, dicamba, dichloroprop, fenoprop, mecoprop and ioxynil. Normally proprietary products contain one or more herbicides. The different combinations increase the number of weed species it is possible to control. The choice of product should be based on the susceptibility of the weed species to any of the available herbicides or a mixture of herbicides. Information is available and the table lists a selection of common weeds and their susceptibility as mature plants to various herbicides and mixtures.

Broad-Leaved Weeds and Their Herbicide Susceptibility as Mature Plants

Common Name	Botanical Name	MCPA	2,4-D	Mecoprop	Mecoprop/ 2,4–D	Ioxynil/ mecoprop
Creeping buttercup	*Ranunculus repens*	S	S	MR	S	MS
Bulbous buttercup	*Ranunculus bulbosus*	MS	MS	MR	MS	MR
Mouse-ear chickweed	*Cerastium holosteoides*	MS	MR	S	S	S
Common chickweed	*Stellaria media*	MS	MS	S	S	S
Pearlwort	*Sagina procumbens*	MR	MR	S	S	S
Blinks	*Montia fontana*	—	—	—	MR	—
Black medick	*Medicago lupulina*	R	R	MS	MS	MS
Suckling clover	*Trifolium dubium*	R	R	MR	MR-MS	MS
White clover	*Trifolium repens*	MR	R	MS	MS	S
Cinquefoil	*Potentilla reptans*	MR-MS	MR-MS	MR-MS	MR-MS	MS
Parsley piert	*Aphanes arvensis*	R	R	MR-MS	MR-MS	MS
Sheep's sorrel	*Rumex acetosella*	MS	MS	R	MS	MS
Common sorrel	*Rumex acetosa*	MS	MS	R	MS	MS
Curled dock	*Rumex crispus*	MS	MS	MR	MS	—
Slender speedwell	*Veronica filiformis*	R	R	MR	MR	MS
Self-heal	*Prunella vulgaris*	MR	MR	MS	MS	MS
Broad-leaved plantain	*Plantago major*	S	S	S	S	S
Ribwort plantain	*Plantago lanceolata*	S	S	S	S	S
Common ragwort	*Senecio jacobaea*	MS	MS	—	MS	—
Daisy	*Bellis perennis*	MR	MS	MR	MS	MR
Yarrow	*Achillea millefolium*	MR	MR	MR-MS	MR-MS	MS
Cat's ear	*Hypochaeris radicata*	MS	MS	MS	MS	MS
Mouse-ear hawkweed	*Hieracium pilosella*	S	S	S	S	MS
Dandelion	*Taraxacum officinale*	MS	MS	MR	MS	MR
Toadrush	*Juncus bufonius*	R	R	MR	MS	MS
Field woodrush	*Luzula campestris*	R	R	MR	MR	MR

Note: Herbicides used at full recommended rates according to manufacturers' instructions.

Key: S = Susceptible, one application kills
    MS = Moderately susceptible, one application usually kills, sometimes a second needed
    MR = Moderately resistant, 2 to 3 applications needed
    R = No useful effect
    — = No information

CONTROL OF BROAD-LEAVED WEEDS WITH APPLICATION OF SELECTIVE WEEDKILLERS

(1) General

Selective weedkillers or herbicides will control most broad-leaved weeds of turf. They may contain one or more active ingredients. At least one of the active ingredients is normally a foliage-applied translocated herbicide with growth-regulating activity, such as MCPA, 2,4-D or mecoprop. These chemicals are taken into plants chiefly through leaves, but also through roots, and upset normal plant growth processes and distort growth within susceptible weed species. Effects can be seen in twisting of leaves and distorted growth within a day or two of application, but weeds may not die for four to eight weeks. Resistant species may take in less chemical (e.g. because of angle and type of leaf, which partly accounts for selectivity between grasses and broad-leaved species) and also avoid the toxic effects in various ways. Some herbicides, e.g. ioxynil, act primarily by contact, producing a rapid contact scorch and then yellowing of foliage on susceptible plants as photosynthesis and other processes are affected.

Selective herbicides are sold as proprietary products containing variable amounts of active ingredient (a.i.). For some herbicides, the active ingredient is expressed as acid equivalent (a.e.). Although the two terms are not the same, they have a similar meaning for the layman, both being used to distinguish the active ingredient from the 'carrier' or solvents in a proprietary product. The proportion of active ingredient varies between products. Thus, if two firms sell weedkillers with the same active ingredient, firm A may formulate its product with 20% a.i. while firm B formulates its product with 30% a.i. Manufacturer's label recommendations must be followed at all times.

(2) Approved Products

All pesticides, including herbicides, currently used must be approved by MAFF; this can be checked by ensuring the product label displays a MAFF number. Details of the approval process are given in Section 10.

(3) Choice of Application Equipment

Herbicide application generally gives the best results for professional users. The spray droplets give good cover, reaching at least partially the undersides of leaves and lower parts of the plants, but spray drift may give risks to non-target plants, the operator and the general public.

There is a wide range of spraying equipment available. For comparatively small areas or for spot treatment (putting greens) a knapsack sprayer may be acceptable. For larger areas there are 'knapsacks on wheels' or other pedestrian equipment, e.g. Walkover sprayers, while for larger areas, e.g. fairways, tractor-mounted or tractor-drawn models are available.

The volume of liquid applied by a sprayer depends partly on the machine itself (e.g. pump output), partly on nozzle size, and partly on speed of movement over the ground (see "Calibration of equipment" below). The following are generally accepted definitions of the various volumes of application appropriate to conventional sprayers with nozzles:–

$$
\begin{array}{lll}
\text{low volume} & - & 55 - 225 \text{ litre ha}^{-1} \\
\text{medium volume} & - & 225 - 675 \quad " \\
\text{high volume} & - & 675 - 1125 \quad " \\
\end{array}
$$

Details of application volumes for herbicides may be found on product labels and must be strictly followed.

Controlled droplet application (CDA) sprayers based on a spinning disc principle work at very low (11–55 litre ha⁻¹) or ultra-low volumes (1–11 litre ha⁻¹).

There are several traditional application methods still in use, e.g. wick applicators, fluted rollers, or a watering can with a rose or dribble bar). These methods are generally less efficient than spraying and the product label must be checked to ensure these methods are recommended.

For areas containing low populations of weeds only, spot treatment may be appropriate. This is often difficult to achieve with any degree of accuracy in practice.

(4) Checking Spraying Equipment

Prior to every spraying operation make sure that the application equipment is in good working order and that pressure hoses, joints and unions are watertight. Ensure that the jets and filter screens of spraying machines are free from blockages and are suitable for the job in hand. The nozzles fitted should be of the type and size specified by the equipment manufacturer or, for particular jobs, those recommended by the chemical manufacturer as described on the product label.

Make sure nozzles are clean and giving their proper spray pattern. As part of the calibration process check their uniformity of output, by operating a stationary water-filled sprayer with a beaker under each nozzle and rejecting nozzles from which output differs from average by more than $\pm5\%$.

The spray boom needs to be positioned so the nozzles are at the correct height from the ground, so that the 'cones' or 'fans' of spray just overlap when they meet the turf surface.

To keep this correct height consistently, make sure that on a 3- or 4-wheel sprayer the boom is level and securely fixed at the right height, and that a 2-wheel sprayer can always reliably be held at the correct distance from the ground (e.g. using a chain of just the right length hanging from the boom). The nozzles of hand-held booms on knapsack sprayers or the working height of controlled droplet applicators are even more difficult to keep a consistent height above target level during operation, but unless this is done, calibration will be meaningless and the application rate quite different from what is intended.

Cleanliness of spray machines is of paramount importance, especially where one machine is used for many different products. If equipment is shared with other users, it is advisable to wash it out thoroughly both after spraying is complete and also before the next use. Ideally, a separate sprayer should be kept for total herbicides or other similar chemicals, to avoid problems of contamination which could result in damage to turf.

(5) Calibration of Equipment

The first essential of accurate treatment is to know what volume per unit area you will actually be applying when you start work: otherwise you cannot possibly work out the correct rates of chemical. Establishing this volume per unit area is calibration. Calibration is not a magical or mysterious process, but it is all important. It must be done afresh every time you spray and must also be done every time equipment is altered or changed, or a change in herbicide product is made.

The volume of liquid applied by a sprayer depends on:

(i)   nozzle size
(ii)   pressure
(iii) travelling speed.

If you have a sprayer in which throughput is geared to travelling speed, e.g. tractor-mounted sprayers, you have only two factors to consider, nozzle size and throughput. Depending which equipment you have, follow instructions A or B below.

(Note: These instructions apply in principle to all sprayers, but are most suited in detail to pedestrian-operated or small tractor-towed sprayers: calibration of tractor-mounted sprayers may be more conveniently done according to the procedure recommended by the Agricultural Training Board.)

The following procedure will allow accurate calibration of small spraying equipment.

Steps

[1] *Select type and size of nozzle to be used*
eg: D/2.25/1.0

D	=	deflector type nozzle
2.25	=	flow rate (litres per minute)
1.0	=	pressure (1 bar)

[2] *Set pressure*
Some sprayers are fitted with a pressure control valve. The settings will vary between different manufacturers and types. For example, the Cooper Peglar knapsack may have the following:

H	=	high approx 40 psi
L	=	low approx 20 psi

or	15, 30, 45	= psi
or	1, 2, 3	= bar

Remember these values are not very accurate so it may be useful to fit a pressure gauge to check the pressure being delivered.

Record your settings here [ ]

[3] *Speed of walking*
The next step is to record the amount of time it takes the operator to walk over 100 metres at his normal walking speed, wearing the correct protective clothing and spraying out water. You may need to get an average of 3 or 4 separate runs. Ensure you maintain a consistent rate of pumping.

Record this information here; seconds per 100 m [ ]
eg: 95 seconds

[4] *Calculate speed of walking*
eg: 95 seconds per 100 metres

To discover kilometres per hour (kph) divide 360 by the number of seconds it took to cover the 100 metres

eg: $\dfrac{360}{95} = 3.8$ kph

Record your speed here [ ] kph

[5] *Spacing of nozzles or swath width if using a single nozzle*
Discover this by getting the operator to hold the lance in a comfortable position and measure the swath width

eg: 1.7 metres

Record your information here [   ]

[6] *Flow rate*
Record the amount of water which comes out of a single nozzle for the 1 minute. Do this by getting the operator to spray water into a bucket for 1 minute

eg: 2.2 litres

Record your quantity here [   ]

So now we know the following, eg:

[a] width of spray (swath width) = 1.7 m
[b] walking speed   = 3.8 km/h
[c] amount of water   = 2.2 ltr

Record your information here

Swath width   [   ] metres

Walking speed   [   ] metres

Amount of water [   ] litres

[7] *Volume per hectare*
The next step is to discover the amount of water which will be sprayed out over one hectare.

Do this by calculating the following:

600 x flow rate per minute ÷ spraying width ÷ speed of walking = litres per hectare

eg: 600 x 2.2 ÷ 1.7 ÷ 3.8 = 204.33

rounded up to 205 litres per hectare or 18.2 gallons per acre.

Record your information here

600 x [   ] ÷ [   ] ÷ [   ] = [   ]

rounded up to [   ] litres per hectare

[8] *Dose rate*

Now obtain the dose rate per hectare (chemical label)

For this exercise assume the rate of chemical to be applied is 5.5 litres per hectare which needs to be contained in the amount of water shown in Section 7

eg: 205 ltrs.

Next, find out the number of tanks full per hectare

eg: 205 ÷ 20 ltrs (size of tank) = 10.25.

Now find out amount of concentrate per tank full

eg: 5.5 ÷ 10.25 = 0.54 litres per tank full.

If not, you may have to use a nozzle with a different flow rate.

Record your rates here:

Litres per hectare

Capacity of sprayer

No. of full tanks per hectare

Concentrate per hectare

Amount of concentrate per tank

(6) Calculating How Much Chemical is Needed for Each Fill of the Sprayer Tank

With proper calibration records there is no problem.

The sprayer set up as in the example above applied 390 litre ha^{-1}.

Total tank capacity is 30 litres.

Therefore, each fill of the tank should contain $\frac{30}{390}$ i.e. $\frac{1}{13}$ of the recommended rate of chemical for one hectare.

If that rate is 20 litres per hectare, use $\frac{20}{13}$ = 1.54 litres of chemical in each tank-fill, with water to bring it up to 30 litres.

(7) Mixing

Mix, as accurately as possible, only the quantity of spray required for the area to be treated. This will avoid the need to dispose of excess material, which is wasteful of chemical and difficult to do safely.

Always wear suitable protective clothing when mixing chemicals. (Refer to product label for details.) Follow any specific instructions given on the label but, as a general rule, add half the required quantity of water, then the chemical, then the remainder of the water (which can be used to rinse out the container in which the chemical was measured). Powder formulations can usually be added to the water and stirred to give a suspension or solution, but it may be necessary to pre-mix the powder by adding a small amount of water to it and mixing thoroughly, to the consistency of a thin cream. This 'cream' can then be added to half the quantity of water in the spray tank and topped up in the normal way.

(8) Patterns of Spraying

Accurate marking of strips is essential to minimise misses or overlaps. If chemicals do not contain a dye, or sprayer wheelings cannot be followed, lines and/or marker pegs should be used or a marker dye added to the spray, particularly on important areas such as golf greens.

For such areas, it is also advisable to spray twice over with a half-strength tank mix, the second time at right angles to the first. This makes misses or overlaps less serious.

All spray work using a boom should be done in parallel lines, not curves (to avoid different speeds at the two ends of the boom). Even with single-nozzle equipment, parallel working is more methodical.

(9) Special Points on Applying Growth-Regulator Herbicides Against Broad-Leaved Weeds

(9a) Timing

Apply any time from spring to early autumn, preferably in fine, warm weather when the soil is moist and growth is vigorous. Late spring is generally considered best. Avoid applying herbicide treatments during hot, dry weather, or in late autumn (when weed control may be good but the turf may not fill in adequately before winter). Heavy rain shortly after application may reduce effectiveness. Wind gives risk of drift, but a slight constant breeze may allow better work than light variable winds.

(9b) Fertiliser

Growth-regulator herbicides act best when both weeds and grass are growing vigorously. Therefore, if the turf normally receives nitrogenous fertiliser, give some a week or two before spraying. Fertiliser/herbicide mixtures are convenient and avoid risks of spray drift, but they do not boost growth in readiness for herbicide treatment like a separate fertiliser dressing, and a granular herbicide may be washed off by rain more easily than a spray, especially a rain-fast one.

(9c) Mowing before and after spraying

[i]   *Turf mown infrequently (every seven to ten days, or more)*
A large leaf area of weeds allows maximum herbicide absorption: therefore delay spraying until a few days before a cut. But then make sure not to cut for two to three days, to give time for herbicide absorption before weed leaves are removed by mowing.

[ii]   *Frequently mown turf*
Weed growth between cuts will not matter. Some people would advise not to spray freshly cut grass, but many greenkeepers mow fine turf and spray the same day with no apparent damage. Also, there is no need to refrain from mowing to allow herbicide uptake if all weed foliage is below mowing height.

(9d) Disposal of clippings

After use of growth-regulator herbicides, the clippings from the first four mowings must not be used directly as a mulch round broad-leaved plants or shrubs but may be incorporated into compost heaps, provided that they remain there for at least six months before the compost is used for broad-leaved plants or shrubs. After the first four mowings no special precautions are needed.

(9e) Grass Weeds

The three most common grass weeds found in fine turf are annual meadow-grass (*Poa annua*), Yorkshire fog (*Holcus lanatus*) and perennial ryegrass (*Lolium perenne*). There are no suitable chemicals available for their control in fine turf and the best way to avoid them is by employing suitable management practices. Removal of grass weeds is possible on a small scale by, for example, hand weeding, plugging or returfing.

Certain resistant broad-leaved weeds may require more than one application of herbicide for effective control. Consult the product label for instructions on repeat treatments.

(10) Precautions

Growth-regulators are very powerful and can affect non-target plants even in minute doses. Risks are very real where crops and plants other than grass and cereals are grown in the vicinity of spraying. Do not treat areas of turf near valued plants in flower beds, etc. except on a calm day. If contamination of such plants is suspected, wash them down copiously with clean water. Clean out spraying equipment thoroughly after use.

All herbicides are potentially harmful to the user; follow safety instructions on the product label carefully. Always be careful when measuring out and mixing concentrated herbicides, avoid inhaling the spray, and store and dispose of containers carefully. Always wear minimum protective clothing, i.e. gloves, protective clothing and face mask. Above all, read everything on the label before opening the container. It should be understood that herbicide users are under an obligation to comply with legal requirements governing the usage of such materials and that the instructions included with each product are mandatory, including instructions regarding application rates. Users should be familiar with the Food and Environment Protection Act (1985)m Part 3 : Control of Pesticides Regulations (1986).

AQUATIC WEED CONTROL

Excessive weed growth in drainage channels, streams and rivers can obstruct the flow of water, causing flooding, impeding drainage and, through increased silting, channel deterioration. The appearance of water features on golf courses may be impaired by weed growth itself, or by the collection of rubbish and debris caught in the weeds. Furthermore, weed growth may interfere with the use of water for irrigation purposes.

The weeds found in or near water can be put in different categories, from truly submerged weeds to bankside plants. Algal growth may also constitute a problem, particularly in sluggish or static water.

Methods of Control
Cutting
The traditional method of eradicating aquatic weeds in small areas has been to cut using scythes, hooks or chain scythes, followed by raking and clearing. In larger areas or depths of water, specially designed weed cutting boats or weed cutting 'buckets' on long-reach excavators can be employed. These methods are both slow and laborious and can also stimulate rapid regrowth, thereby exacerbating the problem.

With both mechanical and hand cutting it is essential to remove all cut material from the water to prevent it blocking pump intakes, etc. and deoxygenating the water as it decomposes.

Chemical Control
The following list details those herbicides which are approved for controlling aquatic weeds or weeds growing along the banks of watercourses. Water that has been treated with these products can only be used for irrigation purposes after defined periods of time have elapsed to prevent any phytotoxicity effects. This period is known as the "safety interval before irrigation".

CHEMICAL	PRODUCT	WEEDS CONTROLLED	SAFETY INTERVAL BEFORE IRRIGATION
asulam	Asulox	docks, bracken	nil
2,4-D	Atlas 2,4-D Chipman 2,4-D Dormone	water weeds, dicotyledon weeds on banks	3 weeks
dalapon	BH Dalapon	bulrushes, reeds, grass weeds on banks	5 weeks
dichlobenil	Casoron G Casoron G-SR	aquatic weeds	2 weeks
diquat	Midstream Reglone	aquatic weeds	10 days
fosamine	Krenite	woody weeds	nil
glyphosate	Mascot Sonic Roundup Pro Spasor	reeds, rushes, sedges, waterlilies, grass weeds on banks	nil
maleic hydrazide	Bos MH 180 Regulox K	suppression of grass growth on banks	3 weeks
terbutryn	Clarosan	aquatic weeds	7 days

When using herbicides the Manufacturer's instructions found on the product label should be followed carefully – many of them are now legally binding. All those concerned with pesticides should make themselves aware of legislation and obligations by consulting the publications listed below.

Additional Information
There are several informative leaflets available from the MAFF Publications Unit, Lion House, Alnwich, Northumberland, NE66 2PF.

These include a general leaflet "Pesticides: Guide to the New Controls" reference UL79 and a booklet "Guidelines for the Use of Herbicides in or Near Watercourses and Lakes" (B2078). This is essential for all those people intending to apply aquatic herbicides as it details the choice, correct application procedures and obligation to consult the appropriate River Authority Catchment Board, River Purification Authority or Water Undertaking before the spraying of such areas is carried out.

Other relevant publications are listed in the Bibliography.

GROWTH RETARDANTS

There is nothing new in the idea of using chemicals to retard the growth of grass. Maleic hydrazide, the original grass growth retarder, was introduced in 1948 and has been used regularly, but has never really made a big impact on the management of amenity grass. Cutting, costly and labour intensive though it is, still remains our main method of management, even for relatively low grade grass areas.

What are Grass Growth Retardants?
Grass growth retardants are part of a group of chemicals described as plant growth regulators. They enter the grass plant via the leaves or roots and are translocated through the plant to their sites of action. Here they begin to affect the growth rate of the plant, slowing down leaf development and in some cases halting the production of flowering stems. Used at higher doses they will quite efficiently kill plants just like conventional herbicides, but at the correct doses the retarding effect wears off in eight to twelve weeks and normal growth resumes.

What Growth Retardants are Available?
There are three growth retardants currently available for use on grass, maleic hydrazide, mefluidide and paclobutrazol. Maleic hydrazide was tested by local authorities in the 1950's for retarding grass growth on road verges, parks and cemeteries and also for retarding hedges and shrubs. Unfortunately, the early formulations of maleic hydrazide were not rainfast, and in Britain's rapidly changeable weather many users found that the compound was washed out by the rain before it had a chance to enter the grass. Yet, other users found that the rather narrow range of safe application rates could result in accidental scorching of swards when the chemical was applied by unskilled operators. Much of the early enthusiasm for the product lapsed in the light of these experiences. However, some authorities still use maleic hydrazide for road verges with great success. The more recent formulations of maleic hydrazide include stickers that help to make them rainfast so that more reliable results can be obtained.

Following the discovery of maleic hydrazide a number of other growth regulator compounds for use in agriculture and horticulture appeared but it was not until 1975 that a new grass retarder, mefluidide was produced. Mefluidide has a number of advantages over maleic hydrazide that should make it easier to use and more effective and reliable. Like maleic hydrazide it enters the grass plant via the leaves and is translocated through the plant to the growing points. Mefluidide checks the grass growth faster than maleic hydrazide and in mixed grass swards it is better at preventing the formation of flowering heads. Mefluidide produces a very tidy looking sward and its effects last up to twelve weeks. Mefluidide has a relatively wide dose range and the danger of discolouration and damage to the sward is consequently less than with maleic hydrazide. Mefluidide can also be used on closer mown swards than maleic hydrazide with less risk of phytotoxicity.

The third growth retarder, paclobutrazol, differs from maleic hydrazide and mefluidide in that it is taken into the plants via the roots. Uptake is therefore dependent upon the soil being moist enough to allow transport of the chemical to the rootzone of the grasses. In years with very dry spring weather this could be somewhat of a disadvantage with chemical retardation delayed, though in drought situations grass growth is naturally retarded to an extent. A rather more serious disadvantage is that paclobutrazol acts predominantly on the shallower rooting finer grasses. Coarse grasses with deeper root systems are not adequately retarded so that the sward can appear untidy and coarse in appearance. In addition, paclobutrazol has little or no effect upon the production of flowering heads, again making treated swards untidy. In its favour it has a longer period of suppression, with effects sometimes carrying over to the following year.

Table 1 compares the three available grass growth retardants.

TABLE 1
Comparison of Growth Retarders

FACTOR	MALEIC HYDRAZIDE (M.H.)	MEFLUIDIDE	PACLOBUTRAZOL
Trade name	Mazide (Synchemicals) Regulox (Diamond Shamrock) Royal Slogro (Uniroyal)	Mowchem (Rhône-Poulenc)	Holdfast (ICI)
Mode of Uptake	Foliar	Foliar	Roots
Typical reduction in dry matter yield from a single application under 'best' conditions	Up to 25%	Up to 45% (*Festuca/Poa* spp.) Up to 60% (*Agrostis* spp.)	Up to 45%
Duration of effects	Up to 8 weeks	Up to 12 weeks	Up to 14 weeks, occasionally carry over to following season
Effects on sward composition	Tends to favour finer species of grass – in particular *Festuca rubra*. There is some suppression of flowering and seedhead production. Some increase in broad-leaved weeds	Encourages finer grasses at the expense of coarser species. Very good seedhead suppression. Tends to produce a finer and much tidier sward than M.H.	Poor suppression of some deeper rooted coarse species. No seedhead suppression. Long term use where coarse species are present may lead to untidy appearance
Discolouration	The rate of use is critical otherwise there can be severe scorching, browning and death of more susceptible species	Tends to make the sward greener and more lush in appearance. Some discolouration in drought conditions with high dose rates	Occasional browning of sward
Reliability	Unpredictable results due to climatic effects – dose rate critical. Rainfast formulation essential	Very reliable in use with a relatively wide dose tolerance by most species	Relatively inactive in dry conditions but acts reliably when soil moisture is high and therefore during periods of growth
Flexibility of application	Fairly critical – rainfall after application can negate effects	Rainfall shortly after application can somewhat reduce effectiveness	Considerable flexibility in timing and season. Leached slowly

Cost Effectiveness

Whether or not the new generation of grass growth retarders make an impact on amenity grass management depends to a large extent upon their cost effectiveness. The greenkeeper may expect between eight and twelve weeks control of grass growth following application. The usual alternative is regular mowing which is labour intensive and for which costs vary according to the situation. A second alternative is to sow new grass areas with low growing cultivars, a range of which are now available. Only the greenkeeper can decide which alternative is most cost effective in his circumstances. A second factor that cannot be costed in monetary terms is the improvement in sward composition that repeated use of maleic hydrazide or mefluidide can produce. Finer grasses are encouraged at the expense of coarser species, leading to a more pleasing appearance and reduced cutting requirements.

Should You Consider Using Grass Growth Retardants?

If you deal exclusively with fine turf the answer is definitely not. None of the currently available retardants are suitable for golf surfaces, whether greens, tees or fairways. They are however sometimes used on awkward areas – around trees, on steep banks and perhaps other odd corners of the rough. Rarefly, growth retardants might be used on bunker edges or for helping control particularly heavy rough, but their suitability for such purposes depends on individual circumstances. Difficult to maintain areas are the places where growth retardants can be very cost-effective and where they will find increasing use.

Remember always to follow the manufacturer's instructions on the label when applying growth retardants.

MOSS, ALGAE AND LICHENS

Mosses are found in very many situations, e.g. on stones, soil, tree trunks, in turf, etc. Only a limited number of species are found in turf.

Causes of Moss

Moss soon establishes on thin swards where there is a lack of competition from vigorous turf. Most mosskillers are palliative – the moss soon returns unless the factors responsible for a thin sward are removed. A strong, healthy turf is the best answer to moss.

The following factors can favour the growth of moss:–

(a) A moist turf – poor drainage encourages the fern-like and tufted mosses.
(b) A very dry soil, e.g. over drains, on mounds and ridges – inadequate watering or over-drainage – encourages the upright type.
(c) Cutting too closely or poor surface levels causing scalping.
(d) A soft, spongy sward with a thick fibre (thatch) layer.
(e) Low fertility, e.g. deficiencies of plant foods, lime, etc. or insufficient soil depth.
(f) Over-consolidation of the soil – compaction.
(g) Shade.

Main Groups of Mosses

Type 1 Fern-like, usually trailing: *Hypnum* and *Eurhynchium* spp. Present in many types of turf but often overlooked. Characteristic of moist, rather spongy swards where there is a soft surface mat. Such mosses are often a problem in turf cut from the rough where the fibre is thick.

Type 2 Tufted, mat forming: *Ceratodon purpureus, Bryum* spp. Very troublesome types of moss especially on acid soils. *Ceratodon purpureus* is common and is the so-called "winter" moss since it appears to die out in spring when active growth starts, only to reappear in the autumn. Tends to become progressively worse unless checked.

Type 3 Upright: *Polytrichum* spp. Most common on dry mounds surrounding greens, bunker faces, etc. Not normally very troublesome, except occasionally under acid conditions.

Control of Moss

Find the cause then remedy it. Mosses can be encouraged by poor surface drainage or alternatively *Polytrichum* mosses are an indicator of excessively dry conditions and hence occur on mounds where surface water is being shed into nearby hollows. Moss is also favoured by excessively close mowing or scalping, low fertility, excessive acidity, shade, compacted soil and the presence of thatch or fibre layers. The correction of such factors can significantly reduce persistent moss problems.

Effects of Sulphate of Iron on Moss, Algae and Weeds

Sulphate of iron applied at 10 g/m^2 is a traditional treatment for moss control, applied alone or in conjunction with sulphate of ammonia and a carrier such as sand. Moss is killed very quickly by sulphate of iron although duration of control is generally short. However, as it is very cheap to purchase it is probably the most cost-effective pesticide for moss control available. Sulphate of iron applied at the moss killing rate may also be effective against algae in turf. However, whilst some suppression of algae may be achieved by repeated application, long lasting control will only be achieved by correcting the cultural conditions (shade, poor drainage etc.) which favour algal growth (see later article on "squidge"). Additional benefits of regular sulphate of iron application may be gained in the control of broad-leaved weeds, especially when used in conjunction with sulphate of ammonia as a fertiliser treatment.

CHEMICAL CONTROL. This works well in the long-term only if it is combined with cultural control. The traditional chemical for moss in turf is sulphate of iron, applied in the calcined form, with or without sulphate of ammonia.

Sulphate of iron gives a fast kill and is cheap but is not long-lasting. It can be used alone bulked with a carrier such as sand, especially in winter, but is more often used for spring or summer application in lawn sand, e.g. a mixture of 1 part sulphate of iron : 3 parts sulphate of ammonia : 10-20 parts carrier (sand or compost). This mixture is used at 140 g/m^2.

Dichlorophen. Fairly quick acting and moderately persistent. This is now the most effective and most popular mosskiller. Several proprietary preparations are available.

Mosskillers for Non-Turf Areas Only

Moss on paved areas or non-grass paths can be controlled using proprietary total weedkillers containing atrazine or simazine applied at makers' recommended rates. Cresylic acid may also be used.

Algae

Bare ground in turf areas is often quickly covered by a green scum which may be a mixture of algae and moss protonema (filaments from which the adult moss develops). Once grass is established on the bare ground, the algae growth usually disappears.

Squidge

During the cold wet winter months when grass growth is slow, turf may be affected by a problem known as squidge. Squidge is caused by an extensive colonisation of the turf by algae (tiny one-celled plants with no true stem or leaves). Algae are common in turf but they generally do not occur in sufficient numbers to cause problems. The algae which cause squidge produce copious amounts of slime to protect themselves from desiccation during dry weather. Rainfall is absorbed by these algae to form a gelatinous mass which rises to the turf surface rendering it very slippery and consequently presents a hazard to greenkeepers and the golfer. Squidge (the term was first used by Scottish greenkeepers) gets its name from the fact that if affected areas are walked on the algal slime rises to the surface, sticks to foot-wear and becomes exceedingly squelchy – an apt description of the problem.

Recognition

Squidge is usually first seen as dark green or black gelatinous masses on the turf surface. Often these masses are discrete from each other measuring approximately 10 mm^2. In severe cases these gelatinous masses will coalesce and form large areas of affected turf. Examination using a high power microscope often reveals several different algae present (over six different types have been identified in research at STRI) together with moss protonema, fungi and various soil fauna in the slime. The turf is also very slimy to the touch and in severe cases handfuls of algae can be removed from a small area of turf.

Recommendations for Control

Long term control of squidge can only be achieved by rectifying the conditions which favour its development. Squidge is often found on sloping turf where water is running across the surface rather than through the soil profile. Slitting or spiking and installing a drainage system where necessary will aid water movement downwards and consequently create a drier turf surface, to the detriment of the algae which cause squidge. Operating machinery on slopes which are affected is very dangerous and it is therefore best to do all slitting and spiking by hand until the problem has been alleviated. Top dressing with a coarse sand will also improve traction and provide a free draining surface, thus inhibiting squidge development. Shaded and sheltered areas are also prone to squidge development due to slow evaporation of surface water by the wind or sun. Shaded areas could be opened up by possibly removing bushes or trees etc. which cast excessive shade. Highly acidic turf is also prone to squidge due to the absence of predatory soil animals who normally feed on squidge, but cannot tolerate acidic conditions. Applications of lime can therefore be made to control squidge but this is recommended in only exceptional circumstances as lime can favour certain diseases such as fusarium patch or take-all patch.

When a squidge problem occurs the first control measure to be deployed is to remove excessive algae and slime from the turf using a brush or reverse side of a rake. Once the bulk of the squidge has been removed, certain pesticides may be effective in suppressing recolonisation to allow time for the predisposing cultural conditions to be rectified. Research at STRI has evaluated 6 possible chemical treatments for squidge and of these, three proved effective – cresylic acid, dichlorophen and sulphate of iron. However, satisfactory results were only achieved with repeated applications – three applications at ten day intervals. Finally, it must be remembered that these chemicals are only useful in creating enough time to rectify the underlying problems and cannot be relied on solely to give effective control.

Lichens
These plants, which are a combination of alga and fungus, can occur on walls, tree trunks, soil, rocks, etc. They also occur on damp turf areas or in dry, acid situations where grass growth is weak. Rarely as troublesome as moss.

Control
Cultural control is best, by improving grass growth. More adequate fertiliser treatment and liming may be required. Lawn sand used at the rate recommended for moss is effective if chemical control proves necessary.

CONTROL OF SQUIDGE

During the cold wet winter months when grass growth is slow, turf may be affected by a problem known as squidge. Squidge is caused by an extensive colonisation of the turf by algae (tiny one-celled plants with no true stem or leaves). Algae are common in turf but they generally do not occur in sufficient numbers to cause problems. The algae which cause squidge produce copious amounts of slime to protect themselves from desiccation during dry weather. Rainfall is absorbed by these algae to form a gelatinous mass which rises to the turf surface rendering it very slippery and consequently presents a hazard to greenkeepers and the golfer. Squidge (the term was first used by Scottish greenkeepers) gets is name from the fact that if affected areas are walked on the algal slime rises to the surface, sticks to foot-wear and becomes exceedingly squelchy – an apt description of the problem.

Recognition

Squidge is usually first seen as dark green or black gelatinous masses on the turf surface. Often these masses are discrete from each other measuring approximately 10 mm^2. In severe cases these gelatinous masses will coalesce and form large areas of affected turf. Examination using a high power microscope often reveals several different algae present (over six different types have been identified in research at STRI) together with moss protonema, fungi and various soil fauna in the slime. The turf is also very slimy to the touch and in severe cases handfuls of algae can be removed from a small area of turf.

Recommendations for Control

Long term control of squidge can only be achieved by rectifying the conditions which favour its development. Squidge is often found on sloping turf where water is running across the surface rather than through the soil profile. Slitting or spiking and installing a drainage system where necessary will aid water movement downwards and consequently create a drier turf surface, to the detriment of the algae which cause squidge. Operating machinery on slopes which are affected is very dangerous and it is therefore best to do all slitting and spiking by hand until the problem has been alleviated. Top dressing with a coarse sand will also provide a free draining surface and thus inhibit squidge development. Shaded and sheltered areas are also prone to squidge development due to slow evaporation of surface water by the wind or sun. Shaded areas could be opened up by possibly removing bushes or trees etc. which cast excessive shade. Highly acidic turf is also prone to squidge due to the absence of predatory soil animals who normally feed on squidge, but cannot tolerate acidic conditions. Applications of lime can therefore be made to control squidge but this is recommended in only exceptional circumstances as lime can favour certain diseases such as fusarium patch or take-all patch.

When a squidge problem occurs the first control measure to be deployed is to remove excessive algae and slime from the turf using a brush or reverse side of a rake. Once the majority of the squidge has been removed, certain pesticides may be effective in suppressing recolonisation to allow time for the predisposing cultural conditions to be rectified. Research at STRI has evaluated 6 possible chemical treatments for squidge and of these, three proved effective - cresylic acid, dichlorophen and sulphate of iron. However, satisfactory results were only achieved with repeated applications – three applications at ten day intervals. Finally, it must be remembered that these chemicals are only useful in creating enough time to rectify the underlying problems and cannot be relied on solely to give effective control.

SECTION 9

PESTICIDES AND LEGISLATION

GOLF CLUBS AND RECENTLY INTRODUCED LEGISLATION CONCERNING PESTICIDES AND OTHER HAZARDOUS SUBSTANCES

FOOD AND ENVIRONMENT PROTECTION ACT PART III : CONTROL OF PESTICIDES REGULATIONS 1986 (COPR)

CONTROL OF SUBSTANCES HAZARDOUS TO HEALTH REGULATIONS (COSHH)

This section outlines some of the obligations placed on golf clubs by the COPR and COSHH Regulations. To obtain full details golf clubs must consult the publications listed at the end of this article and check their specific requirements and duties with their Local Authority and local office of the Health and Safety Executive Agricultural Inspectorate.

CONTROL OF PESTICIDES REGULATIONS 1986

Aims: the FEPA legislation aims to protect the health of human beings, creatures and plants, to safeguard the environment and to secure safe, efficient and humane methods of controlling pests. If also seeks to make information regarding pesticides available to the public.

Pesticides: are anything used for destroying any pest, ie. the fungicides, herbicides, insecticides, earthworm and moss killers commonly used on golf greens and other parts of the course, are all pesticides. Plant growth regulators are also included. Outside the scope of the regulations are fertilisers, soil conditioners and wetting agents, as no pest control is involved.

The main restrictions under COPR can be summarised as follows:-

[a] Approved products:
Only products approved for use in amenity horticulture may be used, as listed in "Pesticides 1989" or any subsequent edition available from HMSO bookshops. Providing you obtain your pesticides from a reputable turf products supplier, and a MAFF number and a **recommendation for use on turf** can be found on the label then it is likely that the product is approved. It is advisable to only purchase pesticides from a salesman qualified under the British Agrochemical Standards Inspection Scheme (BASIS).

[b] Greenkeeper training and certification:
The golf club must ensure that its greenkeepers have received adequate training and are competent to use pesticides. To achieve this, appropriate training followed by an examination leading to a certificate of competence being issued is necessary. There are exemptions under the so-called "grandfather clause" for those born before 1 January 1965. A person so exempted may use pesticides if he has received adequate instruction and guidance in the safe efficient and humane use of pesticides and is competent for the duties which he is called on to perform. In the event of accident, misuse or incorrect storage of pesticides the employer will be criminally responsible for the actions or failings of the employee. "Competence" could well be interpreted as meaning capable of passing the requisite exam to obtain a certificate. Further, only a certificate holder may supervise others. Certification for all users is the direction in

which things are likely to proceed in the future with more and more users being brought into the categories of mandatory certification. Training and certification is highly recommended for **all** users of pesticides. For details of pesticide training courses, contact your local horticultural college. Training is conducted in "modules". The foundation module (coded PA1), hand-held applicator (PA6) and ground crop sprayer (PA2) modules are probably most suitable for golf greenkeepers. Examinations are organised by the National Proficiency Tests Council, National Agricultural Centre, Stoneleigh, Kenilworth, Warwickshire, CV8 2LG and are detailed in their booklet "Pesticides Application". As a rough guide, a training course, examination and certification will cost approximately £50-100 depending on the subjects taken.

[c] Legally binding parts of the label:
Every pesticide container carries instructions, many of which are **now mandatory**. For example, any instructions on maximum dose rates, maximum number of treatments, limitations on area to be treated or quantity of pesticide to be used and latest time of application must be followed strictly. Also, the label may have statements on environmental protection, e.g. avoid contamination of waterways, protective clothing (which **must be** provided by the club and **worn** by greenkeepers during spraying) and greenkeeper training. Any breach of these or other statutory conditions will constitute a criminal offence. Generally speaking, however, if the greenkeeper is trained, possesses appropriate certificates of competence and follows strictly the statements on the pesticide label, he can feel confident that he is working within the COPR.

[d] Storage of pesticides:
For moderate to large quantities of pesticides likely to be stored at a golf course, special lockable metal vaults are available commercially or a purpose built store may be erected. Guidance on storage is given in the next section "Storage of Pesticides".

CONTROL OF SUBSTANCES HAZARDOUS TO HEALTH REGULATIONS
Aims: Applied from 1 January 1990, the COSHH regulations provide the framework for the control of substances at work which may be hazardous to health.

The COSHH and COPR regulations are intended to complement one another and operate together. Whilst COSHH is primarily aimed at protecting people at work, COPR covers creatures, plants and the environmental as well as human health. It must be emphasised that COSHH is concerned not only with pesticides but with all potential hazardous substances which may be present in the workplace.

(1) Risk Assessment
It is necessary to assess the risk to health arising from working with pesticides and other hazardous substances, and to determine what precautions are needed. Risk is defined as the likelihood that it will cause harm in the circumstances of use. An assessment of risk must be made by the employer which must usually take the form of a written document. First, the hazard, i.e. its potential to cause harm, of each particular pesticide should be determined, and then the potential risk can be assessed. Proprietary pesticides currently available are all Approved by the Ministry of Agriculture, Fisheries & Food (MAFF) and a MAFF number is displayed on the product label. Consequently, in this case it is evident that the pesticide in question has satisfied MAFF from the safety viewpoint. However, some pesticides are safer than others and it is the essential point of COSHH that the employer has to decide which pesticide to use. Pesticide product labels also contain relevant statements on safety, advice on protective clothing and a standard warning sign such as "harmful" or "irritant". These are just some of the considerations to be made when assessing the hazard which a pesticide represents.

The risk assessment must be in written form. It is important that the assessment is received and if appropriate revised, whenever a new member of staff is employed, a new hazardous substance introduced to the golf club or responsibilities changed. All revisions should be dated and a copy served to **all** members of staff and to those club members responsible for ensuring compliance with the Regulations.

(2) Reduction of Exposure to Hazardous Substances

Once risk has been determined, then work procedures must be examined critically to prevent or reduce exposure to hazardous substances. For example, the potential hazard posed by a pesticide may be eliminated if a non-pesticidal method of achieving the same aim is practicable. Reduced exposure to a pesticide may be achieved by the employee wearing suitable and adequate protective clothing, which is the employer's responsibility to provide and ensure it is worn by employees. Again, refer to the product label for specific guidance on protective clothing. To prevent or control exposure to hazardous substances, COSHH lists the control measures in the following order or priority. Firstly, substitute the substance with a safer alternative. Secondly, introduce technical or engineering methods of safety, for example, use a sprayer with a specially designed filler pump rather than pouring the pesticide into the spray tank manually. Finally, reduce exposure by following safe systems of work - correct storage and handling of pesticide concentrates, protective clothing etc.

(3) Information and Training

Employees must be trained in the use of and informed about the pesticides with which they are asked to work. The COPR training courses available currently for users of pesticides would seem essential towards the requirements of COSHH. Safety and toxicological information, usually available as technical safety data sheets from the manufacturers of pesticides, must also be made available to all concerned, so the risk may be assessed before a spraying operation. In summary, employees have to be informed about the risks arising from their work and the precautions to be taken.

(4) Recording Exposure to Hazardous Substances

The exposure of employees to hazardous substances must be monitored and a record kept. Standard risk assessment sheets, to be completed by the employer **before** a spraying operation, are available, together with COPR log books for monitoring pesticide usage for these purposes.

FURTHER READING
Pesticide Regulations

The "Code of Practice for the Amenity Use of Pesticides" giving much useful information applicable to golf clubs has been drawn up jointly by the National Turfgrass Council and the National Association of Agricultural Contractors.

The Ministry of Agriculture has issued a free explanatory leaflet UL79 Pesticides : guide to the new controls (revised 1987). A further revision is due shortly. Write to: Ministry of Agriculture, Fisheries and Food (Publications), Lion House, Alnwick, Northumberland, NE66 2PF.

The Health and Safety Executive issue the following leaflets and booklets, available from HSE Library & Information Services, Broad Lane, Sheffield, S3 7HQ. Tel: (0742) 752539.

COSHH Assessments (a step by step guide to assessment and the skills needed for it).

Introducing Assessment (a simplified guide for employers).

Hazard and Risk Explained.

Control of Substances Hazardous to Health Regulations 1988, Approved Code of Practice *Control of Substances Hazardous to Health* and Approved Code of Practice *Control of Carcinogenic Substances*, HMSO, ISBN 0 11 885468 2.

Guidance Note EH40/89 (and subsequent editions) *Occupational Exposure Limits*, HMSO, ISBN 0 11 885411 9.

NOTE This section contains no more than a summary of statutory regulations and requirements and does not set out in full the obligations and responsibilities of employers and employees. The purpose of this leaflet is to draw attention to matters requiring consideration and reference must be made to the Code of Practice and other publications mentioned above and the authorities mentioned therein.

STORAGE OF PESTICIDES

The requirements of the Food and Environmental Protection Act 1985 and the Control of Pesticides Regulations 1986 with regard to the safe storage of pesticides are set down in detail in the 'Code of Practice for the use of Approved Pesticides in Amenity Areas'. More detailed advice can be obtained from the Health and Safety Executive in the form of a guidance note entitled "Storage of Approved Pesticides: Guidance for Farmers and Other Professional Users". The Health and Safety Executive Agricultural Inspectorate are the enforcing body for this legislation, and for specific queries relating to individual sports clubs it is strongly recommended that the local HSE be contacted, their telephone number should be in your local directory.

This section summarises the information on storage of pesticides contained in the Code of Practice and HSE guidance note. It is highly recommended that the documents referred to above should be consulted for comprehensive information on the subject.

Criteria for Pesticide Storage

Depending on the quantity of pesticide involved, the necessary storage facilities can be provided by a specially made metal cabinet or by a purpose built store. Whatever storage facility is chosen, the following criteria apply:–

(a) the store should be suitably sited;
(b) of adequate storage capacity;
(c) soundly constructed of fire resistant materials;
(d) provided with suitable entrances and exits;
(e) capable of containing spillage and leakage;
(f) dry and protected from frost where necessary;
(g) suitably lit;
(h) suitably ventilated;
(i) marked and secure against theft and vandalism;
(j) equipped and organised to accommodate the intended contents.

Application of These Criteria to Metal Cabinets

If only a relatively small amount of pesticide is stored, e.g. at a private bowling club, cricket club or 9-hole golf course, then metal cabinets that are currently available should meet the storage requirements. The following companies have marketed containers of capacity from 65 litres or kilogrammes to 1300 litres or kilogrammes of total pesticide quantity:-

Cleveland Sitesafe Limited	Portasilo Limited	Rhone-Poulenc Environmental
High Farm	Huntington	Products
Old Lackenby	York	Regent House
Eston	YO3 9PR	Hubert Road
Middlesbrough	Tel: 0904 624872	Brentwood
Cleveland TS6 8DN		Essex CM14 4TZ
Tel: 0642 464986/453629		Tel: 0277 261414

These cabinets are sufficiently robust so as not to be significantly damaged by any reasonably foreseeable accidental impact and are capable of containing any leakage up to a total capacity of the contents stored. They are designed to be fire resistant and are lockable to prevent unauthorised access.

The storage container should be marked with an approved notice consisting of a yellow triangle with black edge and exclamation mark, at least 125 mm long on all three sides, the notice also being displayed on the outside of any building in which the container is housed.

The pesticide store should not be sited within a staffroom, office, human or animal food store or food processing area, a dwelling house or building adjoining and directly accessible from a dwelling house. It is also recommended that emergency eye-wash facilities, First Aid kit, list of cabinet contents and a 9 litre aqueous fire extinguisher are provided.

Application of Criteria to Buildings
If large amounts of pesticides need to be stored (over the quantities that can be stored in metal cabinets), then a purpose built store will have to be constructed. The criteria for purpose built stores are numerous and are summarised on the diagram attached.

Useful Information
The Health and Safety Executive publication is available from MAFF Publications Unit, Lion House, Willowburn Trading Estate, Alnwick, Northumberland, NE66 2PF.

'Pesticides: Guide to the New Controls (Control of Pesticides 1986)'. MAFF Leaflet UL79 (revised 1987).

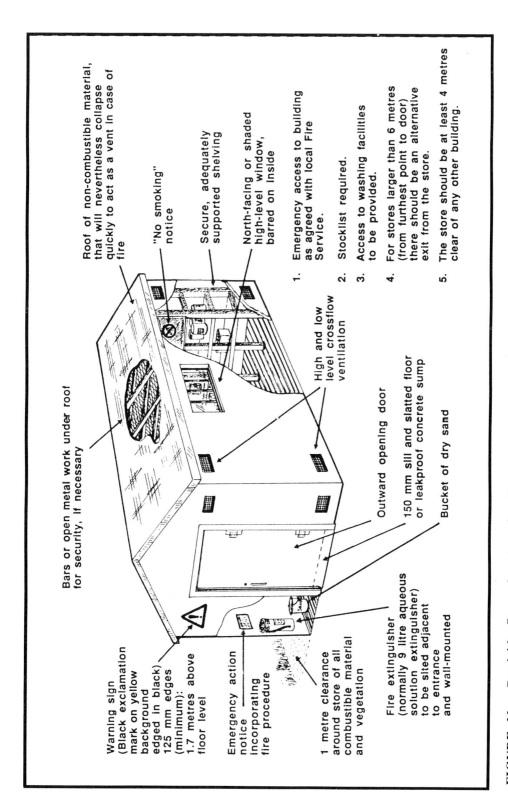

FIGURE 22: Pesticide Store for Amenity Use.

Roof of non-combustible material, that will nevertheless collapse quickly to act as a vent in case of fire

"No smoking" notice

Secure, adequately supported shelving

North-facing or shaded high-level window, barred on inside

1. Emergency access to building as agreed with local Fire Service.

2. Stocklist required.

3. Access to washing facilities to be provided.

4. For stores larger than 6 metres (from furthest point to door) there should be an alternative exit from the store.

5. The store should be at least 4 metres clear of any other building.

High and low level crossflow ventilation

Bars or open metal work under roof for security, if necessary

Outward opening door

150 mm sill and slatted floor or leakproof concrete sump

Bucket of dry sand

Warning sign (Black exclamation mark on yellow background edged in black) 125 mm edges (minimum): 1.7 metres above floor level

Emergency action notice incorporating fire procedure

1 metre clearance around store of all combustible material and vegetation

Fire extinguisher (normally 9 litre aqueous solution extinguisher) to be sited adjacent to entrance and wall-mounted

PAPERWORK FOR SPRAYING

Hopefully, greenkeepers are now fully aware of their responsibilities for the safe use of pesticides under the Control of Pesticides Regulations Act 1986 (COPR). An integral part of those regulations relates to the need to maintain accurate records of spraying operations. The implementation of the Control of Substances Hazardous to Health Regulations (COSHH), which have been in force since 1st October 1989, now means that further paperwork is necessary to conform to the law. This article will briefly outline and, hopefully, reinforce the user's obligations relating to paperwork under COPR and also provides a guide to the type of information which should be recorded as part of the risk assessment under COSHH.

Requirements Under COPR

An accurate record should be kept of every spraying operation, and this includes details such as operator name, product, reason for use, rate of application, quantity used, timing, weather conditions, etc. An example of a suitable format for these records is provided in the "Pesticides Code of Practice for the Use of Approved Pesticides in Amenity Areas" booklet which is obtainable from the STRI. The Institute suggests that separate sheets are prepared for each sprayer and include details of calibrations so that application rates for different nozzle sizes, tractor speeds and boom widths are available. These record sheets should be stored in a separate area from the chemicals.

Requirements Under COSHH

This article will deal specifically with the written assessment of risk which needs to be completed in order to conform with this new legislation. Remember that these regulations apply to all substances which are hazardous to health, so it will be necessary to include materials other than pesticides such as cleaning fluids, fuel, dust (which may be generated during top dressing preparations for example). However, for the purposes of this article, I will outline a risk assessment checklist aimed at pesticide use. Only include pesticides which are considered to be hazardous, these are usually identified with a warning symbol or other information on the product label. The assessment should be completed at the **beginning** of the year prior to spraying, to be updated on, say, an annual basis. The employers are responsible for the implementation of this procedure, in the case of a Golf Club the Secretary would be the appropriate person. However, he has the power to delegate the responsibility to the Head Greenkeeper, who would be in a better position to assess the risks.

The risk assessment could take the following format:

Step 1: Identify the weed/pest/disease/ other problem which will require control.

Step 2: List alternative methods of control other than chemicals, i.e. management techniques.

Step 3: Identify and list all the hazardous pesticides which you are planning to use. At this stage, include information about the chemical, such as formulation, degree of hazard, e.g. are there any warning signs, any special instructions on the label? If there are any specific worries, further information should be sought from the manufacturers, who are obliged to provide safety data sheets for their products.

Step 4: Assess the area of use and risk to the general public, e.g. adjacent to housing, public footpaths may cross the area. Publicise details of spraying operations, Golf Clubs should inform the membership on the notice board for example.

Step 5:   Detail the method of application, i.e. tractor-mounted sprayer or knapsack, hydraulic nozzle or CDA, operating pressure, etc.

Step 6:   Assess the measures which will be taken to control exposure or contamination. Include the various stages of possible risk, i.e. transportation, storage and methods for mixing and bulking into the spray tank. Provide details of the operations, i.e. National Profession Test Certificate (NPTC), experience, supervision, etc., and any written instructions to them.

Step 7:   Make a decision and choose the product which is the least hazardous to be applied by the safest method. At this stage, consider the protective clothing which is necessary rather than using it as an excuse to choose a product at an earlier stage. Remember that you must be able to justify a decision to choose a hazardous chemical, the question of efficacy is important but should not be the first consideration.

Step 8:   Check the decision process.

Step 9:   Decide on the steps necessary to comply with COSHH, i.e. ensure that exposure is prevented and the hazard no longer constitutes a risk.

Step 10: Give details of risks to contractors or non-employees in the work place.

Step 11: Monitor exposures if necessary and keep a record of results, e.g. it may be necessary to monitor dust productions from top dressing mixing.

Step 12: Monitor the health of staff.

These steps are a reduced version of the British Agrochemical Association (BAA) leaflet, which provides a more detailed explanation of all the procedures. This is available from the British Agrochemicals Association Ltd, 4 Lincoln Court, Lincoln Road, Peterborough, PE1 2RP (Tel: 0733 49225) and is called "The COSHH Assessment for Pesticides – A Plain Man's Guide for the Amenity User".

The important point is that management is seen to uphold the spirit of the law and in this respect written documentation provides evidence that risk evaluation has been completed and that employees and staff are aware of the dangers.

Further Reading
The Health and Safety Executive (HSE) produce several relevant publications available from your local HSE office. A series of leaflets are available, free of charge, which give a concise introduction to COSHH. An Approved Code of Practice is also available together with a step by step guide to assessment and the skills needed for it.

SECTION 10

ADMINISTRATION & FACILITIES

COURSE MANAGEMENT: A GUIDE TO A POLICY DOCUMENT

Changes in Green Committee on a regular basis (ie. every one to two years) do not provide the continuity required to develop a golf course on a long term basis. Invariably there are changing policies with changing Committees. For example, bunkers which have been put in one year may be taken out again within four or five years at the whim of a new Committee which is a waste of valuable time and money. To eliminate the risk of sweeping and continued changes, Clubs should formulate their own course management policy document, working to a five and/or ten year plan. Such a document should be obligatory for all Green Committees and Club officials to implement.

This leaflet is set out to help Committees formulate their own document for their own situation which can then be drawn up, voted on possibly at an Annual General Meeting. Several people should be involved in compiling the document, but of particular importance are the Chairman of the Green Committee, the Green Committee, the Head Greenkeeper, the Club Secretary/Manager and the Club's Agronomist.

Introduction
Roles and Responsibilities: Mention should be made of the "Chain of Command" of the Green Committee and greenkeeping staff, confirming the individual's roles and responsibilities within the Club.

Course Management Objectives
This section should identify the characteristics which typify the course, eg. heathland, parkland, links, etc., and the type of vegetation that should be aimed for on various parts of the course.

Stated management objectives should include playing characteristics and structural features of putting greens, surrounds and aprons, tees, fairways, rough and semi-rough, together with areas not in immediate play but which still contribute to the course, eg. woodlands, gorse, heather, etc., which can provide valuable areas for conservation.

Course Management Policy
Having established objectives, broad but detailed principles of the management of the various areas should be laid down. Where professional advice is required, it should be taken from experienced qualified consultants with a proven record.

Resources
The optimum number of greenstaff should be identified by a project management exercise and a commitment made to training and education. A complete inventory of machinery should be made with a phased programme of replacement. Only specified materials should be applied to the course. Quality should not be sacrificed – it is often a false economy (particularly applicable to top dressing for greens and sand for bunkers, etc.).

Usage
There should be a clear understanding and statement of policies relating to temporary greens and winter tees, etc., and certainly avoidance of over-use. Furthermore, there should be properly identified periods when essential maintenance work should be carried out.

Professional Advice

(a) Agronomist

The Club should have a policy of regular (at least annual) monitoring visits undertaken by an experienced professional Agronomist.

(b) Architecture/Construction Work

Any alterations or additions to the course should only be undertaken after consultation with a member of the British Association of Golf Course Architects. Construction work must only proceed after advice from the Architect or an Agronomist. Bunker or tee alterations or additions should form part of a staged phased construction programme.

(c) Ecology/Conservation Management

A proper programme of ecological/conservation management should be started after consultation with a recognised Ecologist sympathetic to the needs of the golfers.

Once a management policy has been drawn up, implementation should be obligatory but with some small scope for necessary minor adjustment agreed by all parties involved in course management. Any major changes should only happen after broad consultation with the membership.

LIST OF APPROVED COLLEGES FOR GREENKEEPER TRAINING

Askham Bryan College
Askham Bryan
York
Tel: 0904 702121
Contact: Nick Bisset

Cannington College
Cannington
Bridgewater
Somerset
Tel: 0278 652226
Contact: Nick Rigden

Cheshire College of Agriculture
and Horticulture
Reaseheath
Nantwich, Cheshire
Tel: 0270 625131
Contact: Dennis Mortram

Elmwood College
Cupar
Fife, Scotland
Tel: 0334 52781
Contact: Mike Taylor

Lancashire College
Myerscough Hall
Bilsborrow
Preston, Lancashire
Tel: 0995 40611
Contact: Richard Gibbs

Langside College
Buchanan Drive
Rutherglen
Glasgow
Scotland
Tel: 041 647 6300
Contact: Archie Morrison

Oaklands College
St Albans
Tel: 0727 50651
Contact: Ian Merrick

Oatridge Agricultural College
Ecclesmachan
Broxburn, Scotland
Tel: 0506 854387
Contact: Quentin Allardice

Plumpton College
Plumpton
Lewes
Tel: 0273 890454
Contact: David Blackmur

Sparsholt College
Sparsholt
Hampshire
Tel: 096 272 441
Contact: Bob Young

Teagasc National Botanic Gardens
Glasnevin, Dublin 9
Republic of Ireland
Tel: 00 01 371 636
Contact: Pat Suttle

Warwickshire College
Moreton Morrell
Warwick
Tel: 0926 651367
Contacts: Hugh Nunn/Roy Nelson

Welsh College of Horticulture
Northop, Mold
Clwyd, Wales
Tel: 035286 861
Contact: Graham Wright

PLAYER/GREENKEEPER RELATIONSHIPS

There is possibly always the foundation for something of a mutual antagonism between the man who looks after the turf and the player who wears it out. Blame for an unsatisfactory relationship can be apportioned to the greenkeeper or to the player or to both depending on circumstances.

Both Sides can be at Fault

Sometimes a greenkeeper, embittered by some injustice imagined or real, will give up all pretence of using his undoubted skill and experience to produce the quality of playing surface he prepared in the past. He can even occasionally be deliberately obstructive. In other cases it may be the player, unfairly critical or clamouring to be allowed to play on a turf which is unfit, probably due to weather conditions, who upsets a hitherto well-balanced apple cart. Ultimately a very difficult situation can arise.

In view of the conflicting interests, the wonder of it is really that, in the majority of golf clubs, such a good rapport exists between ground staff and players. An appreciation of the other side's point of view is essential and here are some ideas which may be helpful in preserving harmony.

Maintenance Work is Essential . . .

The average golfer does not know much about growing grass (though he thinks he does sometimes!). He is therefore quite innocently unaware of the necessity for the annual maintenance jobs which, although they temporarily interfere with his game, are completely necessary if a suitable playing surface is to be preserved. An obvious instance comes to mind of the annual autumn scarifying of golf greens which is needed on most courses these days in order to keep putting surfaces true and firm and free from excessive soft fibre. This scarifying is bound to make the greens a little rough for a week or so and complaints from the golfers can be loud and long, and extremely irritating to a conscientious greenkeeper. The Club Secretary in fact can prevent a good deal of fuss in cases like this by pinning on the notice board in the Clubhouse a short announcement of what is to be done shortly on the course and the reason for it.

On the other hand every man working on a golf course, if he does not actually play the game for which he caters must have an extremely good knowledge of it, so that he knows exactly what is required from the turf by the players. He must be able to dovetail his work as neatly as practicable into the programme of fixtures so that any disturbance he does cause is minimal. For example, a good time to put a summer dressing of sulphate of ammonia, sulphate of iron and compost on golf greens is usually on a Monday, so that by the time the busy weekend arrives the putting surfaces are practically clean again, although Tuesday is often Ladies' day and they can object to compost on greens early in the week.

No Play when Grounds are Unfit

Suspension of play when the playing surface is unfit is a very common source of grievance. Considerable damage can be done to golf greens when they are played upon in frosty weather, particularly when surfaces are thawing out over a still frozen under-surface. When such conditions prevail the golfers should be playing on temporary greens and the best way to reduce the number of complaints is to do sufficient work on these temporary greens during the growing season to ensure putting surfaces with a reasonable finish. Here again a notice displayed in the clubhouse outside the Secretary's office helps considerably to turn away wrath.

The Hazards of Greenkeeping!

Nobody likes to be set up as a target, but this is the unfortunate position in which a greenkeeper sometimes finds himself when, for example, mowing greens on a golf course. Determined golfers, with the bit in their teeth, will occasionally brook no interruption and it is rather sad to have to record that the 'gentler sex' in this context are often said to be the readier to loft an approach shot on to the head of a preoccupied greenkeeper. They have been known in fact not to spare advisory agronomists in the pursuance of their lawful duties! The introduction of the triple greens mower has had one indisputable advantage in that it has allowed the greenkeeper to mow a green quickly and then rapidly get out of range!

One Boss is Sufficient

Too many masters, especially when they give conflicting orders, can be a great source of irritation. There should really be only one official at any Club who has the supreme authority to give instructions to the Head Greenkeeper. Ordinary Golf Club members for instance, playing a round of golf, should have no brief to stop by the greenkeeper for a chat and a few words about filling the second bunker on the previous hole!

Good Results

Consideration and thoughtfulness by all concerned (players, members, committees, staff) in relation to sensitive aspects of ground maintenance such as those described here usually lead to good playing conditions and happy job satisfaction.

COMMUNICATIONS WITHIN THE GOLF CLUB

Introduction

Just as an inability to listen in the widest sense is a common human failing, so too is an unwillingness to listen to the other person's point of view. But without good, structured communications no organisation can operate efficiently, least of all a Golf Club. Members, officials and staff must all strive to achieve effective communications in the interests of the Club's most important asset – its course.

Communications on the Course

The effective management of golf courses hinges on the Head Greenkeeper and depends just as much on his skill as a communicator as it does on his practical abilities and technical know-how. Course maintenance requires team effort, hence the head man must be able to instruct each of his assistants as to which jobs require doing, including where, when and how. In addition, the Head Greenkeeper must make it understood that he is also a receiver of information from assistants acting as scouts; in this way he should be able to spot the first signs of trouble with the turf or machinery, so that small problems may be promptly dealt with.

This, then, is communication, namely a two-way movement of information which is received and interpreted on the same level at which it is formulated and transmitted. To prevent a breakdown in this process, explanations must be sufficiently detailed, simple and clear and put over patiently. Many people are poor listeners and can only concentrate for short periods, so the Head Greenkeeper must allow for this when helping young lads in particular. He must also be a good listener, so that as well as receiving direct messages, he should pick up hints and clues of possible sources of trouble, and follow up as necessary. There is never any harm in double-checking. Getting the right level of communication between the Head Greenkeeper and his assistants can only improve the standard of maintenance. It should also prevent silly mistakes which reflect adversely upon the reputation of the Head Greenkeeper and his staff. If poor spread of fertiliser, slow response to breakouts of disease, misapplication of sprays, scalping with mowers, poor pin positions, doing the right job but on the wrong area, etc., can be prevented, then golf courses, golfers and Head Greenkeepers will benefit.

Explanations of what assistants should do *and why* they should be doing it must benefit the younger members of the greenkeeping fraternity too. This takes time and trouble, but if interest is stimulated the standard of workmanship will improve; a foundation will also have been laid which will help to raise the future standard of greenkeeping.

Communication with the Club House

The quality of course maintenance does not fail solely through poor communication on the course and in the mess room. Many problems on golf courses seem to stem from a breakdown in communication between the Head Greenkeeper and those in the Club House too. The outcome of such a breakdown is frustration, with each side feeling that the other is not getting the message. Such situations can – and frequently do – explode to the detriment of all concerned and, not least, to the condition of the course as well.

To prevent this happening, it is essential that every Golf Club sets up a structure for communication, and accepts that this communication has to be a two-way process, as the Head Greenkeeper should be the person within the Club most technically qualified to comment upon ideas coming from the Club House and how these will affect the golf course in the long term. If, in any situation, he is in doubt, reference should be made to an independent body, such as a golf course agronomist or a golf course architect, who can comment upon the situation impartially. Seeking outside advice does not reflect ignorance – it is the intelligent who have an open mind to receiving information and to assessing its value.

In setting up a structure for communication between the green staff and Club members *one* is a key word. While the Head Greenkeeper does have a duty to talk with and listen to members who, after all, are his ultimate employers, concerning factors which affect the running of the course, the Head Greenkeeper should be dealing with only one person on matters of maintenance policy. This person should be the appointed representative of the members, and whether it be the Chairman of the Green Committee, Course Care Director or Club Manager, it is important that the appointment be of sufficiently long duration to allow the development of both an appreciation of the work done on the course and a working relationship with the Head Greenkeeper. By this means each will acquire an understanding of the other's problems. Day to day running of the course is the Head Greenkeeper's responsibility but it is necessary to have someone with whom he can liaise for the development of a framework of long term policy, and through whom feedback on results should be channelled. A situation in which any Club official may issue orders to the Head Greenkeeper or his staff leads to confusion and contradiction. Similarly, it is wrong for Club members to pass comment or criticism upon the work of green staff. After all, imagine the disruption which would be created if any shareholder were allowed to walk into a factory and give direct orders to a production manager, foreman or workers!

Communication within the Club House
It is the task of the Club official having responsibility for the course to communicate with other officials and with the membership as a whole. He must be sufficiently primed on the projected maintenance programme and its cost when presenting his budget to the finance committee: about the effects of levels of play resulting from visiting societies and projected tournaments: and have answers for the grumblers! Success in golf course maintenance is achieved through long term planning over a period of years, inaugurating an integrated programme of treatments, and ensuring that jobs are done at the right time. There must be a clear, agreed programme, based on the needs of the course as a whole, rather than upon the pet theories of individuals, and adequate funding. The right time for treatments is not always the most convenient time to golfers, and compromise in such matters means give and take from *both* sides.

The collation of statistics relating to levels of play during the weeks throughout the year will provide a guide as to when treatments can be applied with least disruption, as well as to when play should be reduced for the long term good. Information from the Head Greenkeeper's diary, e.g. work done in the past, under what conditions and with what success, could modify these decisions, as could also the seeking of advice from an outside agency on the timing and effectiveness of individual operations, and where any changes might be made.

The Club representative needs to keep abreast of costs and expenditure too, so that he can ensure priority consumables are always available, repairs can be effected promptly, and machines replaced before they collapse into a pile of scrap. All this is to ensure that the best possible surfaces for golf are provided at all times of the year. Being the Club representative in charge of a golf course is not a job to be taken on lightly; it is hard work and unlikely to ensure universal popularity. Neither is it just a job involving dealings with committee people: the membership as a whole also has to be kept in touch with problems and development.

Both the Club representative and the Head Greenkeeper should be available to members to discuss course matters on a general basis, so long as it is appreciated that they are not just there to be the butt of hostilities. A Club rule that suggestions and complaints about the course must be put in writing and posted in a marked box for discussion at the next course care meeting can reduce the number of frivolous complaints. Such an approach tends to concentrate attention on longer term problems, rather than all those small items that someone has got steamed up about after a bad round! But as with all other matters, communication with the membership must be a two-way process too because to produce a successful golf course the backing of the majority is a prerequisite. An occasional newsletter can be a useful way of getting over long term aims and giving an update on progress. In addition, posting bulletins of work to be done during the following month can take the element of surprise out of disruptive procedures on any one day. When giving information to members, avoid the purely technical approach – try to relate more to the effect on their game, time scales and value for money, plus the fact that all work done is for their ultimate benefit even though this may not be immediately apparent.

Projecting the Greenkeeper
Finally, a point to the Head Greenkeeper. If the status of greenkeeping is to be elevated to its proper level, the Head Greenkeeper must try to project a favourable image at all times, both individually and through associations of greenkeepers. Be polite, keep up appearances, make people aware of the technicalities and difficulties but try to do this without a lot of moaning; facts and figures are far more persuasive. The golfing public holds the key to the status of greenkeeping, and it is only with direct communication or with communication through indirect channels that they will become aware that the greenkeeper is no longer just the odd job man.

THOUGHTS ON THE ROLE OF THE CHAIRMAN OF GREEN

For all the faults in the Committee System at Members Clubs, as highlighted in the R&A's discussion document "The Way Forward", the Chairman of Green remains the pivotal point around which golf course management revolves, and is likely to remain so for the foreseeable future. This being the case, one might then ask if there is an effective way of defining the role of the Chairman of Green, with a view to creating the basis for a successful management framework for the running of a golf course and minimising the potential pitfalls of the job.

This is not easy, because the position of the Chairman of Green and his longevity in office is very variable from Club to Club. However, if at the outset we remove the major pitfalls involved with the false assumptions that the Chairman's job is day to day running of the course, and that his election is an autonomous unit, then a start can be made. Day to day running is the job of the Head Greenkeeper/Course Manager/Links Supervisor. Whilst any one Chairman is not a mainspring, but merely a cog in a long line of cogs in the life span of a golf course, each and every Chairman must interlink smoothly with the previous incumbent and do the same with his or her successor, to achieve vital continuity.

The processes which require continuity with respect to the golf course may be broken down into five sections: the setting of standards; man management; communication; planning; and budgeting. It may be said these form the primary functions to be controlled by the Chairman of Green on behalf of the Club, but not necessarily in any order of importance – they are all important.

Setting Standards

Any organisation must set standards and lay down broad policies for their application within manageable units of time.

In terms of a golf course, policies may involve, for example, how presentation is to be developed, or how the course is to be used in winter. But having set objectives, the Committee function then stops at ensuring the wherewithal to meet the desired standards can be provided, having taken advice on whether or not such standards are achievable in each individual circumstance.

Man Management

Investment in and motivation of good staff is vital at any Club. The Chairman must fight hard to persuade the membership that greenkeeping is not cutting grass in summer and playing cards in winter, so that members are prepared to pay for skilled staff in adequate numbers. Good greenkeepers are hard to find, and the competition for their services, both home and abroad, is increasing rapidly.

Not only does each Club need to attract staff, but also to keep them (within reasonable bounds of individual career development). Money is not the only motivational factor in keeping good staff who are interested in the job, and indeed salary increases are very short term in effect in this respect. Of equal importance is to ensure staff become part of the Club in a broad sense, through constructive communication and involvement, through the availability of ongoing training and promotion prospects, and basically trying to avoid an 'us and them' situation.

Of course, there has to be discipline too, but a structural appraisal, not ongoing bickering, and certainly only a defined disciplinary procedure, not each and every player feeling free to bend the ear of the first available greenkeeper he or she comes across. Then, to balance out the discipline, there has to be the converse – praise – preferably broadcast praise of a job well done.

Planning
Planning is an obvious function, but often something which is not done well, tending to be vague and haphazard, with no defined ideas of a conclusion, or the effect of one set of operations on others of equal or greater importance.

Planning basically involves deciding what can be achieved out on the course within a year to year programme, given money, materials, equipment and manpower in set amounts. It is also an item to cover course development which, to be effective in raising standards whilst maximising the throughput of play and controlling costs, has to be set down on paper and carried through successive Committees.

The Head Greenkeeper must have an input on any planning, because he is in the best possible position to know what is possible and practical and what is not. In addition, an input from outset agencies – the Agronomist, the Course Architect, or even an Ecologist in some cases – can be invaluable in focusing ideas, and taking the whim of Clubhouse politics off the agenda, to allow for a concentration upon practical necessity.

Then, having formulated plans, the next step is to make sure what is planned happens!

Communication
Each Club, via the Chairman, should be aiming to let members and visitors know what work is going on out on the course from month to month, and why it is being done. (In giving explanations, keep them simple and aim to provide conclusions which illustrate the likely effects on play, rather than getting bogged down in greenkeeping jargon.)

Regular bulletins, say quarterly, are readily produced for members, while it is not too difficult to make sure societies will know in advance of any work which may affect their visit – forewarning takes a lot of sting out of the odd green out of play.

It should be pointed out that communication is a two-way process, and any Chairman must welcome ideas and suggestions. However, there have to be limits, and a rule that all communication to the Chairman should be in writing unless there is an emergency is something every Club could adopt with benefit. This avoids the need for instant answers, and anyway cuts down what needs to be answered because there has to be strong feeling before members will commit themselves to paper and a signature. Such a rule also gives the Chairman a chance for a quiet meal or drink when he or she dares to venture into the Clubhouse.

Budgeting
The most important function of all has been saved until last – the creation of a budget for the Green.

The concept of what is a budget is the crux here, and it has been best defined as a plan for effective investment. What a budget is not is a means of cheapening expenditure.

An adequate sum is required every year for both revenue and capital items, and a shortfall on either will reflect both poorly on the course and heavily on future incumbents in the position of Chairman. Making an unnecessarily cheap budget is passing the buck on financial reality in the long term.

The five major functions of a Chairman of Green as outlined above are obviously not mutually exclusive, as each runs into the others. However, they do provide a framework for a 'job description' whereby the new Chairman can operate effectively within his term of office and pass on smoothly to whoever succeeds. The scope is there too to allow the Chairman to work in partnership with the Head Greenkeeper to the benefit of the course, and to delegate individual functions to either the Head Greenkeeper or other members of Committee, to provide a corporate structure.

The position of Chairman of Green is never an easy job to be taken on at any Club, not least because what it takes to run a golf course and deal with technical problems is the least well understood part of a Golf Club's field of operations (compared with, say, House or Handicaps). Nevertheless, if the Chairman is prepared to take out the technical aspect to a large degree and concentrate upon the management element (most Chairmen understand the running of a business), then all can be successful. Not necessarily spectacularly successful, but spectacular success in any job is the exception, not the inevitable result of every term of office.

THE ROLE OF BUDGETING IN GOLF COURSE MANAGEMENT

The dictionary definition of a budget is "an estimate of income and expenditure" normally prepared on an annual basis. A reliable budget is as essential to the smooth operation of a Golf Club as it is to one's personal finances.

Preparation of such a document is one of the basic responsibilities of the Head Greenkeeper with regard to course maintenance and as such is often stipulated in his job description and contract.

The budget will detail all maintenance requirements for the year to come and should be prepared in a form that is easily understood by laymen on the Green Committee, or the owner or Manager of the course. Each request for funds under various headings should be accompanied by an explanation and reason for each item, along with an accurate estimate. If this is linked, as it should be, with a detailed course maintenance plan, which states as simply as possible the objectives and standards that are required on the course, the chances of receiving adequate funding are enhanced.

A thoroughly prepared budget can be used as a reference through the year to ensure that targets at the start of the year are being met – or otherwise. It will help in assuring that funds are spent in an orderly manner, since monthly requirements will be known. At the same time it should identify all expenses and may indicate means of cost reduction or more efficient use of labour.

Budget Preparation

Two types of budget will normally be required covering capital expenditure and normal running costs. A capital budget covers those items such as machinery and equipment which have an expected life greater than a year. The operating budget covers costs that are incurred only in the forthcoming year.

The budget will be developed systematically by passing through several stages. The starting point must be a review of the Club's objectives for the coming year covering maintenance levels, policies and any constructional projects that are planned. The establishment of target dates for the start and completion of, say, tee construction or drainage projects helps with their planning in relation to normal daily maintenance, and these must be correctly timed in respect of anticipated weather conditions, which in turn may involve adjustment of the golf calendar of events.

The second stage is to evaluate existing maintenance practices and techniques, discussing items which have cropped up during the year's work with the First Assistant, Foreman or Mechanic to determine whether there is scope for increased efficiency or improvement with any job or item of equipment.

Clearly, it is necessary to have available adequate records of routine maintenance operations and the basic needs are for:–

(1) *Labour Utilisation* – Since cost of salaries amounts to some 70% of the operating budget, careful use of this resource is vital to the proper running and efficiency of the course. Minimum records are an employee's daily log which identifies by code the job, time expended and area, collected into monthly and annual summaries.

(2) *Equipment Records* – The basic requirement is for a machine record sheet for each unit of equipment – often a simple card file works well, with details of expected life and date of disposal. The card should also show the maintenance and service repairs that are necessary, so a complete history for each unit can be built up giving an invaluable guide as to serviceability, routine maintenance and any expensive breakdown repairs. This allows realistic budgeting for routine maintenance and likely bills, as well as an overall assessment of the operational record. There should never be a need to rack one's brain trying to remember how many times and how many hours a particular machine was unserviceable, or the cost of repairs. With the facts at one's fingertips, a clear case can be made for scrapping an inefficient machine before its allotted replacement date. Alternatively, the record can show when a unit reaches the end of its reliable working life and, of course, picks out equipment which has been excellent in service – the same type can then be purchased with some degree of confidence. Committees appreciate a concise statement of the facts such as well kept records allow and good presentation will certainly smooth the path for the new acquisitions or replacement machinery.

(3) *General Running Costs* – The high cost of fuel these days emphasises the need for maintaining accurate records of fuel and lubricants. The daily log for each of the staff should tally fuel consumption for individual items. Petrol has historically always been much more expensive than diesel and it is likely that differentials will persist, so information on fuel use must figure in decisions about new purchases where there is choice of diesel or petrol engines. It goes without saying that there should be records of fertiliser, seed, sand and top dressing. If it was not common sense before, there is now a legal requirement to maintain a record of purchase and usage of pesticides. Remember that the broad term covers not only the obvious, i.e. herbicides, fungicides and insecticides, but also substances such as soil sterilants, wood preservatives and animal repellents. There should also be a record of water use on the course – for irrigation, washing down equipment, spraying, etc.

Budget Content
Having assembled the facts needed to cover the capital side of expenditure, the data necessary for normal day to day running costs can be drawn from the records mentioned above. The various categories within the budget will include:–

(a)   *Capital Improvements*: value added to property such as new maintenance buildings, bridges, shelters, paths; course construction work such as new tees, bunkers, fairway drainage; landscaping work such as tree planting; irrigation systems.

(b)   *Capital Expenses*: will cover new equipment and vehicles, as well as office furniture, staff lockers, etc.

(c)   *Operating Expenses*:
[i]   Salaries and wages – covering tax, personnel, insurance, any pension provision, expense allowances including meals, cost of phone calls, car running costs whilst on Club business. Also part-time employees, students taken on in summer.

[ii]   Training and education – covering cost of apprentice training, staff attendance at seminars, publications, manuals and subscriptions.

[iii]   Clothing – including both safety foot and headwear, protective clothing, both rainwear and safety spray overalls, face shields and gloves.

[iv]   Materials – including top dressing, soil and sand, bunker sand, turf, seed, fertiliser, pesticides (includes herbicides, fungicides and insecticides).

[v]   Fuel – separate amounts allowed for petrol, diesel, oil.

[vi]   Irrigation – water costs averaged over five years if supplies are metered, annual maintenance costs. As the system ages allow for replacement pop-up heads.

[vii] Equipment repairs and maintenance – based on past costs available from records and projected for new equipment.

[viii] Hire of equipment.

[ix]   Sundries – covering flags, flag pins, out of bounds and hazard markers, hole cups, tee markers, boxes and litter baskets. An item to cover theft and vandalism based on past costs.

Long Term Planning

Every Golf Club should have a planned approach to course improvement and general maintenance strategy. This should be based over at least five years, drawn up by the current Committee and made available for the general membership to examine and discuss over a period. It should be presented with appropriate amendment at the Annual General Meeting and passed by the membership as a whole. The Head Greenkeeper or Course Manager then has a clear statement of where the Club is going – basic management strategy is approved – areas that need improvement are agreed, capital building or construction projects are laid out and costings can be applied to each item in a logical way.

Budget Presentation

Presentation of the operating budget to the Green Committee or Directors of the course will normally be the responsibility of the Head Greenkeeper in conjunction with the Chairman of Green. At some Clubs the capital budget may be presented by the Chairman of the Green Committee, but always after consultation with the Head Greenkeeper, or it may be a joint presentation. A copy of the proposed budget should be sent to each Committee member before the crucial meeting. In presentation, the main items of the budget can then be summarised and backed up with appropriate supporting information. Try to keep the presentation as short and concise as possible without waffling, but you must effectively get over your proposals and justifications. Simple language is always better than trade or scientific terms, because most Committee members may be unfamiliar with jargon.

With construction projects, use visual aids – drawings, overheads, etc. to graphically illustrate your aims. Finally, always allow adequate time for discussion and questions.

MAINTENANCE SHEDS ON THE GOLF COURSE

For years the accommodation provided for men and machinery has been neglected. Even today many Clubs are still living in the dark ages with regard to this aspect of course management. Typically, we find an ex-Services building, such as a Nissan hut, totally inadequate in size, dark, damp, lacking mains services and tucked away out of sight of the Clubhouse and membership.

Little wonder the average member has no conception of the size, scope and sheer intensive hard work and effort that goes into producing and maintaining the playing surfaces so essential to his game.

Fortunately, the wind of change is reaching even these out of the way places as Clubs realise just how much they have invested in 'hardware' – at least £80,000 as new cost on the average 18-hole course. It does not make sense to have such expensive items depreciating faster under poor storage conditions, to say nothing of vandalism and theft. In addition, bad working conditions lead to a casual slap-dash approach to cleaning and daily maintenance, shortening the life of a unit as well as increasing the risk of breakdowns. Health and Safety at Work legislation and the Control of Pesticides Regulations 1986 have all helped to bring momentum for change.

Planning
Take time to be thorough in producing a plan of requirements. A well researched scheme is more likely to meet the needs of the Club now and in future years, as well as gaining that vital initial acceptance from the Committee. Planning permission for the new or replacement building will have to be sought from the Local Authority and meet appropriate Building Regulations – check fire precautions and safety aspects with the local Fire Service, and appropriate storage for chemicals with the Local Pollution Control Officer.

Location
The ideal location will be central to the course to minimise travel time between base and working areas. However, it is important not to make the location too isolated, specially near large towns and cities where theft is likely to be a problem. The overriding considerations will be those of access via a road capable of taking large delivery vehicles, and the location of services – electricity, water and sewage disposal.

The site must be well drained, and not subject to casual flooding. Choose a relatively flat area with plenty of space around the building for manoeuvring large items of equipment. Remember safety aspects, keeping well away from golf holes to limit the risk of stray shots hitting staff or equipment.

Car Parking/Storage Areas
Ensure provision of adequate hard standing, at least double the area of concrete indoors to provide temporary parking for machines and washing-down facilities. On this hard base bulk supplies of topsoil, etc. can be tipped for temporary storage or lifted cleanly and moved under cover immediately.

Adequate car parking space must also be provided, well clear of the main access routes and working areas. Ensure enough room for employees' cars as well as visitors.

Landscaping
It will be worthwhile allowing for screening the new building and working area, both from aesthetic and safety aspects. There may be surplus topsoil and subsoil from building and road

foundations which can be used to form a mound on the course side of the compound. Strip topsoil and use surplus subsoil to build up the required height, then replace topsoil to provide at least 300 mm depth. Complete planting with a mix of rapid-growing conifers, such as Lawsons' Cypress, and longer term Scots pine and lodgepole pine to give windbreak and screening effects through winter. A mix of small-leaved deciduous trees – birch, oak and beech –where appropriate can make up the balance of the planting to provide something to attract wildlife and for summer interest.

Building Cost Estimates
Must include for site survey and preparation of plans and working drawings. It will be necessary to install an electricity supply, telephone lines, water, and connect to the sewers. Internal fittings may also have to be included – storage racks, shelving, tables and chairs for the mess room, possibly cooking facilities and office equipment.

Building
The basic requirement is for a large shed with side or end opening doors, ideally doors at both ends to permit through traffic flows. Most go for prefabricated concrete beam, plastic-coated, steel clad agricultural building. Span should be at least 9.5 metres and, better, nearer 11 metres. Length should be as long as the Club can afford, but certainly 14 metres, and up to 18.5 metres is not extravagant. It is essential to have a concrete block wall construction to about 1.2 metre height. Higher than this can be counterproductive, especially when soil or prepared top dressings are stored as there is a temptation to build up stocks against the wall, which must then be buttressed. It can be extremely useful to provide a loading/unloading bay. Eaves and lintel heights should be just tall enough to get a tractor, cab and front loader in comfortably. You cannot tip modern bulk lorries in anything much less than an aircraft hangar, so you may as well settle for a less obtrusive and cheaper low elevation building.

It is hardly worth wasting money on expensive roller doors – sliding doors are expensive enough, and perfectly adequate. Do provide for a separate personnel access door.

Floor Plan
When working out size requirements and where internal structures, such as offices, mess room and opening doors, are to be sited, it helps to draw the site and building to scale. Use cut-outs to the same scale of the various items of equipment so that use of floor space can be planned economically, and internal partitions, storage racks and doors sited to best advantage. Bear in mind:

(a) Doors should be kept away from the windy side of buildings.

(b) Windows should be at such a height they can be seen out of when sat at a chair.

(c) Allow wide enough aisles in equipment storage areas, and access walkways to walls that are useful for hanging up tools in a tidy rack and for extra shelving.

(d) A lower ceiling height over office and mess rooms not only conserves heat but, if adequate joists and floor grade chipboard is put in, loft space can serve as additional storage area for lighter items.

(e) Separate office, mess room, washroom with shower and toilets should be provided, normally of blockwork construction, with internal walls plastered or tiled. Keep the office furthest away from noisy working areas. Chemical storage must be kept entirely separate from the above areas. Depending on the quantities stored, it may be necessary to provide a separate, secure and fireproof structure, with a bund to retain spillage, facility for washing down and suitably signed. For small quantities of pesticides, proprietary lockable metal bins are available which meet requirements of legislation.

(f) As a minimum, allow for an area to accommodate work bench, vice and storage of machinery maintenance tool kits – preferably under lock and key. At larger establishments employing a maintenance fitter or, indeed, any 18-hole course where staff have the necessary skills to carry out more than just routine maintenance, provide a separate workshop with adequate light, heating, bench and storage space.

Services
As a minimum, an electricity power supply, preferably 3-phase, will be required, with separate circuits to irrigation systems. Ensure the electrician details on plan the wiring system. Switches for lights, etc. must be within easy reach, and provide enough power outlet sockets – at least two in the workshop and two in the equipment storage area.

Water supply pipe should be at least 37 mm, with oversize stop valve on the incoming supply. Provide stop valves for mess and washroom, and another in the service area.

Provide floor drains in the storage area, and outside ensure an adequate hard standing wasn-down area with separate drainage and silt and grass clipping traps.

Downspouts from roof gutters must be led to a positive outlet into the surface water drainage system.

Safety
Plan with safety in mind, providing features such as chain barrier fences around loading bays and hand rails to steps. Make provision for First Aid kits, fire extinguishers and ensure fire hydrant points and exits are clearly signed, and access is not blocked.

Finally
Plan well and thoroughly – the building will have to last a long time and you want to get it right first time. Visit and study facilities provided at other courses, and talk to other Head Greenkeepers. All are useful ways of increasing your own background knowledge, learning from other people's mistakes, as well as their successes. Each course has its own unique requirements, e.g. provision of separate soil storage and mixing areas for top dressings, but consideration of the points mentioned will help in preparing thoroughly and well, which goes a long way towards achieving Committee approval.

When plans finally come to fruition, what could be more appropriate than a change of name too – a discrete directional sign labelled 'Course Management Centre' is far more in keeping with the highly professional approach we must all bring to the job today.

COMPACT TRACTORS

An acceptable definition of a compact tractor would be those machines with a horse power rating of below, say, 26 (DIN). They were originally developed to meet the requirements for a small, economical to run power unit on Japanese farms which only average 1.6 hectares.

UK distributors soon realised the potential for compact tractors in a wide range of applications, particularly on amenity turf areas such as golf courses. Nearly all compact tractors are still manufactured in Japan and include the now household names of Iseki, Kubota Hinimota and Yanmar, together with those machines which masquerade under Anglo-Saxon names such as Ford or Massey Ferguson. Also, the American compact tractor, the John Deere, has a Japanese engine.

What Are the Advantages?

One of the major advantages of the compact tractor is its extreme versatility. To complement the extensive range of attachments which have been specifically designed for use with compact tractors it is possible to fit implements from other maintenance systems. For example, the Sisis Hydromain implements can be attached directly to the tractor 3-point linkage or adapted for use with a compact tractor by means of a special mounting frame which allows downward pressure to be applied to the implements through the hydraulic system. In addition, the tractor must be fitted with an auxiliary spool valve of the doubt-acting type.

Many Golf Clubs have realised the potential applications of the compact tractor and have purchased a suitable power unit to fulfil a variety of functions around the course. The high power to weight ratio means that a set of three gangs can be towed with relative ease (or driven off the tractor's PTO) yet the tractor can still be used on the vulnerable putting surfaces with safety due to advances in low ground pressure tyre technology.

The more powerful compact tractors can pull five gang units, although it is important not to over-burden the tractor as this will result in a reduction of its effective working life span.

The high ground clearance of the compact tractors enables mid-mounted rotary mowers to be fitted or the option of front or rear mounting of a range of flail or rotary mowers is available for specific models. Fully mounted, hydrostatic-driven mowers have also been developed for grass areas where a higher quality finish is required. This offers the advantage of a purpose-built, self-propelled machine with the bonus of out of season availability of the 'prime-mover' for other work.

Routine turf maintenance operations such as spiking, scarifying, spraying and top dressing can easily be accomplished on golf greens, tees and other fine turf areas by attachment of the appropriate implement. The compact tractor can easily exert sufficient pulling power for carrying out such operations as mini mole ploughing of greens, tees and approaches – which are particularly susceptible to soil compaction. In addition, modern compact tractors have the necessary hydraulic muscle to operate loaders, excavators and similar equipment. Therefore, drainage work can be accomplished, tees can be built, bunkers dug and ditches cleared without the need to hire suitable equipment. Various cultivation operations can be carried out both quickly and efficiently. A special advantage of the compact tractor is that it can accomplish the above functions in areas which may be inaccessible to standard machines while minimising turf wear and damage to the underlying soil structure on peripheral areas or the main traffic routes to and from the site of work.

Safety Must Have Priority
Safety should not be neglected in the interests of economy and a roll bar should be fitted to a compact tractor, particularly if it is to be used on sloping ground, to reduce the risk of the operator being injured in the case of an accident.

Desirable Features
Selection of a suitable compact tractor will depend to a large extent on its intended range of functions. Therefore, certain features may be considered to be of greater importance than others.

Four-wheel drive is highly desirable as this feature will improve traction as well as offering the benefits of a smoother ride and better balance on any ground contours in either muddy or wet conditions. Indeed, four-wheel drive is a prerequisite when using implements which require downward pressure – exerted through a double-acting back ram – to operate efficiently, as this will reduce traction through the rear wheels.

Hydrostatic transmission provides an infinite number of speeds within a defined range so that the pace of the compact tractor can be precisely tailored to implement activity. At very low creep speeds trenching is facilitated.

Direct comparison with integrated maintenance systems such as those produced by Cushman and Sisis or even the larger types of tractor is tempting, although impractical since the role of the compact tractor overlaps into each of these two categories, as well as performing specific functions of its own.

Not a Replacement for a Larger Tractor
Larger tractors, in both horse power and size, take up considerably more room in the shed and cannot manoeuvre or negotiate narrow paths with the same ease as compact tractors. However, they are particularly useful workhorses for carrying out operations such as routine mowing or deep spiking of fairways. Therefore, a compact tractor should not be seen as a replacement for the larger tractor (with a rating of between, say, 35–40 h.p.) but as a complementary unit. Work in the rough and peripheral areas of the course with difficult access or restrictions imposed on manoeuvrability are not 'out of bounds' for the compact tractor if rotary mowing, hedge trimming, post hole boring or cutting back of under-growth is necessary.

Reduced Running Costs
An important consideration which favours the compact tractor is the reduced running costs when compared with their big brothers. In particular, the new breed of highly efficient diesel engines give much improved fuel economy and reduce maintenance costs when fitted to compact tractors.

In summary, compact tractors have the capability of performing a vast range of difficult jobs in combination with a formidable array of compatible implements. This versatility, combined with economy, has been the major factor responsible for establishing a niche for compact tractors on golf courses.

GOLF TROLLEYS: BOON OR BANE!

Judging by their inexorable proliferation on the golf course, this is undoubtedly 'the age' of the golf trolley and more specifically the sleek, electrically powered models. The procession of golfers following in the wake of their occasionally 'self-willed' machines up and down our fairways has perhaps eased the burden of carrying clubs, but what are the implications of using trolleys in terms of course conditions?

Their primary drawback can be related to the constant attrition of the same 'paths', notably around the main playing areas of greens and tees. Without restrictions being enforced the most economical routes are adopted and at the extreme this can culminate in the golfer navigating a precipitous path between putting surface and adjacent greenside bunkers! The inevitable consequences of the same routes being exploited through narrow entry and exit areas are worn turf surfaces and compacted soils where the weight of golf traffic has been focused. In contrast, golfers who prefer to carry their clubs can circumvent obstacles with greater ease and traverse the putting surfaces, thus adopting a much wider range of traffic routes. Furthermore, the restrictions placed on golf trolleys can reduce the pace of throughput, notably when the ball strays from the 'straight and narrow' into rough! This is a source of frustration for the golfer and the cumulative effects may impinge on the potential playing levels which can practically be supported by the course.

The pressures imposed by golf trolleys are particularly acute during the late autumn and winter months when the decline is aggravated by the lack of natural turf recovery and vulnerability of the 'wet' soils to compaction forces. The rigidity of traffic flow patterns, enforced by the use of trolleys, around tee and green sites is often reflected by distinct, heavily worn arcs or muddy streaks in the following spring which are slow to make a satisfactory recovery. The advent of wide-wheeled trolleys (to replace the narrow-wheeled versions) has eased the pressure to a degree, but the emergence of heavier electrically driven trolleys has increased the 'scouring effect' on the turf – notably under wet surface conditions.

An appropriate course of action should be formulated in accordance with the individual site conditions, but the following factors should be taken into consideration:–

- The drainage potential of the course.
- Course layout and design, eg. compact or expansive, flat or undulating.
- The aspect of the course, ie. exposed or protected.
- The prevailing ground and weather conditions.
- The intensity of play and its distribution throughout the year.

Undoubtedly, the temporary winter suspension of the use of golf trolleys will, in most instances, have a marked influence on the viability and quality of the turf surfaces. Enforcing a local rule that clubs must be carried will help to 'break the pattern' and spread the 'load' of golf traffic more evenly. The majority of golfers should be sufficiently fit to carry a golf bag without significantly diminishing their enjoyment of the game. Indeed, a golfer armed with a few clubs and a lightweight 'pencil bag' may appreciate a different perspective of the course without a significant increase in exertion! There may be mitigating circumstances on the grounds of ill-health.

A ban on trolleys will prove most effective through the winter months (eg. December through to February inclusive) when the surfaces are most vulnerable, although this needs to be tailored to each site's requirements. This should encompass both the pulled and powered trolleys as this will prove simpler and less divisive. Where good channels of communication are established and co-operation of the golfers assured, then temporary suspensions – in accordance with prevailing ground and weather conditions – may be a workable compromise. However, this strategy is usually less effective due to the difficulties of decision making, monitoring and enforcement within the usual structure of course management.

The use of trolleys is inextricably linked with the need for adequate traffic control directives. These can take several forms including ropes, hoops and white lines; backed-up by clear, strategically placed signs. Through these means vulnerable areas can be protected and different traffic routes are brought into use. The designation of 'trolley parks' may serve a similar purpose and dictate an alternative route from fairway to green and green to the next tee. To realise the potential of these devices requires good channels of communication to be established at all levels within the Club so the strategies can be agreed and objectives clearly defined prior to implementation.

Development of separate 'alternative' tees mainly for winter play, but possibly pressed into use during the summer if required, can have a profound influence on patterns of traffic flow. Where there is scope, within the confines of the course layout, for the strategic placement of these tees the golfers will be forced to take alternative routes to those adopted during the summer. This will ease the pressures on the turf surfaces, provide a valuable period of recuperation and enable the benefits of remedial procedures to be realised. Furthermore, the introduction of purpose-built paths, to take the weight of trolley traffic, may be warranted in certain situations, eg. alongside tees, but they **must** satisfy golfing, management and aesthetic criteria.

The above measures should not be regarded as a substitute for a temporary trolley ban, but rather as being **complementary** with the objective of countering the increasing pressures on our golf courses and maintaining optimum playing conditions year-round!

BIBLIOGRAPHY

BOOKS AND BOOKLETS : MODERN GREENKEEPING (1985 to Date)

Anon. (1986). *Nozzle Selection Handbook*. British Crop Protection Council, Farnham, Surrey, 40 pp.

Anon. (1989). *Disease, Insect & Weed Control in Turf* (2nd Ed.). Australian Turfgrass Research Institute, Concord West, N.S.W, Australia, 54 pp.

Anon. (1990). Golf course Europe. *Proc. Int. Exhib. and Conf. on the Design, Construction and Maintenance of Golf Courses and Golf Club Management*. Expoconsult, The Netherlands, 179 pp.

Anon. (1991). *Boom Sprayers Handbook*. British Crop Protection Council, Farnham, Surrey, 60 pp.

Anon. (1991). *Code of Practice for the Use of Approved Pesticides in Amenity and Industrial Areas*. National Assoc. of Agric. Contractors and National Turfgrass Council, 72 pp.

Baker, S.W. (1990). *Sands for Sports Turf Construction and Maintenance*. Sports Turf Research Institute, Bingley, 67 pp.

Baldwin, N.A. (1990). *Turfgrass Pests and Diseases*. Sports Turf Research Institute, Bingley, 57 pp.

Cochran, A.J. (Ed.) (1990). Science and golf. *Proc. 1st World Scientific Congress of Golf*. E.&F.N. Spon, London, 374 pp.

Daniel, W.H. & Freeborg, R.P. (1987). *Turf Managers' Handbook* (2nd Ed.). Harvest Pub. Co., Ohio, U.S.A., 437 pp.

Decker, H.F. & Decker, J.M. (1988). *Lawn Care: A Handbook for Professionals*. Prentice-Hall, N.J., U.S.A., 270 pp.

Gibeault, V.A. & Cockerham, S.T. (Eds.) (1985). *Turfgrass Water Conservation*. Co-op. Ex., University of California, CA., U.S.A., 155 pp.

Gilbert, D. & Macrory, R. (1989). *Pesticide Related Law*. British Crop Protection Council, Farnham, Surrey, 68 pp.

Gould, C.J., Goss, R.L. & Byther, R.S. (1985). Diseases of turfgrasses. *Extension Bulletin 713*. Washington State Univ. Co-op. Extension, U.S.A., 32 pp.

Greenkeeping Panel (1989). *The Way Forward: Discussion Document of British Golf Course Management*. Royal & Ancient Golf Club, St. Andrews, Scotland, 33 pp.

Hope, F. (1990). *Turf Culture: A Manual for the Groundsman* (2nd Ed.). Cassell Pubs. Ltd., London, 293 pp.

Jarrett, A.R. (1985). *Golf Course and Grounds: Irrigation and Drainage*. Prentice-Hall Inc., N.J., U.S.A., 246 pp.

Lawson, D.M. (1991). *Fertilisers for Turf*. Sports Turf Research Institute, Bingley, 47 pp.

Park, E. (1990). *Real Golf*. Privately Pub. Mrs. N. Park, Woodsetts, Nottinghamshire, 179 pp.

Park, E. (undated). *The Management of British Golf Courses*. Pub. by Golf Monthly Magazine, London, 26 pp.

Robinson, R. (1990). *Turf Spraying: A Practical Guide*. Turfgrass Technology, Seaford, Victoria, Australia, 60 pp.

Shildrick, J.P. (Ed.) (1985). The mower for the job. *Workshop Report No.6*. National Turfgrass Council, Bingley, W. Yorks., 60 pp.

Shildrick, J.P. (Ed.) (1989). Turf nutrition '88. *Workshop Report No.15*. National Turfgrass Council, Bingley, W. Yorks., 79 pp.

Shildrick, J.P. (Ed.) (1990). Pesticide use after COSHH. *Workshop Report No.18*. National Turfgrass Council, Bingley, W. Yorks., 76 pp.

Modern Greenkeeping Cont.

Shildrick, J.P. (Ed.) (1991). Safe disposal of amenity pesticides. *Workshop Report No.22.* National Turfgrass Council, Bingley, W. Yorks., 86 pp.

Shildrick, J.P. & Marshall, E.J.P. (Eds.) (1985). Growth retardants for amenity grassland. *Workshop Report No.7.* National Turfgrass Council, Bingley, W. Yorks., 77 pp.

Shurtleff, M.C., Fermanian, T.W. & Randell, R. (1987). *Controlling Turfgrass Pests.* Prentice-Hall Inc., N.J. U.S.A., 449 pp.

Smiley, R.W., Dernoedan, P.H. & Clarke, B.B. (1992). *Compendium of Turfgrass Diseases.* American Phytopathological Soc. Press, MN, U.S.A., 128 pp.

Smith, J.D., Jackson, N. & Woolhouse, A.R. (1989). *Fungal Diseases of Amenity Turf Grasses.* E.&F.N. Spon, London, 401 pp.

Turgeon, A.J. (1985). *Turfgrass Management* (rev. Ed.). Prentice-Hall Inc., N.J., U.S.A., 416 pp.

Walmsley, W.H. (Ed.) (1990). *Fungicides for Turfgrass Disease Control.* New Zealand Turf Culture Institute, Palmerston North, N.Z., 26 pp.

Watkins, J.A. (1987). *Turf Irrigation Manual.* Telsco Industries, Texas, U.S.A., 363 pp.

Weaver, C. & Weaver, M. (1989). *Ransomes 1789–1989 A Bicentennial Celebration.* Ransomes Sims & Jefferies PLC, Ipswich, 132 pp.

BOOKS AND BOOKLETS : GREENKEEPING PRE-1985

Anon. (1933). *Improvement of Lawns, Golf Greens and Fairways.* I.C.I. Ltd., London, 23 pp.

Anon. (circa 1940). *Ransomes Royal Records 1789–1939.* Ransomes Sims & Jefferies Ltd, Ipswich, 79 pp.

Anon. (1971). *Turf Culture.* New Zealand Institute for Turf Culture (2nd Ed.), 362 pp.

Anon. (1979). *Turfgrass Diseases.* Sports Turf Research Institute, Bingley, 36 pp.

Beale, R. (1924). *Lawns for Sports: Their Construction and Upkeep.* Simpkin Marshall Hamilton Kent & Co. Ltd., London, 276 pp.

Beale, R. (1931). *The Book of the Lawn: A Complete Guide to the Making and Maintenance of Lawns & Greens for All Purposes.* Cassell & Co. Ltd., London, 151 pp.

Beard, J.B. (1973). *Turfgrass Science and Culture.* Prentice-Hall Inc., N.J., U.S.A., 658 pp.

Beard, J.B. (1982). *Turf Management for Golf Courses.* Macmillan Pub. Co. & U.S.G.A., N.Y., U.S.A., 642 pp.

Beard, J.B. (1983). *Better Turfgrass Nutrition.* Par Ex Prof. Products, Florida, U.S.A., 22 pp.

Cave, L.W. (1967). *Cave's Guide to Turf Culture.* Pelham Books Ltd., London, 188 pp.

Clouston, D. (1937). *The Establishment and Care of Fine Turf for Lawns and Sportsgrounds.* D. Wyllie & Son, Aberdeen, 121 pp.

Colvin, T.S. (1974). *Grounds Keeping Equipment Vol.1 Operating Tractors for Grounds Keeping & Ornamental Horticulture.* Americ. Assoc. for Vocational Instructional Materials, Georgia, U.S.A., 95 pp.

Couch, H.B. (1962). *Diseases of turfgrasses.* Reinhold Pub. Corp., N.Y., U.S.A., 289 pp.

Darwin, B. (1931). *Science and Greenkeeping.* Reprint from Country Life, 19 December 1931, 4 pp.

Dawson, R.B. (1939). *Practical Lawncraft* (1st Ed.). Crosby Lockwood & Son Ltd., London, 300 pp.

Dawson, R.B. & Evans, T.W. (1932). *Lectures on Greenkeeping 1931–32.* Scottish Golf Union (Western District), Glasgow, 60 pp.

Dickenson, L.S. (1930). *The Lawn: The Culture of Turf in Park, Golfing and Home Areas.* Orange Judd Pub. Co. Inc., N.Y., U.S.A., 128 pp.

Emmons, R.D. (1984). *Turfgrass Science and Management.* Delmar Pub. Inc., N.Y., U.S.A., 451 pp.

Greenkeeping Pre-1985 Cont.

Escritt, J.R. (1978). *ABC of Turf Culture.* Kay & Ward Ltd., London, 239 pp.

Farley, G.A. (1931). *Golf Course Commonsense: A Non-technical Treatise on the Subject of Golf Course Maintenance.* Farley Libraries, Ohio, U.S.A., 256 pp.

Faulkner, R.P. (1950). *The Science of Turf Cultivation.* The Technical Press Ltd, London, 64 pp.

Greenfield, I. (1962). *Turf Culture.* Leonard Hill Ltd., London, 364 pp.

Hackett, N. (1928). *Soil Acidity: The Vital Importance of Top Dressing and Other Notes.* Private Pub., Bradford, W. Yorks., 37 pp.

Halford, D.G. (1982). *Old Lawn Mowers.* Shire Album No.91. Shire Pubs. Ltd., Aylesbury, Buckinghamshire, 32 pp.

Hanson, A.A. & Juska, F.V. (1969). *Turfgrass Science.* American Society of Agronomy Inc., Wisconsin, U.S.A., 715 pp.

Hawthorn, R. (Rev.) (1977). *Dawson's Practical Lawncraft* (7th Ed.). Crosby Lockwood Staples, London, 313 pp.

Hayes, P. (1984). *Technical Terms in Turf Culture.* Sports Turf Research Institute, Bingley, 76 pp.

Howard, F.L., Rowell, J.B. & Keil, H.L. (1951). *Fungus Diseases of Turf Grasses.* Agric. Exp. Stn., Univ. of Rhode Island, U.S.A., 56 pp.

Hutchinson, H.G. (Ed.) (1906). *Golf Greens and Greenkeeping.* Country Life Ltd., London, 219 pp.

Kreitlow, K.W. & Juska, F.V. (1960). Lawn diseases: how to control them. *Home & Garden Bulletin No.61.* U.S. Dept. Agric., Washington D.C., U.S.A., 16 pp.

Levy, E.B., Kiely, W.A. & Horton, W.M. (1951). *Construction, Renovation and Care of the Golf Course.* New Zealand Institute for Turf Culture, Palmerston North, N.Z., 101 pp.

Lewis, I.G. (1948). *Turf: A Book About Golf Greens, Tennis Courts, Bowling Greens and Playing Pitches No less Than Lawns: Their Making and Keeping According to Modern Practice.* Faber & Faber Ltd., London, 141 pp.

Macdonald, J. (1923). *Lawns, Links and Sportsfields.* Country Life Ltd. and George Newnes Ltd., London, 78 pp.

Macself, A.J. (1924). *Grass: A New and Thoroughly Practical Book on Grass for Ornamental Lawns and All Purposes of Sports and Games.* Cecil Palmer, London, 204 pp.

Macself, A.J. (undated c.1925). *Lawns and Sports Greens.* W.H. & L. Collingridge Ltd., London, 134 pp.

Madison, J.H. (1971). *Principles of Turfgrass Culture.* Van Nostrand Reinhold Co., N.Y., U.S.A., 420 pp.

Madison, J.H. (1971). *Practical Turfgrass Management.* Van Nostrand Reinhold Co., N.Y., U.S.A., 466 pp.

Murray, C.M. (1932). *Greenkeeping in South Africa: A Treatise on Scientific Methods for the Establishment and Maintenance of Turf for Sporting Purposes & Garden Lawns.* Pub. by "South African Golf", Cape Flats, S.A., 104 pp.

Musser, H.B. (1950). *Turf Management.* U.S.G.A. & McGraw Hill Book Co., N.Y., U.S.A., 354 pp.

Peterson, F. (1973). *Handbook of Lawn Mower Repair.* Emerson Books Inc., N.Y., U.S.A., 253 pp.

Piper, C.V. & Oakley, R.A. (1929). *Turf for Golf Courses.* The Macmillan Co., N.Y., U.S.A., 262 pp.

Sanders, T.W. (1920). *Lawns & Greens: Their Formation and Management.* W.H.& L. Collingridge, London, 138 pp.

Smith, J.D. (1965). *Fungal Diseases of Turf Grasses.* Sports Turf Research Institute, Bingley, 97 pp.

Greenkeeping Pre-1985 Cont.

Sprague, H.B. (1976). *Turf Management Handbook* (2nd Ed.). The Interstate Printers & Publishers Inc., Illinois, U.S.A., 255 pp.

Stinson, R.F. (Ed.) (1981). *Greenkeeping.* Teacher Education Series, Vol.22, No.6, Instructional Materials Services, Pennsylvania State University, Penn. U.S.A., 103 pp.

Sutton, M.A.F. (Ed.) (1933). *Golf Courses: Design, Construction and Upkeep.* Simpkin Marshall Ltd., London, 152 pp.

Sutton, M.H.F. (1912). *The Book of the Links: A Symposium on Golf.* W.H. Smith & Son., London, 212 pp.

Sutton, M.H.F. (undated). *The Laying Out and Upkeep of Golf Courses and Putting Greens.* Simpkin, Marshall, Hamilton, Kent & Co. Ltd., London, 46 pp.

BOOKS AND BOOKLETS : GOLF COURSE CONSTRUCTION AND DEVELOPMENT

Anon. (1964). *Making Room for Golf.* Golf Foundation Ltd., London, 52 pp.

Anon. (1978). *Golf: An Interim Strategy for Provision in the Lothian Region.* Lothian Regional Council, Edinburgh, ? pp.

Anon. (1988). *Golf Course Development.* English Golf Union, Leicester, 18 pp.

Anon. (1989). *Aspects of Golf Development.* English Golf Union, Leicester, 40 pp.

Bengeyfield, W.H. (Ed.) (1989). *Specification for a Method of Putting Green Construction.* United States Golf Assoc., N.J., U.S.A., 24 pp.

Cook, W.L. & Holland, R. (1964). *Public Golf Courses: A Guide to Their Development and Operation.* National Recreation & Park Assoc., Washington D.C., U.S.A., 36 pp.

Davidson, A.W. & Leonard, J.E. (1975). Land for leisure. (Proceedings of Conference October 1974) Centre for Advanced Land Use Studies, Reading, Berkshire, 49 pp.

Ferguson, M.H. (1968). *Building Golf Holes for Good Turf Management.* United States Golf Assoc., N.Y., U.S.A., 55 pp.

Finger, J.S. (1972). *The Business End of Building or Rebuilding a Golf Course.* Private Pub., Houston, Texas, U.S.A., 47 pp.

Jones, R.L. & Rando, G.L. (1974). Golf course developments. *Technical Bulletin No.70.* Urban Land Inst., Washington D.C., U.S.A., 112 pp.

Nicholls, D.C. & Massey, D.W. (1969). *Study of Golf Course Provision in Britain.* Dept. of Social & Economic Res., University of Glasgow, 37 pp.

Shildrick, J.P. (Ed.) (1988). The recreational diversification of farmland. *Workshop Report No.13.* National Turfgrass Council, Bingley, W. Yorks., 94 pp.

Shildrick J.P. (Ed.) (1991). Minimum standards for golf course construction. *Workshop Report No.20.* National Turfgrass Council, Bingley, W. Yorks., 94 pp.

Stutt, J.H. (1980). *The Reclamation of Derelict Lands for Golf.* Golf Development Council, London, 12 pp.

Various Authors (1964). *Municipal Golf Courses: Their Layout, Upkeep and Economics.* Journal of Park Admin. & C.R. Books Ltd., London, 20 pp.

BOOKS AND BOOKLETS : GOLF ARCHITECTURE

Anon. (1972). *Elements of Golf Course Layout and Design.* Golf Development Council, London, 24 pp.

Bauer, A. (1913). *Hazards: The Essential Elements in a Golf Course Without Which the Game Would be Uninteresting.* Tony Rubovits, Chicago, U.S.A., 61 pp.

Colt, H.S. & Alison, C.H. (1920). *Some Essays on Golf Course Architecture.* Reprint 1990 by Grant Books, Droitwich, Worcestershire, 78 pp.

Cornish, G.S. & Whitten, R.E. (1981). *The Golf Course.* Rutledge Press: W.H. Smith Pub. Inc., N.Y., U.S.A., 320 pp.

Golf Architecture Cont.

Green, R. & Morgan, B. (1989). *Classic Golf Holes: 72 of the World's Greatest.* Willow Books, William Collins Sons & Co. Ltd., London, 160 pp.

Hawtree, F.W. (1983). *The Golf Course: Planning, Design, Construction & Maintenance.* E.&F.N. Spon, London, 212 pp.

Hawtree, F. (1991). *Colt and Co. Golf Course Architects.* Cambuc Archive, Oxford, 214 pp.

Hotchkin, S.V. (undated). *The Principles of Golf Architecture, etc.* Reprint of articles from "Club Sportsman", London, 25 pp.

Hunter, R. (1926). *The Links.* Charles Scribner's Sons, N.Y., U.S.A., 163 pp.

Kirk, J. & Jacobs, T. (Eds.) (1988). *The Golf Courses of Robert Trent Jones Jr.* Bison Books Ltd., London, 191 pp.

Mackenzie, A. (1920). *Golf Architecture: Economy in Course Construction and Greenkeeping.* Simpkin, Marshall, Hamilton, Kent & Co. Ltd., London, 135 pp.

Simpson, T. (1933). *A Broadcast Talk on Golf Architecture.* Pub. by the British Broadcasting Corp., London, 7 pp.

Sorensen, G.L. (1976). *The Architecture of Golf.* Private Pub., College Station, Texas, U.S.A., 106 pp.

Thomas, G.C. (1927). *Golf Architecture in America: Its Strategy and Construction.* Times-Mirror Press, Los Angeles, California, U.S.A., 342 pp.

Wethered, H.N. & Simpson, T. (1929). *The Architectural Side of Golf.* Longmans Green, London, 211 pp. (Revised Ed. 1952 entitled "Design for Golf", Sportsmans Book Club, London.)

BOOKS AND BOOKLETS : GOLF COURSE ECOLOGY & CONSERVATION

Anon. (1983). *Wildlife on the Royal Birkdale.* Interpretive Branch, Nature Conservancy Council, Shrewsbury, 6 pp.

Anon. (1988). *Heathland Restoration: A Handbook of Techniques.* Environmental Advisory Unit, University of Liverpool. Pub. by British Gas PLC, Southampton, 160 pp.

Anon. (1990). *Your Course . . . . Preparing a Conservation Management Plan.* Nature Conservancy Council, Peterborough, 15 pp.

Bunce, R.G.H. (Ed.) (1989). Heather in England & Wales. *Research Pub. No.3.* Institute of Terrestrial Ecology, H.M.S.O., London, 40 pp.

Gilchrist, T.D. (1983). *Trees on Golf Courses.* The Aboricultural Association, Romsey, Hampshire, 134 pp.

Picksley, K. (1988). *A Strategy for Surrey Heathland.* Surrey County Council and The Nature Conservancy Council, Kingston-on-Thames, 40 pp.

Prendiville, B. (1985). *Flora and Fauna of Portmarnock (Golf Course).* Criterion Press Ltd., Dublin, Ireland, 12 pp.

Schofield, M. & Dair, I. (Eds.) (1989). *On Course Conservation: Managing Golf's Natural Heritage.* Pub. by Nature Conservancy Council, Peterborough, 46 pp.

Shildrick, J.P. (Ed.) (1984). Creating Attractive Grasslands. *Workshop Report No.5.* National Turfgrass Council, Bingley, W. Yorks., 92 pp.

Shildrick, J.P. (Ed.) (1988). Wild flowers '87. *Workshop Report No.14.* National Turfgrass Council, Bingley, W. Yorks., 90 pp.

BOOKS AND BOOKLETS : GOLF COURSES – GENERAL INTEREST

Allen, P. (1987). *Play the Best Courses: Great Golf in the British Isles.* Stanley Paul & Co. Ltd., London, 210 pp.

Allen, P. (1989). *The Sunley Book of Royal Golf.* Stanley Paul & Co. Ltd., London, 160 pp.

Anon. (1937). *Golf Round London.* Whitefriers Press Ltd, London (1st Ed.), 275 pp.

General Interest Cont.

Anon. (1989). *A History of Golf Clubs in Fife.* The Fife Golfing Assoc., St. Andrews, Scotland, 164 pp.

Arlott, J. (Ed.) (1975). *Oxford Companion to Sports & Games.* Oxford University Press, London, 1143 pp.

Booth, A. & Hobbs, M. (1987). *The Sackville Illustrated Dictionary of Golf.* Sackville Books Ltd., London, 192 pp.

Brasch, R. (1972). *How Did Sport Begin?* Longmans Group Ltd., London, 279 pp.

Browning, R. (1955). *A History of Golf: The Royal & Ancient Game.* Reprint 1990. A. & C. Black Ltd., London, 236 pp.

Campbell, M. (1991). *The Encyclopaedia of Golf: The Definitive Guide to the Game – Its Courses, Characters & Traditions.* Dorling Kindersley Ltd., London, 336 pp.

Clougher, T.R. (Ed.) (1929). *Golf Clubs of the Empire: The Golfing Annual* (3rd Ed.). The Clougher Corp. Ltd., London, 510 pp.

Crowther, J. (1991). *Managing Your Golf Club.* Harper Trade Journals, London, 147 pp.

Darwin, B. (1910). *Historic Golf Courses of the British Isles* (2nd Ed. 1987). Gerald Duckworth & Co. Ltd., London, 253 pp.

Darwin, B. (undated). *Green Memories.* Hodder & Stoughton, London, 333 pp.

Dickinson, P. (1951). *A Round of Golf Courses. A Selection of the Best Eighteen.* Reprint 1990. A. & C. Black Ltd., London, 159 pp.

Editors of Golf World Magazine (1987). *Golf in Scotland and Ireland: The Complete Guide to Courses, Clubs, Accommodation & Travel.* Sackville Books Ltd., London, 160 pp.

Edmund, N. (Ed.) (1991). *Following the Fairways 1991: The Distinguished Companion to the Golf Courses of Great Britain & Ireland* (4th Ed.). Kensington West Productions, London, 315 pp.

Elliott, A. & May, J.A. (1990). *Illustrated History of Golf.* Hamlyn Pub. Group Ltd., London, 256 pp.

Evans, W. (1974). *Encyclopaedia of Golf* (2nd Ed.). Robert Hale & Co., London, 319 pp.

Ferrier, B. (1990). *The World Atlas of Golf Courses.* Hamlyn Pub. Group Ltd., London, 208 pp.

Fittis, R.S. (1891). *Sports and Pastimes of Scotland.* Alexander Gardner. Reprint 1975 E.P. Pub. Ltd., Wakefield, W. Yorks., 212 pp.

Gibson, W.H. (1988). *Early Irish Golf: The First Courses, Clubs and Pioneers.* Oakleaf Publications, Naas, Co. Kildare, Republic of Ireland, 303 pp.

Green, R. (1987). *Golf: An Illustrated History of the Game.* Willow Books, William Collins Sons & Co. Ltd., London, 208 pp.

Hobbs, M. (1988). *The World's Great Golf Courses.* The Apple Press, London, 112 pp.

Kelly, G.M. (1971). *Golf in New Zealand: A Centennial History.* New Zealand Golf Assoc., Wellington, N.Z., 262 pp.

Kennington, D. (1981). *The Sourcebook of Golf.* Library Assoc. Pub. Ltd., London, 255 pp.

Lawless, P. (Ed.) (1937). *The Golfer's Companion.* J.M. Dent & Sons, London, 498 pp.

Leigh-Bennett, E.P. (1930). *Some Friendly Fairways.* Southern Railway, London, 57 pp.

Lyle, S. & Ferrier, B. (1989). *The Championship Courses of Scotland.* Lennard Publishing, Oxford, 288 pp.

May, J.A. (1991). *The Complete Book of Golf: A Guide to Equipment Techniques & Courses.* (W.H. Smith) Hamlyn Pub. Group Ltd., London, 192 pp.

Menton, W.A. (1991). *The Golfing Union of Ireland 1891–1991.* Gill and Macmillan, Dublin, 399 pp.

Miller, D. (1977). *America's Greatest Golfing Resorts.* Bobbs-Merrill Co. Inc., Indianapolis/N.Y., U.S.A., 239 pp.

Morgan, B. (1988). *A World Portrait of Golf.* Aurum Press Ltd., London, 224 pp.

General Interest Cont.

Morrison, J.S.F. (Ed.) (1939). *Around Golf.* Arthur Barker Ltd., London, 246 pp.

Pennink, F. (1962). *Golfer's Companion: A Guide to 128 of the Finest Courses in Great Britain and Ireland.* Cassell & Co. Ltd., London, 311 pp.

Plumridge, C. (1988). *The Illustrated Encyclopaedia of World Golf.* (W.H. Smith) Marshall Cavendish Books Ltd., 256 pp.

Pottinger, G. (1972). *Muirfield and the Honourable Company.* Scottish Academic Press, Edinburgh, 146 pp.

Price, R. (1989). *Scotland's Golf Courses.* Aberdeen University Press, Aberdeen, 235 pp.

Salmond, J.B. (1956). *The Story of the R. & A.* Macmillan & Co. Ltd., London, 256 pp.

Saunders, V. (1989). *The Golf Handbook.* Marshall Editions Ltd., London, 223 pp.

Scott, T. (1978). *The Concise Dictionary of Golf.* Bison Books Ltd., London, 256 pp.

Shapiro, M., Dohn, W. & Berger, L. (1986). *Golf: A Turn of the Century Treasury.* Castle Book Sales Inc., N.J., U.S.A., 467 pp.

Steel, D. & Ryde, P. (Eds.) (1975). *The Shell International Encyclopaedia of Golf.* Ebury Press & Pelham Books Ltd., London, 478 pp.

Stirk, D. (1987). *Golf: The History of an Obsession.* Phaidon Press Ltd., Oxford, 160 pp.

Vardon, H. (1905). *The Complete Golfer.* Methuen & Co. Ltd., London, 283 pp.

Various Authors (1931). *The Game of Golf.* Lonsdale Library, Vol.9, Seeley Service & Co. Ltd., Lonsdon, 251 pp.

Viney, N. & Grant, N. (1978). *An Illustrated History of Ball Games.* William Hernemann Ltd. (Book Club Associates), London, 201 pp.

Wind, H.W. (Ed.) (1954). *The Complete Golfer.* William Heinemann Ltd., London, 398 pp.

CURRENT PERIODICALS (U.K. Only)

The Journal of the Sports Turf Research Institute.
Formerly the Journal of the Board of Greenkeeping Research. Published annually, 1929 to date. Britain's leading Scientific Journal of Turf Research. Sports Turf Research Institute, Bingley, West Yorkshire, BD16 1AU (Tel: 0274 565131).

The Sports Turf Bulletin.
Articles and information for Greenkeepers, Groundsmen, Committee Members, etc. Published quarterly, January 1951 to date. Sports Turf Research Institute, Bingley, West Yorkshire, BD16 1AU (Tel: 0274 565131).

Turfgrass Seed.
Evaluations of currently available turfgrass cultivars. Published annually, 1977 to date. Sports Turf Research Institute, Bingley, West Yorkshire, BD16 1AU (Tel: 0274 565131).

Turf Management.
Monthly. Haymarket Trade & Leisure Pubs. Ltd., 38-42 Hampton Road, Teddington, Middlesex, TW11 0JE (Tel: 081 943 5023).

The Golf Club Secretary.
Monthly, May 1991 to date. Briefing and Practical Advice for Golf Club Administrators. Articles on greenkeeping topics. J.V. Wilson, Broadside Publishing, Broadside, Kent Hatch Road, Limpsfield Chart, Oxted, Surrey, RH8 0SZ (Tel: 0883 730270).

Amateur Golf.
Official Journal of the English Golf Union. Eleven Issues per year. The English Golf Union, 1-3 Upper King Street, Leicester, LE1 6XF (Tel: 0533 553042).

Current Periodicals Cont.

Greenkeeper International.
> Journal of the British & International Golf Greenkeepers Association. Monthly since January 1991. David White (Editor), 13 Firle Close, Seaford, East Sussex, BN25 2HL (Tel: 0323 891291).

The Groundsman.
> Official Journal of the Institute of Groundsmanship. Monthly. Gene Price (Editor), 42 West End Avenue, Pinner, Middlesex, HA5 1BJ (Tel: 081 868 3600).

Golf Club Management.
> Official Journal of the Association of Golf Club Secretaries. Monthly. Steve Rankin (Editor), Harper Trade Journals, Harling House, 47-51 Great Suffolk Street, London, SE1 0BS (Tel: 071 261 1604).

Parks, Golf Courses & Sportsgrounds.
> Monthly. Alan Guthrie (Editor), Clarke & Hunter (London) Ltd., 61 London Road, Staines, Middlesex, TW18 4BN (Tel: 0784 461326).

National Turfgrass Council News.
> Bi-monthly. J.P. Shildrick, 3 Ferrands Park Way, Harden, Bingley, West Yorkshire, BD16 1HZ (Tel: 0535 273188).

Golf Link.
> Several issues per year plus an annual edition. Includes a section entitled "The Ulster Greenkeeper", Edited by A. Abercrombie. Main Editor R. Bingham, Link Publications, 328 Antrim Road, Belfast, BT15 5AB (Tel: 0232 740471).